THE THEORY OF MAGNETISM

HARPER'S
PHYSICS SERIES

Frederick Seitz, EDITOR

THE THEORY

OF

MAGNETISM

An Introduction to the Study of Cooperative
Phenomena

Daniel C. Mattis, Ph.D.

THOMAS J. WATSON RESEARCH CENTER

INTERNATIONAL BUSINESS MACHINES

CORPORATION

YORKTOWN HEIGHTS, NEW YORK

HARPER & ROW

PUBLISHERS

NEW YORK, EVANSTON, AND LONDON

To Noémi, My Wife

CONTENTS

CHAPTER 4   MANY-ELECTRON WAVEFUNCTIONS   81

Part II   Statics and Dynamics of Magnetism

CHAPTER 5   SEMICLASSICAL THEORY OF MAGNETISM   117

PRINCIPAL
TABULAR MATERIAL

FOREWORD

One of the most active fields of theoretical physics at the present time is the study of cooperative phenomena, such as magnetism and superconductivity, in systems of large numbers of interacting particles. Powerful mathematical methods, borrowed in part from quantum field theory, have been developed to treat such problems. We are beginning to get an understanding of the difficult problem of phase transitions as well as to understand the properties of the cooperative state itself. These developments have had an impact in other fields of physics, such as the theory of elementary particles. This book is the first authoritative account of the remarkable progress which is being made in our understanding of magnetism as a cooperative phenomenon.

In a very interesting and beautifully written historical introductory chapter (done in collaboration with his wife), Dr. Mattis tells us how an explanation of magnetism has challenged the mind of man through the ages. It has long been one of the central problems of physics. An adequate theory was of course impossible prior to the discovery of quantum mechanics in 1926. Important beginnings were made at that time, but until the past decade progress has been slow. Major advances made soon after 1926 include Heisenberg's model based on exchange interaction between neighboring atoms and the theory of spin waves. Later, there have been parallel developments of the itinerant electron, or band model.

Particularly during the last ten years, there has been a flowering of both experimental and theoretical work on spin waves, the theory being based mainly on the Heisenberg model. This model has also been used as the basis for the great progress made in understanding insulating magnetic materials, including the nature of ferromagnetic and antiferromagnetic phase transitions. Less well understood are ferromagnetic transition metals such as iron and nickel. Mattis adopts the view and gives convincing arguments that intra-atomic exchange (Hund's rule), as proposed by J. C. Slater many years ago, is basic for our understanding of the magnetic properties of these materials.

Designed primarily for the beginning student, the book should also be of interest to the expert and to physicists in other fields who would like to be brought up to date on recent advances. It may be hoped that it will help stimulate graduate courses in magnetism, which in the past have been all too rare in our universtities, probably because most research on magnetism, due to its technological importance, has been done in industrial rather than university laboratories. Dr. Mattis has performed a real service in giving a timely, lucid, coherent account of a large and active field of central interest to physics.

A professor takes pride in the careers of his former students and is pleased to see them carry the advancement of knowledge far beyond what he himself could do. With these feelings in mind, it is a pleasure and a privilege to be able to contribute a foreword to this important book.

JOHN BARDEEN

University of Illinois

PREFACE

Magnetism is rapidly becoming a field so varied and complex that no single individual is able to comprehend it in its entirety. A recent bibliography of the literature published in a single year runs over two hundred printed pages,[1] and any reader of current scientific journals will agree that this is only the beginning of a veritable explosion. The time is therefore ripe to set down between covers at least a part of what is now known, that part which is likely to help in the formulation and solution of new problems, that is, the theory of magnetism. Even so, the scope is so vast that other processes of selection have been needed to keep the length of this book within reasonable bounds. All time-dependent or irreversible phenomena were omitted, as were spin-orbit coupling and other causes of magnetic anisotropy. The emphasis has been on strong interactions among two or more particles, in quantum theory or statistical mechanics, particularly where collective phenomena are involved. Quite aside from references to works used in the preparation of the text, there is included a Bibliography of articles and books touching many aspects of magnetism not covered in the text, such as the experimental and technical properties, or the theory of the Landé g factor in solids, etc.

Principally we present to the reader an introduction to some aspects of the physics of cooperative phenomena, in addition to some facts about magnetism. This is advantageous for the reason that modern solid-state physics has progressed beyond the solution of one-body problems to the statement, if not always the solution, of the many-body problem. That magnetism provides a good example of this is not surprising, since historically the study of magnetism has always tended to reflect the main currents of physical thought. This will be apparent from our first chapter; it concerns itself exclusively with the history of the theory of magnetism, but reads so much like a history of physics that we may hope it serves to illuminate the latter.

The first three months of an introductory course in quantum mechanics provides sufficient background for most of the material. No previous study of statistical mechanics is required, and indeed the entire work is viewed as introductory to the study and appreciation of solid-state physics. But with the needs of the theorists in mind, we have delved somewhat deeper than this in the fundamentals, and also in three applications: in the theories of spin waves, of magnetism in metals (including tabular

---

[1]*Magnetic Materials Digest, 1962*, (M. W. Lads, Philadelphia, 1963).

material in the Appendix), and of the Ising model; all of which remain today at the very frontiers of knowledge. When some day these topics become obsolete, as indeed they shall, it will be principally because they have been mastered by those who have proceeded beyond them to open wider horizons. At the present date the greatest advances are being made in the discovery of new magnetic materials and effects, and in their ever widening application to technology. And if we believe that history repeats itself, this stage will be followed by a resurgence of theoretical activity. It is this which the present book is designed to stimulate, by addressing itself to the level of students early in their formative period, when their minds are most open to the joys of intellectual exploration.

And after all, is this not the most interesting and delightful of subjects? Else "why should I, in so vast an ocean of books by which the minds of men are troubled and fatigued . . . why should I, I say, add aught further to this so perturbed republick of letters?"[2] To satisfy the curiosity of the nonspecialist as well as the specialist, of the chemist and the engineer, and of the physicist, of all who want to know *the mystery of the magnet.*

D. C. M.

Chappaqua, October, 1964

---

[2]William Gilbert, Preface to *De Magnete* (1600), rev. ed., Basic Books, Inc., New York, 1958.

ACKNOWLEDGMENTS

In the early days of the printing press, authors of scientific works collected the publication fee from wealthy patrons and subscribers, to whom a series of acknowledgments and dedications were made in the work .The second and subsequent editions often carried new dedications and acknowledgments reflecting shifts in the relative generosity of the patrons or a new list of subscribers. Nor was it uncommon for the various chapters to start with distinct lists of dedications when the debt of the author to his publisher was particularly great.

Whatever else may have changed in the twentieth century, the desire of an author to thank all the people who have helped make his book possible has stayed much the same. although, the debts which the present author owes to a long list of individuals cannot be measured in any units of currency. To Dr. Noémi Perelman Mattis, *Docteur en Droit*, Master of Arts, my wife and mother of our two children, who is co-author of Chapter 1 and mainly responsible for the historical research on which it is based, my gratitude for her outstanding contribution is boundless. It is with deep appreciation also that I thank Professor John Bardeen of the University of Illinois for contributing the foreword to the present work.

Professor Paul H. Cutler of the Pennsylvania State University arranged our visit to that campus where parts of this book were written or outlined during the Summer of 1963, and I wish to thank him for this opportunity. Much of the research work was done in collaboration with my colleagues, notably Drs. E. H. Lieb and T. D. Schultz, at the Thomas J. Watson Research Center of the International Business Machines Corporation, and has appeared in previous joint scientific publications. IBM has been generous in permitting use of material first calculated at the Research Center. In the person of Dr. J. Slonczewski, the management of this company has been helpful in every way, particularly in encouraging the work required so that this book may be made available at this time.

Professor J. H. Van Vleck of Harvard University reviewed the manuscript. I thank him for a helpful suggestion concerning the title of the book, and thank Professor Charles Perelman of Brussels University for guidance on Chapter 1. Help by Drs. R. Bozorth, S. Charap, M. Freiser, and M. Gutzwiller is gratefully acknowledged.

D.C.M.

PART 1

THE BASES OF
THE THEORY

CHAPTER 1

HISTORY OF THE
THEORY OF MAGNETISM

It was probably the Greeks who first reflected upon the wondrous properties of magnetite, the magnetic iron ore FeO—Fe_2O_3 and famed lodestone (leading stone, or compass). This mineral, which even in the natural state often has a powerful attraction for iron and steel, was mined in the province of Magnesia.

> The magnet's name the observing Grecians drew
> From the magnetick region where it grew.[1]

This origin is not incontrovertible. According to Pliny's account the magnet stone was named after its discoverer, the shepherd Magnes, "the nails of whose shoes and the tip of whose staff stuck fast in a magnetick field while he pastured his flocks."[2]

PHYSICS AND METAPHYSICS

The lodestone appeared in Greek writings by the year 800 B.C., and Greek thought and philosophy dominated all thinking on the subject for some 23 centuries following this. A characteristic of Greek philosophy was that it did not seek so much to explain and predict the wonders of nature as to force them to fit within a preconceived scheme of things. It might be argued that this seems to be precisely the objective of modern physics as well, but the analogy does not bear close scrutiny. To understand the distinction between modern and classical thought on this subject, suffice it to note the separate meanings of the modern word *science* and of its closest Greek equivalent, ἐπιστήμη. We conceive science as a specific activity pursued for its own sake, one which we endeavor to keep free from "alien" metaphysical beliefs. Whereas, ἐπιστήμη meant *knowledge* for the Greeks, with aims and methods undifferentiated from those of philosophy.

The exponents of one important school of philosophy, the *animists*, took cognizance of the extraordinary properties of the lodestone by ascribing to it a divine

---

[1] Lucretius Carus, *De Rerum Natura*, 1st century B.C. References are to *vv.* 906 ff., in the translation by Th. Creech, London, 1714.

[2] Pliny, quoted in William Gilbert, *De Magnete*, trans., Gilbert Club, London, 1900, rev. ed., Basic Books, Inc., New York, 1958, p. 8 (see also Bibliography).

origin. Thales, then later Anaxagoras and others, believed the lodestone to possess a soul. We shall find this idea echoed into the seventeenth century A.D.

The school of the *mechanistic*, or atomistic, philosophers should not be misconstrued as being more scientific than were the animists, for their theories were similarly deductions from general metaphysical conceptions, with little relation to what we would now consider "the facts." Diogenes of Apollonia (about 460 B.C.), a contemporary of Anaxagoras, says there is humidity in iron which the dryness of the magnet feeds upon. The idea that magnets feed upon iron was also a long lived superstition. Still trying to check on it, John Baptista Porta, in the sixteenth century, reported as follows:

I took a Loadstone of a certain weight, and I buried it in a heap of Iron-filings, that I knew what they weighed; and when I had left it there many months, I found my stone to be heavier, and the Iron-filings lighter: but the difference was so small, that in one pound I could finde no sensible declination; the stone being great, and the filings many: so that I am doubtful of the truth.[3]

But the more sophisticated theories in this category involved effluvia, which were invisible emanations or a sort of dynamical field. The earliest of these is due to Empedocles, later versions to Epicurus and Democritus. We quote a charming accounting by the Roman poet Lucretius Carus showing that in the four centuries since Empedocles, in an era of high civilization, the theory had not progressed:

> Now sing my muse, for 'tis a weighty cause.
> Explain the Magnet, why it strongly draws,
> And brings rough Iron to its fond embrace.
> This Men admire; for they have often seen
> Small Rings of Iron, six, or eight, or ten,
> Compose a subtile chain, no Tye between;
> But, held by this, they seem to hang in air,
> One to another sticks and wantons there;
> So great the Loadstone's force, so strong to bear! ...
>
> First, from the Magnet num'rous Parts arise,
> And swiftly move; the Stone gives vast supplies;
> Which, springing still in Constant Stream, displace
> The neighb'ring air and make an empty Space;
> So when the Steel comes there, some Parts begin
> To leap on through the Void and enter in. ...
>
> The Steel will move to seek the Stone's embrace,
> Or up or down, or t'any other place
> Which way soever lies the Empty Space.[4]

The first stanza is a vivid enough description of magnetic induction, the power of magnetized iron to attract other pieces of iron. Although this fact was already known to Plato, Lucretius was perhaps among the first to notice, by accident, that magnetic materials could also repel. The phenomenon awaited the discovery of the existence of two types of magnetic poles for an explanation.

---

[3] John Baptista Porta, *Natural Magick* (Naples, 1589), reprint of 1st English ed., Basic Books, Inc., New York, p. 212 (see also Bibliography).
[4] Lucretius Carus, *op. cit.*

There followed many centuries without further progress at a time when only monks were literate and research was limited to theological considerations.

The date of the first magnetic technological invention, the compass, and the place of its birth are still subjects of dispute among historians. Considerable weight of opinion places this in China at some time between 2637 B.C. and 1100 A.D., reflecting a historical *uncertainty principle*, no doubt. Many other sources have it that the compass was introduced into China only in the thirteenth century A.D. and owed its prior invention to Italian or Arab origin. In any event, the compass was certainly known in western Europe by the twelfth century A.D. It was an instrument of marvelous utility and fascinating properties. Einstein has written in his autobiography of its instinctive appeal:

A wonder ... I experienced as a child of 4 or 5 years, when my father showed me a compass. That this needle behaved in such a determined way did not at all fit into the nature of events, which could find a place in the unconscious world of concepts (effects connected with direct "touch"). I can still remember—or at least believe I can remember—that this experience made a deep and lasting impression upon me.[5]

Many authors in the middle ages advanced metaphysical explanations of the phenomenon. However, the Renaissance scientist William Gilbert said of these writers:

... they have lost both their oil and their pains; for, not being practised in the subjects of Nature, and being misled by certain false physical systems, they adopted as theirs, from books only, without magnetical experiments, certain inferences based on vain opinions, and many things that are not, dreaming old wives' tales.[6]

Doubtless his condemnation was too severe. Before Gilbert and the sixteenth century, there had been some attempts at experimental science, although not numerous. The first and most important was due to Pierre Pélerin de Maricourt, better known under the Latin nom de plume Petrus Peregrinus. His "Epistola Petri Peregrini de Maricourt ad Sygerum de Foucaucourt Militem de Magnete," dated 1269 A.D., is the earliest known treatise of experimental physics. Peregrinus experimented with a spherical lodestone which he called *terrella*. Placing on it an oblong piece of iron at various spots, he traced lines in the direction it assumed and thus found these lines to circle the lodestone the way meridians gird the earth, crossing at two points. These he called the *poles* of the magnet, by analogy with the poles of the earth.

GILBERT AND DESCARTES

Of the early natural philosophers who studied magnetism the most famous is William Gilbert of Colchester, the "father of magnetism."

> Gilbert shall live till loadstones cease to draw
> Or British fleets the boundless ocean awe.[7]

The times were ripe for him. Gilbert was born in 1544, after Copernicus and before Galileo, and lived in the bloom of the Elizabethan Renaissance. Physics was his

---

[5] P. A. Schilp (ed.), *Albert Einstein: Philosopher-Scientist*, Harper & Row, New York, 1959, vol. I, p. 9.

[6] Gilbert, *op. cit.*, p. 3.

[7] John Dryden, from "epistle to Doctor Walter Charleton, physician in ordinary to King Charles I."

hobby, and medicine his profession. Eminent in both, he became Queen Elizabeth's private physician and president of the Royal College of Physicians. It is said that when the Queen died, her only personal legacy was a research grant to Gilbert. But this he had no time to enjoy, for he died a few months after her, carried off by the plague in 1603.

Some 20 years before Sir Francis Bacon, he was a firm believer in what we now call the experimental method. Realizing that "it is very easy for men of acute intellect, apart from experiment and practice, to slip and err," he resolved to trust no fact which he could not prove by his own experience. *De Magnete* was Gilbert's master-piece, 17 years in the writing and containing almost all his results prior to the date of publication in 1600. There he assembled all the trustworthy knowledge of his time on magnetism, together with his own major contributions. Among other experiments, he reproduced those performed three centuries earlier by Peregrinus with the terrella; but Gilbert realized that his terrella was an actual model of the earth and thus was the first to state specifically that the earth is itself a magnet "which opinion of his was no sooner broached that it was embraced and wel-commed by many prime wits as well English as Forraine."[8] Gilbert's theory of magnetic fields went as follows: "Rays of magnetick virtue spread out in every direction in an orbe; the center of this orbe is not at the pole (as Porta reckons) but in the center of the stone and of the terrella."[9]

Gilbert dispelled superstitions surrounding the lodestone, of which some dated from antiquity, such as, "if a loadstone be anointed with garlic, or if a diamond be near, it does not attract iron." Some of these had already been disproved by Peregrinus in 1269, and even nearer to Gilbert's time, by the Italian scientist Porta, founder of one of the earliest scientific academies. Let Porta recount this:

> It is a common Opinion amongst Sea-men, that Onyons and Garlick are at odds with the Loadstone: and Steersmen, and such as tend the Mariners Card are forbidden to eat Onyons or Garlick, lest they make the Index of the Poles drunk. But when I tried all these things, I found them to be false: for not onely breathing and belching upon the Loadstone after eating of Garlick, did not stop its Virtues: but when it was all anoynted over with the juice of Garlick, it did perform its office as well as if it had never been touched with it: and I could observe almost not the least difference, lest I should seem to make void the endeavours of the Ancients. And again, When I enquired of the Mariners, Whether it were so, that they were forbid to eat Onyons and Garlick for that reason; they said, They were old Wives fables, and things ridiculous; and that Sea-men would sooner lose their lives, than abstain from eating Onyons and Garlick.[10]

But the superstitions survived the disproofs of Peregrinus, Porta, and Gilbert, and have left their vestiges in our own time and in common language. Between super-stition and fraud there is but a thin line, and Galileo recounts how his natural skepti-cism protected him in one instance from a premature Marconi:

> … a man offered to sell me a secret for permitting one to speak, through the attraction of a certain magnet needle, to someone distant two or three thousand miles, and I said to him that I would be willing to purchase it, but that I would like to witness a trial of it, and that it would please me to test it, I being in one room and he being in another. He told me that, at such short distance, the action could not be witnessed to advantage; so I sent him away, and

---

[8] Nathaniel Carpenter, Dean of Ireland, quoted in Mottelay's book, *A Bibliographical History …* p. 107 (see Bibliography).

[9] Gilbert, *op. cit.*, p. 95.

[10] Porta, *op. cit.*, p. 211.

said that I could not just then go to Egypt or Muscovy to see his experiment, but that if he would go there himself I would stay and attend to the rest in Venice.[11]

Medical healers of all times have been prompt to invoke magnetism. For example, mesmerism, or animal magnetism, was just another instance of the magnetic fluids, which we shall discuss shortly, invading the human body. Still seeking to disprove such hypotheses, it was in the interest of science that Thomas Alva Edison, as late as 1892, subjected himself "together with some of his collaborators and one dog" to very strong magnetic fields without, however, sensing any effects.

But how could experiments disprove metaphysics? In spite of their own extensive investigations, Gilbert and Porta were themselves believers in an animistic philosophy, and such were their theory and explanations of the phenomena which they had studied. Note in what sensuous terms Porta describes magnetic attraction:

... iron is drawn by the Loadstone, as a bride after the bridegroom, to be embraced; and the iron is so desirous to joyn with it as her husband, and is so sollicitous to meet the Loadstone: when it is hindred by its weight, yet it will stand an end, as if it held up its hands to beg of the stone, and flattering of it, ... and shews that it is not content with its condition: but if it once kist the Loadstone, as if the desire were satisfied, it is then at rest; and they are so mutually in love, that if one cannot come to the other it will hang pendulous in the air. ...[12]

His explanation, or theory, for this phenomenon is no less anthropomorphic:

I think the Loadstone is a mixture of stone and iron ... whilst one labors to get the victory of the other, the attraction is made by the combat between them. In that body, there is more of the stone than of the iron; and therefore the iron, that it may not be subdued by the stone, desires the force and company of iron; that being not able to resist alone, it may be able by more help to defend itself. For all creatures defend their being.[13]

To which Gilbert, picking up the dialogue 40 years later, retorts:

As if in the Loadstone the iron were a distinct body and not mixed up as the other metals in their ores! And that these, being so mixed up, should fight with one another, and should extend their quarrel, and that in consequence of the battle auxilliary forces should be called in, is indeed absurd. But iron itself, when excited by the Loadstone, seizes iron no less strongly than the Loadstone. Therefore those fights, seditions, and conspiracies in the stone ... are the ravings of a babbling old woman, not the inventions of a distinguished mage.[14]

Gilbert's own ideas are themselves a curious blend of science and myth. On the one hand he dismisses the effluvia theory of magnetism with cogent reasoning, although he admits this concept might apply to electricity. His arguments are pithy: magnetic force can penetrate objects and the lodestone attracts iron through solid materials other than air, which should act as deterrents to any sort of effluvium. Electricity, on the other hand, is strongly affected by all sorts of materials. But when he comes to give his own explanation for magnetic attraction, he states it arises because "the Loadstone hath a soul." He believed the earth to have one, and therefore the loadstone also, it "being a part and choice offspring of its animate mother the earth."[15]

Notwithstanding the shortcomings of his theory, Gilbert had indeed inaugurated the experimental method. At the other pole stands René Descartes (1596–1650). Here

---

[11] Spoken by Sagredus in "Dialogo sopra i due massimi sistemi del mondo Tolemaico e Copernicano," 1632.

[12] Porta, *op. cit.*, p. 201.

[13] *Ibid*, p. 191.

[14] Gilbert, *op. cit.*, p. 63.

[15] *Ibid.*, p. 210.

was a philosopher who ignored the facts, but whose merit it was to exorcise the soul out of the lodestone, laying the foundations of a rational theory. Descartes is the author of the first extensive theory of magnetism, stated in his *Principia*, Part IV, sections 133–183.

Since Descartes was among the "prime forraine wits" to embrace Gilbert's hypothesis linking the lodestone to the earth, his theory of ferromagnetism is accessory to his theory of geomagnetism. Both can be summarized as follows: The prime imponderables were not specifically denoted "effluvia" but rather "threaded parts"

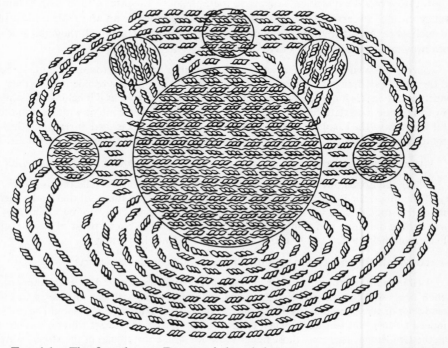

FIG. 1.1. The first theory: Descartes' threaded parts are shown going through the earth (center sphere) and in and around other magnetized bodies.

(*parties cannelées*). These were channeled in one-way ducts through the earth, entering through pores in one pole while leaving through pores in the other. Two kinds of parts were distinguished: those which could only enter the North Pole and leave by the South, and those which made the inverse voyage. The return trip was, in either case, by air. The parts find this a disagreeable mode of travel, and seize upon the opportunity to cross any lodestone in the way. So much so, indeed, that if they chance to meet a lodestone they will even abandon their ultimate destination and stay with it, crossing it over and over again. This is shown in Fig. 1.1. Vortices are thus created in and around the material. Lodestone, iron, and steel are the only materials having the proper channels to accommodate the parts because of their origin in the inner earth. Of these, lodestone ducts are best, whereas iron is malleable, and therefore the furlike cillia which cause the ducts to be one-way are disturbed in the process of mining. The threaded parts—throwing themselves upon the iron with great speed—can restore the position of the cillia, and thus magnetize the metal. Steel, being harder, retains magnetization better.

With this theory, Descartes claimed to be able to interpret all magnetic phenomena known to his time. From today's perspective it is hard to see how he even met Gilbert's objection to the theory of effluvia, stated a generation earlier, nor how this theory could answer the practical questions which arise in the mind of anyone working directly with magnetism. However, such was Descartes' reputation that this theory came to be accepted as fact, and influenced all thinking on the subject throughout his century, and much of the eighteenth. Two of his more prominent disciples in the eighteenth century were the famed Swiss mathematician Léonard Euler and the Swedish mystic and physicist Emmanuel Swedenborg.

Descartes, in his physics and in his philosophy, marks the transition between metaphysical and scientific thought. First, he re-established confidence in the power of reason, which was an absolute necessity for the birth of theoretical science. Second, he postulated a dichotomy of the soul and of the body, which opened the door to the study of nature on her own terms. In that, he was not alone. The beginning of the seventeenth century had witnessed a widespread mechanistic revolution in the sciences, led by such men as Gassendi, Mersenne, Hobbes, Pascal, Huygens and others. These people often went much further than Descartes in divorcing physics from metaphysics. Descartes still believed that physics could be deduced from unprovable first principles, and his mechanism was thus close to the Greeks'. He invoked metaphysics to ascertain his scientific assumptions: his argument was that, since God created both nature and our reason, we can trust that the certitudes He has instilled in us correspond to truth. The other mechanists, however, were content with a more humble approach to nature: let us describe the phenomena, they would say, and not mind the deeper essence of things.

Probably the most important contribution of mechanism to modern science is the adoption of a separate language to describe nature, that of mathematics. At first, there is an intuition. Galileo had already said in 1590: "Philosophy is written in a great book which is always open in front of our eyes (I mean: the universe), but one cannot understand it without first applying himself to understanding its language and knowing the characters in which it is written. It is written in the *mathematical* language."[16] Descartes, almost 30 years later, receives the same idea as an illumination, though he fails to apply it successfully. The new language having been adopted, physics will receive an impetus from the invention of calculus (by Newton and Leibnitz, in the 1680's) and from all subsequent progress in mathematics. The intuition of Galileo and Descartes has been borne out so well by the results that mathematics has now come to replace metaphysics as a set of first principles from which we can deduce and make conclusions.

In magnetism, it is the French monk Mersenne, a friend of Descartes', who is the first, in 1644, to quantify many of Gilbert's observations.[17] Progress in theory remains slow. The mechanists are reluctant to speculate about deeper causes, and the field is left to the neocartesians. Even so, by the year 1700 there is one (as later there will be many) dissident voice singing a new tune. It belongs to John Keill, Savilian professor of astronomy at Oxford, who in his eighth lecture of that year observes:

It is certain that the magnetic attractions and directions arise from the structure of parts; for if a loadstone be struck hard enough, so that the position of its internal parts be changed,

---

[16] *Opera di Galileo Galilei*, Ed. Nazionale, Firenze, 1890–1909, vol. V, p. 232.
[17] Marin Mersenne, "Cogitata physico-mathematica" (1644), the part entitled "Tractatus de Magnetis proprietatibus."

the loadstone will also be changed. And if a loadstone be put into the fire, insomuch as the internal structure of the parts be changed or wholly destroyed, then it will lose also its former virtue and will scarce differ from other stones. ... And what some generally boast of, concerning effluvia, a subtile matter, particles adapted to the pores of the loadstone, etc., ... does not in the least lead us to a clear and distinct explication of those operations; but notwithstanding all these things, the magnetick virtues must still be reckoned amongst the occult qualities.[18]

RISE OF MODERN SCIENCE

It is not until the second half of the eighteenth century that we see the beginnings of a modern scientific attack on the problems of magnetism, characterized by a flexible interplay between theory and experiment and founded in rational hypotheses. For a while, theory becomes variations on the theme of *fluids*. Even Maxwell was to swim in this hypothesis, and it was not until the discovery of the electron that magnetic theory could be placed on more solid ground.

The fluid theory was originally proposed as an explanation for electricity after the discovery by Stephen Gray in 1729 that electricity could be conveyed from one body to another. This was through the medium of metals or other "nonelectric" substances, i.e., substances which conduct electricity and do not lend themselves readily to the accumulation of static charge. An early, and eminent proponent of the "one-fluid" hypothesis was Benjamin Franklin. He interpreted static charge as the lack, or excess, of the electric fluid. One of his scientific disciples, a German *émigré* to St. Petersburg by the name of Franz Maria Aepinus (1724–1802), applied the one-fluid theory to magnetism. His theories of electricity and magnetism appear in *Tentamen Theoriae Electricitatis et Magnetismi*, published in St. Petersburg, 1759.[19] This is an important work for it brought many ideas of Franklin into sharp focus and gave the theories of effluvia the *coup de grâce* by dint of mathematical and experimental reasoning.

In 1733, Charles François duFay, superintendent of the French Royal Botanical Gardens, discovered that there were two types of electricity. These he denoted *vitreous* and *resinous*, each of which attracted its opposite and repelled its own kind. As this idea came into competition with the Franklin one-fluid theory, much thought and many experiments were expended on proving one at the expense of the other.

Some years after electricity was granted a second fluid, so was magnetism. The two fluids were denoted *austral* and *boreal* in correspondence with the two poles. It was said that in the natural nonmagnetic state the two fluids saturate iron equally, but that magnetization parts them and leads them slightly towards their respective poles, where they accumulate. The Swede Johan C. Wilcke, a former student and collaborator of Aepinus, and the Dutchman Anton Brugmans presented this two-fluid hypothesis independently in 1778.

The best-known proponent of the two-fluid theory was Charles Augustin Coulomb (1736–1806), who proposed an important modification in the theory, and whose experiments have immortalized his name as the unit of charge and in connection with the law of force.[20] It was by means of a torsion balance of his invention that he

---

[18] J. Keill, *Introductio ad Veram Physicam*, 1705 (trans., 1776).

[19] Although this work has never been translated from the Latin, a good account of it is given by Père René Just Haüy in his "Exposition raisonnée de la théorie de l'électricité et du magnétisme," 1787.

[20] Almost all of Coulomb's memoirs are collected in a single work published by the *Société française de physique* in 1884, *Collection des Mémoires Relatifs à la Physique*, vol. 1.

established with some precision the law which bears his name: that infinitesimals of either fluid, in electricity as in magnetism, attract or repel in the ratio of the inverse of the square of their distance. After establishing this in 1785, he performed many experiments on the thermal properties of magnets. On the theoretical side, his principal contribution was the realization that the magnetic fluids could not be free to flow like their electrical counterpart, but perforce were bound to the individual molecules. Thus, he supposed each molecule to become polarized somewhat in the process of magnetization. In this manner it could be explained why the analogue of Gray's effect had never been found in magnetism, and why two new poles always appeared when a magnet was cut in twain. Coulomb was also aware that the laws of force he had discovered were *not* applicable on an atomic scale, that a solid body was not in stable equilibrium under the effect of the inverse square law of force alone. However, concerning the unknown laws of molecular repulsion, attraction, and cohesion, he was to write, "It is almost always more curious than useful to seek to know their causes,"[21] a correct (if defeatist) attitude considering the nearly complete ignorance of atomic structure in his day.

Siméon Denis Poisson (1781–1840) is the man who eventually became the best interpreter of the physical constructs which Coulomb discovered. Here was a brilliant mathematician whose scientific career appears to have been predestined from his early successes in school, whose teacher predicted, punning on the verse of La Fontaine:

Petit Poisson deviendra grand
Pourvu que Dieu lui prête vie.[22]

To magnetism, Poisson brought the concept of the static potential, with which he had been so successful in solving the problems of static electricity. And having invented the mathematical theory of magnetostatics, he proceeded by solving a considerable number of problems in that field. This work dates from 1824 onwards, a very exciting time in physics as we shall see in the following section. But Poisson ignored all developments that came after the experiments of Coulomb, and while he gave the full theory of all the discoveries by the master of the torsion balance, he did not participate in the exciting movement which followed and which was to lead science into a totally new direction.

We understand the magnetical work of Poisson today mostly in the manner in which it was extended and interpreted by George Green (1793–1841). Poisson's "equivalent volume and surface distributions of magnetization" are but a special case of one of the later Green theorems. Poisson found it convenient to consider instead of $\mathbf{H}(\mathbf{r})$ the scalar potential $V(\mathbf{r})$ with the property that

$$\mathbf{\nabla} V(\mathbf{r}) = \mathbf{H}(\mathbf{r}) \tag{1}$$

The contribution to $V(\mathbf{r})$ from the point $\mathbf{r}'$ is

$$\left(m_x \frac{\partial}{\partial x'} \frac{1}{|\mathbf{r} - \mathbf{r}'|} + \cdots \right) d_3 r' = \mathbf{m} \cdot \mathbf{\nabla}' \frac{1}{|\mathbf{r} - \mathbf{r}'|} d_3 r' \tag{2}$$

---

[21] *Mémoire lu à l'Institut le 26 prairial, an 7, par le citoyen Coulomb,* Mémoires de l'Institut, vol. III, p. 176.
[22] Little Fish will become great if God allows him but to live.

and the potential from the entire sample is

$$V(\mathbf{r}) = \int_{\text{vol}} \mathbf{m}(\mathbf{r}') \cdot \mathbf{\nabla}' \frac{1}{|\mathbf{r} - \mathbf{r}'|} \, d_3 r' \tag{3}$$

By partial integration, this is transformed into the sum of a surface integral and of a volume integral,[23]

$$V(\mathbf{r}) = \int_{\text{sur}} \frac{1}{|\mathbf{r} - \mathbf{r}'|} \, \mathbf{m} \cdot d\mathbf{S}' - \int_{\text{vol}} \frac{1}{|\mathbf{r} - \mathbf{r}'|} \, \mathbf{\nabla}' \cdot \mathbf{m}(\mathbf{r}') \, d_3 r' \tag{4}$$

the latter vanishing for the important special case of constant magnetization. In that special case, the sources behaved *as if* they were all on the surface of the north and south poles of the magnet, and from this one might suspect that experiments concerning the nature of magnetic fields surrounding various substances would *never* reveal the slightest information about the mechanism within the material. Therefore, the fluid hypothesis seemed as good a working model as any. Poisson also extended the theory in several directions. For example, by means of certain assumptions regarding the susceptibility of magnetic fluids to applied fields he obtained a law of induced magnetization, thereby explaining the phenomenon of which Lucretius had sung.

Poisson, like Coulomb, refused to become excited about any speculation concerning the *nature* of the sources of the field, which is to say, the fluids. This reluctance to discuss the profound nature of things was, of course, an extreme swing of the pendulum away from metaphysics. That attitude was itself developed into an all-embracing philosophy by Auguste Comte. *Positivism*, as it was called, holds that in every field of knowledge general laws can only be induced from the accumulated facts and that it is possible to arrive, in this way, at fundamental truths. Comte believed this to be the only scientific attitude. But, after Poisson, the main theoretical advances will be made by men who will ask *why* as well as *how*. That is, by physicists who will make *hypotheses vaster, simpler, and more speculative than the mere facts allow*. The specialization to the facts at hand answers the *how*; the vaster theory, the *why*.

ELECTRODYNAMICS

As early as the seventeenth century there was reason to connect the effects of electricity and magnetism. For example, "in 1681, a ship bound for Boston was struck by lightning. Observation of the stars showed that 'the compasses were changed'; 'the north point was turn'd clear south.' The ship was steered to Boston with the compass reversed."[24] The fluids had proliferated, and this now made it desirable to seek a relationship among them. The invention of the voltaic pile about 1800 was to stimulate a series of discoveries which would bring relative order out of this chaos.

During the time that Poisson, undisturbed, was bringing mathematical refinements to the theory of fluids, an exciting discovery opened the view to a new science of electrodynamics. In April, 1820, a Danish physicist, Hans Christian Oersted (1777–1851) came upon the long-sought connection between electricity and magnetism.

---

[23] Poisson, *Mémoire sur la théorie du magnétisme*, Mém. de l'Acad., vol. V, p. 247.
[24] F. Cajori, *A History of Physics*, Dover, New York, 1962, p. 102.

Oersted himself had been seeking to find such a connection since the year 1807, but always unfruitfully, until the fateful day when he directed his assistant Hansteen to try the effect of a current on a delicately suspended magnetic needle nearby. *The needle moved.* The theory which had guided his earlier research had indicated to him that the relation should manifest itself most favorably under open-circuit conditions and not when the electric fluid was allowed to leak away, and one can easily imagine his stupefaction when the unexpected occurred. On July 21, 1820, he published a memoir in Latin (then a more universal tongue than Danish), which was sent to scientists and scientific societies around the world.[25] Translations of his paper were published in the languages and journals of every civilized country.

The reaction was feverish; immediately work started, checking and extending the basic facts of electromagnetism. French and British scientists led the initial competition for discoveries. At first the French came in ahead. The French Academy of Science of that time was a star-studded assembly, and besides Poisson it included such personalities as Laplace, Fresnel, Fourier, and more particularly active in this new field, Biot, Savart, Arago, and Ampère.

Dominique F. J. Arago (1786–1853) was the first to report to the Academy the news of Oersted's discovery, on September 11, 1820. Here was a most remarkable scientist, who had been elected to the Academy 12 years earlier at the age of 23 as a reward for "adventurous conduct in the cause of science." The story of his dedication is worth retelling. In 1806, Arago and J. B. Biot had been commissioned to conduct a geodetic survey of some coastal islands of Spain. This was the period of Napoleon's invasion of that country, and the populace took them for a pair of spies. After escaping from a prison, Arago escaped to Algiers, whence he took a boat back to Marseilles. This was captured by a Spanish man of war almost within sight of port! After several years of imprisonment and wanderings about North Africa, he finally made his way back to Paris in the Summer of 1809, and forthwith deposited the precious records of his survey in the *Bureau des Longitudes*, having preserved them intact throughout his vicissitudes. In this, he followed in a great tradition, and today's armchair scientists may well find their predecessors an adventurous lot. Earlier, in 1753, G. W. Richmann of St. Petersburg, had been struck dead by lightning while verifying the experiments of Franklin. The effects of the electricity on his various organs were published in leading scientific journals, and Priestly wrote: "It is not given to every electrician to die in so glorious manner as the justly envied Richmann."[26]

Shortly after his initial report to the Academy, Arago performed experiments of his own and established that a current acts like an ordinary magnet, both in attracting iron filings and in its ability to induce permanent magnetism in iron needles.

Seven days after Arago's report, André Marie Ampère (1775–1836) read a paper before the Academy, in which he suggested that internal electrical currents were responsible for the existence of ferromagnetism, and that these currents flowed perpendicular to the axis of the magnet. By analogy, might not steel needles magnetized in a solenoid show a stronger degree of magnetization than those exposed to a single current-carrying wire? Ampère proposed this idea to Arago, and they jointly performed the successful experiment on which Arago reported to the Academy on November 6, 1820.

---

[25] This memoir refers to the experiment performed "last year," by which Oersted meant "last academic year," viz., "last April." This has often been misinterpreted, and the date 1819 incorrectly given for the discovery.

[26] J. B. Priestly, *Hist. of Elec.*, London, 1775, p. 86.

The English were barely tardy. It took Sir Humphry Davy (1778–1829) until November 16 of that year to report on his similar experiments. Everyone took particular pains to witness and record important experiments and the dates thereof, and thus establish priority. No one on either side of the Channel underestimated the importance of Oersted's discovery nor of the results which flowed therefrom.

After Ampère's death, correspondence to him from Fresnel (one letter undated, the other dated 5 June, 1821) was found among his papers, containing the suggestion that the "Amperian currents" causing ferromagnetism should be molecular rather than macroscopic in dimension. Ampère had hesitated on this point. Fresnel wrote that the lack of (Joule) heating, and arguments similar to those advanced above in connection with Coulomb's theory, suggested the existence of elementary, atomic or molecular currents.[27] This must have accorded well with Ampère's own ideas, and he made some (unpublished) calculations on the basis of such a model. This work was carried on subsequently by W. E. Weber (1804–1891), who assumed the molecules of iron or steel to be capable of movement around their fixed centers. These molecules, in unmagnetized iron or steel, lie in various directions such as to neutralize each other's field; but under the application of an external force, they turn around so that their axes lie favorably oriented with respect to this external field. Precisely the same concept had been stated by Ampère, in a letter addressed to Faraday dated 10 July, 1822, and it proved superior to Poisson's theory in explaining the saturation of magnetization, for example. The final evolution of this idea may be traced to J. A. Ewing (1855–1935), who pivoted tiny magnets arranged in geometric arrays so that they might be free to turn and assume various magnetic configurations. If these magnets could be assumed each to represent a magnetic molecule, and the experimental distance scaled to molecular size, the experiments of Ewing might have been expected to yield quantitative as well as qualitative information about ferromagnets. As Digby had written long before, in connection with Gilbert's terrella, "any man that hath an ayme to advance much in naturall science, must endeavour to draw the matter he inquireth of, into some such modell, or some kind of manageable methode; which he may turne and winde as he pleaseth...." But for the outcome, see ahead, p. 27.

The fact that current loops had been found by Ampère to behave in every manner like elementary magnets did not logically justify the belief that ferromagnetism is caused by internal electric currents. Nevertheless, this was the hypothesis most economical in concepts which could be put forward, and as it turned out, the most fruitful in stimulating new discoveries and in creating "insight" into the "physics" of magnetism. It was Ampère and his followers, rather than Poisson and his school, who acted in the modern style, which we may describe as the harmonious union of theory and experiment.

The modern scientific method, which found in electrodynamics one of its early applications, seeks to imbed every phenomenon into a vaster mathematical and conceptual framework and, within this context, to answer the question of why it occurs, and not merely of how it happens. The long list of discoveries by the electrodynamicists is sufficient tribute to the efficacy of this method, even though their explanations of the cause of magnetism were to be proved wrong. If we dwell on the subject, it is because of the popular misconception that modern science is positivistic, an idea which is not justified by the methods with which science is carried forward today. Einstein wrote: "There is no inductive method which could lead to the fundamental

---

[27] *Collection des Mém. Rel. à la Phys.*, Soc. franç. de phys., 1884, vol. II, pp. 141, 144.

concepts of physics ... in error are those theorists who believe that theory comes inductively from experience."[28]

The nineteenth century was so rich in interrelated theories and discoveries in the fields of atomic structure, thermodynamics, electricity, and magnetism, that it is quite difficult to disentangle them and neatly pursue our history of the theory of magnetism. Fortunately many excellent and general accounts exist of the scientific progress made in that epoch, in which magnetism is discussed in the proper perspective, as one of the many areas of investigation. Here we concentrate only on the conceptual progress which was made and distinguish between progress in the physical theory of magnetism and progress in the understanding of the nature of the magnetic forces.

Much is owed to the insight of Michael Faraday (1791–1867), the humble scientist who is often called the greatest experimental genius of his century. Carrying forward the experiments of the Dutchman Brugmans, who had discovered that (paramagnetic) cobalt is attracted, whereas (diamagnetic) bismuth and antimony are repelled from the single pole of a magnet, Faraday studied the magnetic properties of a host of ordinary materials and found that all matter has one magnetic property or the other, although usually only to a very small degree. It is in describing an experiment with an electromagnet, in which a diamagnetic substance set itself with its longer axis at right angles to the magnetic flux, that Faraday first used the term, "magnetic field" (December, 1845). He was not theoretically minded and never wrote an equation in his life. Nevertheless, his experiments led him unambiguously to the belief that magnetic substances acted upon one another by means of intermediary fields and not by "action at a distance." This was best explained by Maxwell who

> ... resolved to read no mathematics on the subject till I had first read through Faraday's *Experimental Researches in Electricity*. I was aware that there was supposed to be a difference between Faraday's way of conceiving phenomena and that of the mathematicians. ... As I proceeded with the study of Faraday, I perceived that his method ... [was] capable of being expressed in ordinary mathematical forms. ... For instance, Faraday, in his mind's eye, saw lines of force traversing all space where the mathematicians saw centres of force attracting at a distance: Faraday saw a medium where they saw nothing but distance. ... I also found that several of the most fertile methods of research discovered by the mathematicians could be expressed much better in terms of ideas derived from Faraday than in their original form.[29]

Faraday's concept of fields led him to expect that they would influence light, and after many unfruitful experiments he finally discovered in 1845 the effect which bears his name. This was a rotation of plane-polarized light upon passing through a medium in a direction parallel to the magnetization. Beside the Faraday effect, several other magneto-optic phenomena became important. The Kerr magneto-optic effect is the analogue of the above, in the case of light reflected off a magnetic or magnetized material. Magnetic double refraction, of which an extreme example is the Cotton-Mouton effect, is double refraction of light passing perpendicular to the magnetization. But the effect which was to have the greatest theoretical implications was that discovered by Zeeman, which we shall discuss subsequently.

By virtue of the physicomathematical predictions to which it led, the hypothesis of fields acquired a reality which it has never since lost. Henry Adams wrote *ca.* 1900:

> For a historian, the story of Faraday's experiments and the invention of the dynamo passed belief; it revealed a condition of human ignorance and helplessness before the

---

[28] A. Einstein, *The Method of Theoretical Physics*, Oxford, 1933.
[29] James Clerk Maxwell, *A Treatise on Electricity and Magnetism*, 1873.

commonest forces, such as his mind refused to credit. He could not conceive but that some-one, somewhere, could tell him all about the magnet, if one could but find the book. ...[30]

But of course there was such a book: James Clerk Maxwell (1831–1879) had summarized Faraday's researches, his own equations, and all that was known about the properties of electromagnetic fields and their interactions with ponderable matter.[31]

With Faraday, Maxwell believed the electric field to represent a real, physical stress in the ether (vacuum). Because electrodynamics had shown the motion of electricity to be responsible for magnetic fields, the latter must therefore have a physical representation as rates of change in the stress fields. Thus the energy density $E^2/8\pi$ stored in the electric field was of necessity potential energy; and the energy density $H^2/8\pi$ stored in the magnetic field was necessarily kinetic energy of the field. This interpretation given by Maxwell showed how early he anticipated the Hamiltonian mechanics of the quantum theory, and how modern his outlook was.

The harmonic solutions of Maxwell's equations were calculated to travel with a velocity close to that of light. When the values of the magnetic and electrical constants were precisely determined, it was found by H. R. Hertz in 1888 that these waves were precisely those of light, radio, and those other disturbances that we now commonly call *electromagnetic waves*. Later, the special theory of relativity was invented by Einstein with the principal purpose of giving to the material sources of the field the same beautiful properties of invariance which Maxwell had bestowed on the fields alone.

A formulation of Maxwell's equations which is most useful for our purposes introduces the vector potential $A(r, t)$ in terms of the magnetic field $H(r, t)$ and the magnetization $M(r, t)$ as

$$\boxed{\nabla \times \mathbf{A} = \mathbf{H} + 4\pi\mathbf{M} = \mathbf{B}} \tag{5}$$

The vector $\mathbf{B}$ is defined as the **curl** of $\mathbf{A}$, and is therefore solenoidal by definition; that is, $\nabla \cdot \mathbf{B} = 0$, as is instantly verified. The next equation introduces the electric field in terms of the potentials $A(r, t)$ and the scalar potential $U(r)$ without the necessity of describing the sources. More precisely,

$$\boxed{\mathbf{E} = -\nabla U - \frac{1}{c}\frac{\partial \mathbf{A}}{\partial t}} \tag{6}$$

This is but the equation of the dynamo: the motion or rate of change of the magnetic field is responsible for an electric field, and if this is made to occur in a wire, a current will flow. The familiar differential form of this equation,

$$\nabla \times \mathbf{E} = -\frac{1}{c}\frac{\partial \mathbf{B}}{\partial t} \tag{7}$$

is obtained by taking the curl of both sides. Next, the results of Oersted, Ampère,

---

[30] Henry Adams, *The Education of Henry Adams*, Random House, 1931.
[31] Maxwell, *op. cit.*

Arago, and their colleagues almost all were contained in the equation

$$\nabla \times \mathbf{H} = \frac{4\pi}{c}\mathbf{j} + \frac{1}{c}\frac{\partial \mathbf{D}}{\partial t} \tag{8}$$

where $\mathbf{j}$ = real current density, and

$$\mathbf{D} = \mathbf{E} + 4\pi\mathbf{P} \tag{9}$$

relates the electric displacement vector $\mathbf{D}$ to the electric field $\mathbf{E}$ and the polarization of material substances, $\mathbf{P}$. Equation (8) can be transformed into more meaningful form by using the definitions of $\mathbf{H}$ and $\mathbf{D}$ in terms of $\mathbf{A}$, $\mathbf{P}$, and $\mathbf{M}$, assuming $\nabla \cdot \mathbf{A} = 0$:

$$\left(-\nabla^2 + \frac{1}{c^2}\frac{\partial^2}{\partial t^2}\right)\mathbf{A}(\mathbf{r}, t) = 4\pi\left(\frac{1}{c}\mathbf{j} + \frac{1}{c}\frac{\partial \mathbf{P}}{\partial t} + \nabla \times \mathbf{M}\right) \tag{10}$$

This equation shows that in regions characterized by the absence of all material sources $\mathbf{j}$, $\mathbf{P}$, and $\mathbf{M}$, the vector potential obeys a wave equation, the solutions of which propagate with c = speed of light. The right-hand side of this equation provides a ready explanation for Ampère's famous theorem, that every current element behaved, insofar as its magnetic properties were concerned, precisely like a fictitious magnetic shell which would contain it. For if we replace all the currents $\mathbf{j}$ (assumed constant) by a fictitious magnetization $\mathbf{M} = \mathbf{r} \times \mathbf{j}/2c$ the fields would be unaffected. Nevertheless, for the sake of definiteness it will be useful to assume that $\mathbf{j}$ always refers to real free currents, $\mathbf{P}$ to bound or quasibound charges, and $\mathbf{M}$ to real, permanent magnetic moments.

THE ELECTRON

Once these equations permitted a conceptual separation of cause and effect, of the fields and of their sources, progress had to be made in understanding the sources. This was tied in with the nature of matter itself, a study which at long last became "more useful than curious," to turn about the words of Coulomb. A giant step was taken in this direction by the discovery of the electron, one of the greatest scientific legacies of the nineteenth century to our own.

While Faraday, Maxwell, and many others had noted the likelihood that charge existed in discrete units only, this idea did not immediately make headway into chemistry, and Mendeléev's 1869 atomic table was based on atomic weights rather than atomic numbers. The first concrete suggestion was made in 1874 by G. Johnstone Stoney, the man who was to give the particle its name in 1891.[32] We know the electron as the fundamental particle, carrier of $e = 1.26 \times 10^{-19}$ Coulomb unit of charge, and $m = 9.11 \times 10^{-28}$ gram of rest mass, building block of atoms, molecules, solid and liquid matter. But it is amusing to us to recall that it was first isolated far from its native habitat, streaming from the cathode of the gas discharge tubes built in the

---

[32] G. Johnstone Stoney, *Trans. Roy. Dub. Soc.*, 4: 583 (1891).

seventies. Certainly it was of mixed parentage. To mention but two of the greatest contributors to its "discovery," Jean Perrin found in his 1895 thesis work that the cathode rays consisted of negatively charged particles, and Thomson had obtained the ratio e/m to good precision by 1897 (curvature in a magnetic field). Its existence was consecrated at the Paris International Congress of Physics held in 1900 inaugurating the twentieth century with a study devoted to the problems which the discovery of the existence of the electron had finally solved, and the problems which it now raised.[33]

By this time there already was great interest in the spectral lines emitted by incandescent gases, for their discrete nature suggested that the fluids that constituted the atoms were only capable of sustaining certain well-defined vibrational frequencies. In 1896 Zeeman had shown that the spectral lines could be decomposed into sets of lines, *multiplets*, if the radiating atoms were subjected to intense magnetic fields. This experiment had disastrous consequences on various hypotheses of atomic structure which had hitherto appeared in accord with experimental observations, for example, that of Kelvin. Concerning his "gyrostatic" model of the atom as an electrified ring, Kelvin himself, in 1899, was to write its epitaph:

No simplifying suppositions as to the character of the molecule, such as the symmetry of forces and moments of inertia round the axis of the ring, can possibly give Zeeman's normal results of the splitting of a bright line into two sharp lines circularly polarized in opposite directions, when the light is viewed (in a spectrograph) from a direction parallel to the lines of magnetic force; and the dividing of each bright line into three, each plane polarized, when the light is viewed from a direction perpendicular to the lines of force. Hence, although from 1856 till quite lately I felt quite satisfied in knowing that it sufficed to explain Faraday's magneto-optic discovery, I now, in the light of Zeeman's recent discovery, discard my old tempting gyrostatic hypothesis for an irrefragable reason. ....[34]

It was Zeeman's teacher, the Dutch theoretician Hendrik Antoon Lorentz (1853–1928), who provided the first reasonable theory of the phenomenon, and he based it on the electron theory. (Later he extended his electron theory to give a physical basis for all of electrodynamics. "The judgment exhibited by him here is remarkable," wrote Sommerfeld, "he introduced only concepts which retained their substance in the later theory of relativity."[35]) Most useful for our purpose is Lorentz' formulation of the force exerted by electric and magnetic fields on a (nonrelativistic) particle of charge e and velocity $\mathbf{v}$:

$$\mathbf{F} = e\left(\mathbf{E} + \frac{\mathbf{v}}{c} \times \mathbf{B}\right) \tag{11}$$

In the Lorentz theory of the Zeeman effect, one assumes the electron to be held to the atom by a spring (of strength K) and a weak magnetic field $H(=B)$ applied along the z direction. Thus, by the laws of Newton and Lorentz,

$$m\ddot{\mathbf{r}} = \mathbf{F} = -K\mathbf{r} + \frac{e}{c}\dot{\mathbf{r}} \times \mathbf{H} \tag{12}$$

---

[33] For a more complete account of the birth of the electron, see D. L. Anderson, *The Discovery of the Electron*, Van Nostrand, Princeton, N.J., 1964.

[34] "Mathematical and Physical Papers of W. Thomson, Lord Kelvin," vol. V, Cambridge, 1911.

[35] A. Sommerfeld, *Electrodynamics*, Academic, New York, 1952, p. 236.

The motion $z(t)$ proceeds at the unperturbed frequency

$$z(t) = z(0) \cos \omega_0 t \qquad \text{with} \qquad \omega_0 = \sqrt{\frac{K}{m}} \qquad (13)$$

but in the perpendicular direction there is a frequency shift in the amount

$$\Delta\omega \cong \pm \frac{1}{2} \frac{eH}{mc} + O(H^2) \text{ (assuming } \Delta\omega \ll \omega_0) \qquad (14)$$

corresponding to angular motion clockwise or counterclockwise in the plane perpendicular to the magnetic field. If this is equated to the width of the splittings observed, it yields a value for e/m within a factor of 2 from that which had been established for the cathode rays. This factor was not to be explained for another quarter century.

The thermal properties of magnetic substances were first investigated in a systematic manner by Pierre Curie (1859–1906), who established the law for the susceptibility χ of paramagnetic substances,

$$\chi = \lim_{H \to 0} \frac{\mathscr{M}}{H} = \frac{C}{T} \qquad (15)$$

Curie's constant C assumed different (positive) values depending on the material, with T the temperature measured from the absolute zero. In diamagnetic substances he found little variation of the (negative) susceptibility with temperature. In all ferromagnetic materials, he found a relatively rapid decrease of the magnetization as the temperature was raised to a critical value, now known as the Curie temperature; above this temperature, the ferromagnets behaved much like ordinary paramagnetic substances.[36] While many of these results had been known for isolated materials, the scope and quantitative accuracy of his investigations and the enunciation of these general laws gave particular importance to Curie's research.

The diamagnetism was explained a decade after Curie's experiments, in a famous paper[37] by Paul Langevin (1872–1946), as a natural development of Lorentz's electronic theory of the Zeeman effect. As far as Langevin could see, diamagnetism was but another aspect of the Zeeman effect. Without entering into the details of his calculation, we may merely observe that this phenomenon is apparently already contained in one of the Maxwell equations: Eqs. (6) and (7) indicate that when the magnetic field is turned on, an electric field will result; this accelerates the electron, producing an incremental current loop, which in turn is equivalent to a magnetization opposed to the applied field. Thus Lenz' law, as this is called in the case of circuits, was supposed valid on an atomic scale, and held responsible for the universal diamagnetism of materials. Paramagnetism was explained by Langevin as existing only in those atoms which possessed a permanent magnetic moment. The applied magnetic field succeeded in aligning them against thermal fluctuations. Standard thermodynamic reasoning led Langevin to the relationship

$$\mathscr{M} = f\left(\frac{H}{T}\right) \qquad (16)$$

---

[36] P. Curie, *Ann. Chim. Phys.*, (7) **5**: 289 (1895), and *Oeuvres*, Paris, 1908.
[37] P. Langevin, *Ann. Chim. Phys.*, (8) **5**: 70 (1905), and *J. Phys.*, (4) **4**: 678 (1905).

where f = odd function of its argument. Then, the leading term in a Taylor series expansion of the right-hand side yields Curie's law, Eq. (15), without further ado.

THE DEMISE OF CLASSICAL PHYSICS

As we know, the great development of physics in our century is indebted mainly to the invention of quantum mechanics. Progress in the modern understanding of magnetism has depended, to a great extent, on progress in quantum theory. Conversely, the greatest contributions of the theory of magnetism to general physics have been in the field of quantum statistical mechanics and thermodynamics. Whereas understanding in this important branch was limited in the nineteenth century to the theory of gases, the study of *magnetism as a cooperative phenomenon* has been responsible for the most significant advances in the theory of thermodynamic phase transitions. This has transformed statistical mechanics into one of the sharpest and most significant tools for the study of solid matter.

The initial, and perhaps the greatest, step in this direction was taken in 1907 when Pierre Weiss (1865–1940) gave the first modern theory of magnetism.[38] Long before, Coulomb already knew that the ordinary laws of electrostatics and magnetostatics could not be valid on the atomic scale; and neither did Weiss presume to guess what the microscopic laws might be. He merely assumed that the *interactions* between magnetic molecules could be described empirically by what he called a "molecular field." This molecular field H_m would act on each molecule just as an external field did, and its magnitude would be proportional to the magnetization and to a parameter N which would be a constant physical property of the material. Thus, Weiss' modification of the Langevin formula was

$$\mathcal{M} = f\left(\frac{H + N\mathcal{M}}{T}\right) \tag{17}$$

If the molecular field was due to the usual demagnetizing field caused by the free north and south poles on the surface of a spherical ferromagnet, the Weiss constant would be $N \approx -4\pi/3$ in some appropriate units. In fact, experiments gave to N the value $\approx +10^4$ for iron, cobalt, or nickel, as could be determined by solving the equation above for $\mathcal{M}(N, T)$ and fitting N to secure best agreement with experiment. This was particularly easy to do at high temperature, where f could be replaced by the leading term in the Taylor series development. That is,

$$\mathcal{M} \doteq \frac{C}{T}(H + N\mathcal{M}) \tag{18}$$

predicting a Curie temperature (where $\mathcal{M}/H = \infty$) at

$$T_c = CN \tag{19}$$

---

[38] P. Weiss, *J. de Phys.*, (4) **6**: 661 (1907).

Above the Curie temperature, the combination of the two equations above yields

$$\chi = \frac{C}{T - T_c} \tag{20}$$

the famous Curie-Weiss law which is nearly, if not perfectly, obeyed by all ferro-magnets. This agreement with experiment was perhaps unfortunate, for it meant that the gross features of magnetism could be explained without appeal to any particular mechanism and with the simplest of quasithermodynamic arguments. Therefore any model which answered to those few requirements would explain the gross facts, and a correct theory could be tested only on the basis of its predictions for the small deviations away from the laws of Weiss. It was to be some time before the deviations were systematically measured and interpreted, but the large value of Weiss' constant N was intriguing enough in his day and pointed to the existence of new phenomena on the molecular scale.

To the mystery of the anomalously large molecular fields was added that of the *anomalous Zeeman effect*, such as that observed when the sodium D lines were resolved in a strong magnetic field. Unlike the spectrum previously described, these lines split into quartets and even larger multiplets, which could no more be explained by Lorentz' calculation than the normal Zeeman effect could be explained by Kelvin's gyrostatic structures. In view of the other surprising facts of atomic, molecular, and solid-state structure, these were truly mysteries.

A development now took place which should have effected a complete and final overthrow of the Langevin-Lorentz theory of magnetism. It was the discovery of an important theorem in statistical mechanics by Niels Bohr (1885–1962), contained in his doctoral thesis of 1911. In view of the traditional obscurity of such documents, it is not surprising that this theorem should have been rediscovered by others, in particular by Miss J. H. van Leeuwen in the course of her thesis work in Leyden 8 years later. However, due to rapid and important developments in quantum theory which occurred in that period, the Bohr-van Leeuwen theorem was not universally recognized as the significant landmark it was, until so pointed out by Van Vleck[39] in 1932. Consider the following strong statement of it, valid for classical nonrelativistic electrons: *At any finite temperature, and in all finite applied electrical or magnetical fields, the net magnetization of a collection of electrons in thermal equilibrium vanishes identically.* Thus, this theorem marked the end of the classical phase of the theory of magnetism and the beginning of the reign of the quantum theory. We now proceed to a proof of it.

The Maxwell-Boltzmann thermal distribution function gave as the probability that the nth particle have momentum $\mathbf{p}_n$ and coordinate $\mathbf{r}_n$ the following function:

$$dP(\mathbf{p}_1, \dots, \mathbf{p}_N; \mathbf{r}_1, \dots, \mathbf{r}_N) = \exp\left[-\frac{1}{kT}\mathcal{H}(\mathbf{p}_1, \dots; \dots, \mathbf{r}_N)\right]d\mathbf{p}_1 \cdots d\mathbf{r}_N \tag{21}$$

where k = Boltzmann's constant
         T = temperature
         $\mathcal{H}$ = Hamilton's function, total energy of the system

---

[39] J. H. Van Vleck, *The Theory of Electric and Magnetic Susceptibilities*, Oxford, 1932. Summarizing the consequences of this theorem, he quips: "... on the other hand, when one attempts to apply classical statistics to electronic motions within the atom, the less said the better ..." (p. 104).

The thermal average (TA) of any function $F(\mathbf{p}_1, \ldots ; \ldots \mathbf{r}_N)$ of these generalized coordinates was then simply

$$\langle F \rangle_{TA} = \frac{\int F \, dP}{\int dP} \tag{22}$$

with the integration carried out over all the generalized coordinates, or "phase space."

Next we consider an integral solution of Maxwell's equation, Eq. (8), giving the magnetic field in terms of the currents flowing. As the current density created by the motion of a single charge e_n is $\mathbf{j}_n = e_n \mathbf{v}_n$, the integral solution of Eq. (8) becomes

$$\mathbf{H}(\mathbf{r}) = \sum_{n=1}^{N} e_n \frac{\mathbf{v}_n \times \mathbf{R}_n}{c R_n^3} \tag{23}$$

where $\mathbf{R}_n = \mathbf{r} - \mathbf{r}_n$. (This is the law of Biot-Savart in electrodynamics.) The quantity $\mathbf{v}_n \times \mathbf{R}_n$ which appears above is closely related to the *angular momentum*, discussed in Chapter 3. If we wished to calculate the expected magnetic field caused by the motion of charges in a given body, it would suffice to take the thermal average of $\mathbf{H}(\mathbf{r})$ over the thermal ensemble dP characteristic of that body. For this purpose it is necessary to know something about Hamilton's function $\mathcal{H}$, for particles in electric and magnetic fields. In the absence of magnetic fields, this function is

$$\mathcal{H} = \sum_n \tfrac{1}{2} m_n \mathbf{v}_n^2 + U(\mathbf{r}_1, \ldots, \mathbf{r}_N) \tag{24}$$

where $\mathbf{v}_n = \mathbf{p}_n/m_n = d\mathbf{r}_n/dt$ as a consequence of Lagrange's equations; the first term being the kinetic energy of motion and the second the potential energy due to the interactions of the particles amongst themselves and with any fixed potentials not necessarily restricted to Coulomb law forces. We observe from Maxwell's equation, Eq. (6), that Newton's second law $e_n \mathbf{E} = \dot{\mathbf{p}}_n$ assumes once more the form in which forces are derivable from potentials if we incorporate the magnetic field by the substitution $\mathbf{p}_n \rightarrow \mathbf{p}_n + e_n \mathbf{A}(\mathbf{r}_n, t)/c$. This is in fact correct, and the proper value of the velocity for a particle under the effects of a vector potential is

$$m_n \mathbf{v}_n = \mathbf{p}_n + \frac{e_n}{c} \mathbf{A}(\mathbf{r}_n, t) \tag{25}$$

as is more convincingly shown in any contemporary textbook on Lagrangian mechanics.[40] Substitution of this formula into Eq. (24) gives the *Hamiltonian* in the case of interest. This concludes the preliminaries.

It shall be assumed that a magnetic field is applied to the body, as described by a vector potential $\mathbf{A}(\mathbf{r}, t)$, and the resultant magnetization produces in turn a magnetic field $\mathbf{H}(\mathbf{r})$ as given by Eq. (23). The thermal average of this field can be computed, and three situations are distinguished:

1. $\langle H \rangle_{TA}$ has a finite value which is independent of A in the limit $A \rightarrow 0$. In this case, the substance is evidently a *ferromagnet*.

---

[40] See, for example, H. Goldstein, *Classical Mechanics*, Addison-Wesley, Reading, Mass., 1951.

2. $\langle H \rangle_{TA}$ is parallel to the applied magnetic field $\mathbf{V} \times \mathbf{A}$, but its magnitude is proportional to the applied field and vanishes when the latter is turned off. This is the description of a *paramagnetic* substance.

3. $\langle H \rangle_{TA}$ is proportional but *antiparallel* to the applied field. Such a substance is repelled by a magnetic pole and is a *diamagnet*.

The actual calculation is simplicity itself. In calculating the thermal average of $\mathbf{H}(\mathbf{r})$, we note that the convenient variables of integration are the $\mathbf{v}_n$ and not the $\mathbf{p}_n$. A transformation of variables in the integrals Eq. (22) is then made from the $\mathbf{p}_n$ to the $\mathbf{v}_n$, and according to the standard rules for the transformation of integrals, the integrands must be divided by the Jacobian of the transformation

$$J = \det \left\| \frac{m_n \, \partial v_n}{\partial p_m} \right\| = 1 \tag{26}$$

As is seen, the Jacobian equals unity, and therefore $\mathbf{A}(\mathbf{r}, t)$ simply disappears from the integrals, both from the Maxwell-Boltzmann factor and from the quantity $\mathbf{H}(\mathbf{r})$. Finally, the thermal expectation value of the latter vanishes because it is odd under the inversion $\mathbf{v}_n \rightarrow -\mathbf{v}_n$.

Therefore, actual calculation proved that classical statistical mechanics of charged particles resulted in none of the three categories of substances described by Faraday, but in a *fourth* category, viz., substances with *no* magnetic properties whatever.

QUANTUM THEORY

In the period between 1913 and 1925 the "old quantum theory" held sway. Bohr had quantized Rutherford's atom, and the structure of matter was becoming well understood. Spatial quantization was interpretable on the basis of the old quantum theory, and a famous experiment[41] by O. Stern and W. Gerlach allowed the determination of the angular momentum quantum number and magnetic moment of atoms and molecules. The procedure was to pass an atomic beam through an inhomogeneous magnetic field, which split it into a discrete number of divergent beams. In 1911 the suggestion was made that all elementary magnetic moments should be an integer multiple, of what later came to be called the *Weiss magneton*, in honor of its inventor. Although incorrect, this suggestion was taken up again by Pauli in 1920, the unit magnetic moment given a physical interpretation in terms of the Bohr atom, a new magnitude some five times larger:

$$\mu_B = \frac{e\hbar}{2mc} = 0.927 \times 10^{-20} \quad \text{ergs/gauss} \tag{27}$$

and renamed the *Bohr magneton*. In 1921, Compton[42] proposed that the electron possesses an intrinsic spin and magnetic moment, in addition to any orbital angular momentum and magnetization. This was later proven by S. Goudsmit and G. E.

---

[41] Gerlach and Stern, *Z. Physik.*, **9**: 349 (1922).
[42] A. H. Compton, *J. Franklin Inst.*, **192**: 144 (1921).

Uhlenbeck, then students of Ehrenfest, and in a famous paper in 1925 they demonstrated that the available evidence established the spin of the electron as $\hbar/2$ beyond any doubt.[43] The magnetic moment was assigned the value in Eq. (27), i.e., twice larger than expected for a charge rotating with the given value of angular momentum. The reason for this was yet purely empirical: the study of the anomalous Zeeman effect had led Landé some two years earlier to his well-known formula for the g factor, the interpretation of which in terms of the spin quantum number obliged Goudsmit and Uhlenbeck to assign the anomalous factor $g = 2$ to the spin of the electron. But a satisfactory explanation of this was to appear within a few years, when Dirac wedded the theory of relativity to quantum mechanics.

Developments in a new quantum mechanics were then proceeding at an explosive rate, and it is impossible in this narrative to give any detailed accounting of them. In 1923 De Broglie made the first suggestion of wave mechanics,[44] and by 1926 this was translated into the wave equation through his own work and particularly that of E. Schrödinger. Meantime, W. Heisenberg's work with H. A. Kramers on the quantum theory of dispersion, in which the radiation field formed the "virtual orchestra" of harmonic oscillators, suggested the power of noncommutative matrix mechanics. This was partly worked out, and transformation scheme for the solution of general quantum-mechanical problem given, in a paper by Heisenberg, Born, and Jordan.[45] Max Born and Norbert Wiener[46] then collaborated in establishing the general principle that to every physical quantity there corresponds an operator. From this it followed that Schrödinger's equation and that of matrix mechanics were identical, as was actually shown by Schrödinger[47] also in 1926. It is the time-independent formulation of his equation which forms the basis for much of the succeeding work in solid-state physics and in quantum statistical mechanics, when only equilibrium situations are contemplated. It is

$$\mathcal{H}\left(\frac{\hbar}{i}\,\nabla_n,\,\mathbf{r}_n\right)\psi = E\psi \tag{28}$$

with the operator $\dfrac{\hbar}{i}\,\nabla_n$ replacing the momentum $\mathbf{p}_n$ in Hamilton's function. By radiation or otherwise, a system will always end up with the lowest possible, or ground state, energy eigenvalue E_0. When thermal fluctuations are important, however, the proper balance between maximizing the entropy (i.e., the logarithm of the probability) and minimizing the energy is achieved by minimizing an appropriate linear combination of these, the *free energy*. The important connection between quantum theory and statistical mechanics was forged from the very beginnings, in the introduction of quantization to light and heat by Planck in 1900, through Einstein's theory of radiation (1907), its adaptation by Debye to the specific heat of solids (1912), and most

---

[43] G. Uhlenbeck and S. Goudsmit, *Naturwiss.*, **13**: 953 (1925).

[44] See *Compt. Rend.*, September, 1923, and also De Broglie's thesis. For this work, he was awarded the 1929 Nobel prize in physics.

[45] Max Born et al., *Z. Physik.*, **35**: 557 (1926).

[46] Max Born and Norbert Wiener, *J. Math. Phys.* (M.I.T.), **5**: 84 (1926).

[47] E. Schrödinger, *Ann. Phys.*, (4) **79**: 734 (1926); also C. Eckart, *Phys. Rev.*, **28**: 711 (1926). In these references, and in much of the narrative in the text, we follow a truly fascinating account given by Sir Edmund Whittaker, *A History of the Theories of Aether and Electricity*, Harper & Row, New York, 1960, vol. II.

firmly in the new quantum mechanics. For Heisenberg's uncertainty principle,

$$\Delta p_n \Delta r_n \gtrsim \hbar \tag{29}$$

which expressed the lack of commutativity of $\partial/\partial x_n$ with x_n, gave a natural size to the cells in phase space in terms of Planck's constant $2\pi\hbar$, and more pertinently perhaps, the interpretation of processes in quantum mechanics as statistical, aleatory events seemed an important necessary step in applying this science to nature.

The importance of the energy eigenfunction ψ in the subsequent development of quantum theory was overriding, and is discussed in some detail in Chapters 2 and 4 of this book. Here a bare outline will suffice. In 1927 Pauli invented his spin matrices; the next year Heisenberg and (almost simultaneously) Dirac explained ferromagnetism by means of *exchange*, the mysterious combination of the Pauli exclusion principle and physical overlap of the electronic wavefunctions. The next development was to consider the wavefunction itself as a field operator, i.e., *second quantization*. The importance of this was perhaps not immediately recognized. But the quantization of the electromagnetic field by Planck, leading to the statistics of Bose and Einstein, had here its precise analogue: the quantization of the electronic field by P. Jordan and E. Wigner[48] in 1928. This incorporated Pauli's exclusion principle and led to the statistics of Fermi and Dirac and to the modern developments in field theory and statistical mechanics. In 1928 also, Dirac[49] incorporated relativity into Hamiltonian wave mechanics, and the first and immediate success of his theory was the prediction of electron spin in precisely the form postulated by Pauli by means of his 2×2 matrix formulation, and an explanation of the anomalous factor $g = 2$ for the spin. The anomalous Zeeman effect finally stood stripped of all mystery. The Jordan-Wigner field theory permitted one loophole to be eliminated from the theory, viz., the existence of negative energy states. These were simply postulated to be filled,[50] and a striking confirmation came with the 1932 discovery by Anderson of the positron—a *hole* in the negative energy Dirac sea.

Side by side with these fundamental developments, Hartree, Fock, Heitler, London, and many others were performing the indispensable atomic and molecular calculations that were the direct applications of the new theory of the quantum electron. In 1929 J. C. Slater[51] showed that a single determinant, with entries which are individual electronic wavefunctions of space *and* spin, provides a useful variational many-electron wavefunction for use in problems of atomic and molecular structure. Heisenberg, Dirac, Van Vleck, Frenkel, Slater, and many others contributed to the notions of exchange, and to setting up the operator formalism to deal with it. And so, without further trying to list individual contributions, we can note that by 1930, after four years of the most exciting and brilliant set of discoveries in the history of theoretical physics, the foundations of the modern electronic theory of matter were definitively laid, and an epoch of consolidation and calculation based thereupon was started, in which we yet find ourselves at the date of this writing. We note that 1930 was the year of a Solvay conference devoted to magnetism; for it was time to pause and

---

[48] P. Jordan and E. Wigner, *Z. Phys.*, **47**: 631 (1928).

[49] P. A. M. Dirac, *Proc. Roy. Soc.*, **117A**: 610 (1928).

[50] *Ibid.*, **126A**: 360 (1930). For an interesting sidelight, see D. Mattis and E. Lieb, "Exact Solution of a Many-Fermion System and Its Associated Boson Field," *J. Math. Phys.* (Jan. or Feb. 1965).

[51] J. C. Slater, *Phys. Rev.*, **34**: 1293 (1929).

review the progress which had been made, time to see if "someone ... could tell all about the magnet. ..."

It is not out of place to note the youth of the creators of this scientific revolution, all less than 30 years of age. None of them had ever known a world without electrons or without the periodic table of the atoms. On the one hand their elders saw determinism and causality crumbling: "God does not throw dice!" Einstein was to complain.[52] But determinism was just the scientific substitute for God's prescience[53] and the elders forgot that long before, in the very foundations of statistical mechanics and thermodynamics, such as had been given by J. Willard Gibbs and Einstein himself, determinism had already been washed out to sea. The alarm about causality was unwarranted, for it has retained the same status in quantum theory as in classical theory in spite of all the assaults upon it. On the other hand, the young workers only saw in the new theory a chance finally to understand *why* Bohr's theory, *why* the classical theory worked when they did—and also why they failed when they did. They saw in quantum theory a greater framework with which to build the universe, no less than in the theory of relativity; and being devoid of severe metaphysical bias, they did not interpret this as philosophical retrogression. There is a psychological truth in this which had not escaped the perspicacious Henry Adams: "Truly the animal that is to be trained to unity must be caught young. Unity is vision; it must have been part of the process of *learning to see.*"[54]

MORE ON MAGNETISM

At the same time as the theoretical foundations were becoming firmer, the experimental facts and puzzles were becoming more numerous. Let us recount these with utmost brevity. Foremost was the question, why is not iron spontaneously ferromagnetic? Weiss proposed that his molecular field had various directions in various elementary crystals forming a solid; thus the magnetic circuits are all closed, minimizing the magnetostatic energy. Spectacular evidence was provided by Barkhausen in 1919, who by means of newly developed electronic amplifiers, heard distinct *clicks* as an applied field aligned the various Weiss domains. This irreversible behavior also explained hysteresis phenomena. Measurements of the gyromagnetic ratio gave $g \cong 2$ for most ferromagnetic substances, showing that unlike in atomic or molecular magnetism only the spins participated in the magnetic properties of the solids. In atoms, the mounting spectroscopic data permitted Stoner to assign the correct number of equivalent electrons to each atomic shell and Hund to enunciate his rules concerning the spontaneous magnetic moment of a free atom or ion.

In the study of metals it was found that alloying magnetic metals with nonmagnetic ones resulted in a wide spectrum of technical properties. In metals, unlike insulators, it was also found that the number of magnetic electrons *per* atom was not, in general, an integer. In many respects, knowledge of the magnetic properties of many classes of solids was fairly definitive by 1930. Only the class of solids which are magnetic, but non*ferro*magnetic, ordered structures remained to be discovered, and

---

[52] Quoted by Van Vleck in a talk, "American Physics Becomes of Age," *Physics Today*, **17**: 21 (1964).

[53] I am indebted to Professor Ch. Perelman for this formulation.

[54] Henry Adams, *op. cit.* (italics ours).

only two crucial tools of investigation were lacking: neutron diffraction, and magnetic resonance, each of which has permitted modern investigators to study solids from within.

The progress of the theory of magnetism in the first third of the twentieth century can be followed in the proceedings of the Sixth Solvay Conference of 1930, which was entirely devoted to this topic, and in two important books: Van Vleck's *The Theory of Electric and Magnetic Susceptibilities* (Oxford, 1932), and E. C. Stoner's *Magnetism and Matter* (Methuen, London, 1934). In the first of these books, but one chapter out of thirteen is devoted to the study of magnetism as a cooperative phenomenon. In the other, barely more emphasis is given to this field of study; after all, Heisenberg had written "it seems that till now, Weiss' theory is a sufficient basis, even for the deduction of second-order effects," in his contribution to the Solvay conference. Nevertheless, some attempts at understanding magnetism as a collective phenomenon which had already been made by this time were to lay the groundwork for our present understanding of the subject.

First came the Lenz-Ising formulation[55] of the problem of ferromagnetism; spins were disposed at regular intervals along the length of a *one-dimensional* chain. Each spin was allowed to take on the values ± 1, in accordance with the laws of Goudsmit and Uhlenbeck. This model could be solved exactly (see Chapters 8 and 9), and as long as each spin interacted with only a finite number of neighbors, the Curie temperature could be shown to vanish identically. Did this signify that forces of indefinitely large range were required to explain ferromagnetism?

The introduction by Pauli of his spin matrices showed that spin was a vector quantity; the requirements that the interaction between two spins be an isotropic scalar and the theory of permutations led Dirac in 1929 to the explicit formulation of the operator

$$\mathbf{S}_i \cdot \mathbf{S}_j \tag{30}$$

as the essential ingredient in the magnetic interaction. The coefficient of this operator was a function of the electrostatic force between the electrons, a force so large that the magnetic dipole–dipole interactions (the Amperian forces) could even be neglected to a first approximation. The theory of Weber and Ewing was now obsolete.

As soon as the elementary magnets are interpreted as corresponding to electrons in orbits, or as electron spins, however, it is found that the magnetic forces between neighbouring molecules are far too small to give rise to constraints of the magnitude required in the Ewing treatment of ferromagnetism. Atoms or molecules may in certain cases have some of the characteristics of small bar magnets—in possessing a magnetic moment; but an interpretation of the properties of a bar of iron as consisting of an aggregate of atomic bar magnets ceases to be of value, whatever its superficial success, once it is known that the analogy between atoms and bar magnets breaks down just at those points which are essential to the interpretation.[56]

With Eq. (30) or its equivalent as the basic ingredient in the magnetic Hamiltonian, F. Bloch[57] and J. C. Slater[58] discovered that *spin waves* were the elementary excitations. Assigning to them Bose-Einstein statistics, Bloch showed that an indefinitely large number of them would be thermally excited at any finite positive temperature, no matter how small, in one or two dimensions; but that a three-dimensional

[55] E. Ising, *Z. Phys.*, **31**: 253 (1925). See Bibliography, p. 295.
[56] E. C. Stoner, *Magnetism and Matter*, Methuen, London, 1934, p. 100.
[57] F. Bloch, *Z. Phys.*, **61**: 206 (1930).
[58] J. C. Slater, *Phys. Rev.*, **35**: 509 (1930).

ferromagnet possessed a finite Curie temperature. For the magnetization in three dimensions, Bloch found his "three-halves' power law" (discussed on p. 244),

$$\mathcal{M}(T) = \mathcal{M}(0)\left[1 - \left(\frac{T}{T_c}\right)^{\frac{3}{2}}\right] \tag{31}$$

with T_c calculable from the basic interaction parameters. *Now*, at last, Ising's result, $T_c = 0$, could be understood to have resulted primarily from the one-dimensionality of his array and not necessarily from the old quantum-theoretical formulation of the spins.

The properties of metallic conduction electrons were fairly well understood by the end of the first third of the century. In 1926 Pauli had calculated the spin paramagnetism of conduction electrons obeying Fermi statistics; and not much later Landau obtained their motional diamagnetism (see p. 183); one of the primary differences between classical and quantum-mechanical charges arose in this violation of the Bohr-van Leeuwen theorem. Bloch (see p. 191) then considered the Coulomb repulsion among the carriers in a very dilute gas of conduction electrons in a monovalent metal. In the Hartree-Fock approximation, he found that for sufficiently low concentrations (or sufficiently large effective mass, we would add today) this approximation gave lowest energy to the ferromagnetic configuration. Here are Pauli's mixed reactions to this work:

> Under those conditions [of low concentration, etc.], in fact, the approximation used by Bloch is rather bad; one must, however, consider as proved his more general result, which is, that ferromagnetism is possible under circumstances very different from those in which the Heitler-London method is applicable; and that it is not sufficient, in general, to consider merely the signs of the exchange integrals.[59]

More modern work has fully borne out Pauli's intuition; for example, it is now widely believed that the charged electrons of a metal behave, in most respects, as ideal, noninteracting fermions. Nevertheless, Bloch's approximation has been the basis of many later investigations, the reason for such "errors ... sedulously propagated, ... coming down to our own day, through the writings of a host of men,"[60] being the natural reluctance of physicists to abandon the only model of ferromagnetism other than the Heitler-London theory, which could be characterized as truly *simple*. For an explanation had to be found for the ferromagnetism of certain metals.

In 1932, Néel[61] put forward the idea of *anti*ferromagnetism to explain the temperature independent paramagnetic susceptibility of such metals as Cr and Mn, too large to be explained by Pauli's theory. He proposed the idea of two compensating sublattices undergoing negative exchange interactions, resulting in Eq. (20) with a *negative* Curie temperature—now known as the Néel temperature.

In 1936, Slater and G. H. Wannier both found themselves at Princeton, one at the Institute for Advanced Studies, and the other at the University. This overlap had positive results, for in an issue of the *Physical Review* of the succeeding year there are two consecutive papers of some importance to the theory of magnetic solids. In the first of these, Wannier introduced the set of orthogonal functions bearing his name,[62]

[59] W. Pauli, in *Le Magnétisme* (6th Solvay Conference), Gauthier-Villars, Paris, 1932, p. 212.
[60] W. Gilbert, *op. cit.*, p. 2.
[61] L. Néel, *Ann. Phys. (Paris)*, **17**: 64 (1932), *J. Phys. Radium*, **3**: 160 (1932).
[62] G. H. Wannier, *Phys. Rev.*, **52**: 191 (1937).

of which we shall have much more to say. In the second of these, Slater[63] gave a nontrivial theory of ferromagnetism of metals partly based on the use of Wannier functions. He discussed the case of a half-filled band, which is least favorable to ferromagnetism (see Chapter 7) but is amenable to analysis:

Starting with the theory of energy bands we have set up the perturbation problem and solved approximately the case of a band containing half enough electrons to fill it, all having parallel spins but one. This problem is a test for ferromagnetism: if the lowest energy of the problem is lower than the energy when all have parallel spins, the system will tend to reduce its spin, and will not be ferromagnetic; whereas if all energies of the problem are higher ... we shall have ferromagnetism.[63]

This followed hard upon his band theory of the ferromagnetism of nickel.[64]

The study of nickel–copper alloys was strong evidence for the band theory of ferromagnetism in metals. A single copper atom dissolved in nickel does not succeed in binding the extra electron which it brings into the metal by virtue of its higher valency. This electron finds its way into the lowest unfilled band, which belongs to the minority spins; and therefore decreases the magnetization of the entire crystal in the amount of one Bohr magneton, homogeneously distributed. As pure nickel possesses 0.6 Bohr magnetons per atom, the magnetization should decrease linearly with copper concentration, extrapolating to zero at 60 percent concentration. The experiments accorded beautifully with this hypothesis.[65]

Continuing study of Weiss domains soon indicated that they did not necessarily coincide with the physical crystals, that their size was determined by such effects as magnetostriction, quantum-mechanical exchange energy, etc., as well as the magnetostatic energy. The first complete theory (for Co) was sketched by Heisenberg in 1931, and subsequent work by Bloch, Landau, Bozorth, Becker, and many others have laid the theoretical and experimental bases for the study of domains. More recent attempts to give domain theory a uniform mathematical foundation have coalesced into a new science of *micromagnetics*, created principally by W. F. Brown and collaborators.

The statistical mechanics of magnetism came to be studied on many different fronts. Stoner[66] devised a procedure for metals, in which the Weiss molecular field was wedded to the band picture. In insulators where the Heisenberg Hamiltonian (based on the interaction of Eq. (30)) could be used with more confidence, the problem was more straightforward, albeit insoluble as well (in any exact sense). Opechowski inaugurated the study of high-temperature series expansions which are still under way today, there being no logical place to stop the sequence. An American physicist named Peter Weiss (unrelated to his French namesake) extended a method due to Bethe and Peierls in the study of order-disorder phenomena and of the Ising model, to an examination of the Heisenberg theory. The resulting Bethe-Peierls-Weiss method was superior to the old molecular field approximation, at all but the lowest temperatures where *all* "cluster" methods, based on the exact statistics of a limited number of spins, must fail.[67] It was but the first in a series of proposed cluster methods, some of which are in active use at the present day.[68]

[63] J. C. Slater, *Phys. Rev.*, **52**: 198 (1937).
[64] J. C. Slater, *Phys. Rev.*, **49**: 537 and 931 (1936).
[65] V. Marian, *Ann. Phys.* (*Paris*), (11) 7: 459 (1937). These experimental data are quoted in the review by Bozorth, B.S.T.J., **XIX**: 1 (1940).
[66] E. C. Stoner, *Proc. Roy. Soc.*, **169A**: 339 (1939).
[67] P. R. Weiss, *Phys. Rev.*, **74**: 1493 (1948).
[68] For a review, see J. S. Smart, "Effective Field Theories of Ferromagnetism and Antiferromagnetism," W. B. Saunders, Philadelphia, 1965, and Bibliography, p. 295.

Since World War II, the isotopic separation plants have made available a new series of magnetic elements, the rare-earth metals. Microwave and computer technology created the need for insulating magnetic materials, of which iron ferrite—the familiar lodestone—is one example. These substances have but one thing in common: They cannot be described by the theories given above and their study has spurred a renewal of theoretical and experimental investigations on a grand scale. It has become necessary to understand ordered arrays of spins in which nearest neighbors are anti-parallel, such as had earlier been proposed by Néel. Ordered structures have subsequently been found in which the spins precessed from one plane of atoms to the next, and these *spiral spin configurations* appear to be merely special cases of an even vaster class of magnetic arrangements. The techniques of magnetic resonance and neutron diffraction have added valuable tools to the study of magnetism but, in turn, have posed interesting new problems in the search to understand their basic mechanisms. Indeed, these have become fields of research even vaster than the sciences which spawned them, as is apparent in the literature.[69]

In the following chapters, the reader will find exposed some of the interesting and exciting developments of the past few years in the theory of magnetism. Many of them have not been discussed in this chapter. The emphasis is on the study of cooperative phenomena, a field which will surely grow in importance in the future, and of which there is given but a tentative initial formulation.

> But enough of this; there is such a variety of game springing up before me, that I am distracted in my choice, and know not which to follow.

> —Dryden (on the Canterbury Pilgrims)

---

[69] See, for example, C. P. Slichter, *Principles of Magnetic Resonance*, Harper & Row, New York, 1963.

CHAPTER 2

EXCHANGE

With the simultaneity which has characterized the great inventions of modern physics, Dirac[1] and Heisenberg[2] independently discovered exchange. This effect appeared at first to be quite mysterious, for its origins in the Pauli exclusion principle of quantum mechanics had no classical analogue. But it must be remembered that classical mechanics had failed to provide any explanation of magnetism, and now one could see why. Ferromagnetism cannot exist in the classical correspondence limit $\hbar \to 0$; it is one of the results of quantum mechanics, a manifestation of "exchange."

Loosely speaking, exchange was explained as follows. The Pauli exclusion principle keeps electrons with parallel spins apart, and so reduces their Coulomb repulsion. The difference in energy between the parallel spin configuration and the antiparallel one is the exchange energy, which, however, is favorable to ferromagnetism only in exceptional circumstances. This is because the increase in kinetic energy associated with parallel spins outweighs the favorable decrease in potential energy—as is the case in the helium atom or the hydrogen molecule, for example. In rare cases, such as with metallic iron, a large number of parallel spins produces ferromagnetism because the cost in kinetic energy is not as great as in some other metals, whereas the gain in potential energy is significant. Thus, the forces which are involved are *electrostatic* Coulomb forces and not the far weaker Ampère current, or *magnetic dipole*, forces. These electrostatic forces regulate the spin configurations in atoms, molecules, and solids via the Pauli principle, so that in constructing the foundations of the theory of magnetism, one could to a very good approximation completely ignore the magnetic fields proper. (It is fortunate that cause and effect could be so neatly disentangled.)

It is necessary to anticipate formally some of the material in the next chapter by introducing three common exchange operators named respectively for Majorana, Bartlett, and Heisenberg:[3]

$$\left.\begin{array}{c}\mathscr{P}^M \\ \mathscr{P}^B \\ \mathscr{P}^H \end{array}\right\} \psi(r_1\xi_1; r_2\xi_2; ...) = \left\{\begin{array}{l}\psi(r_2\xi_1; r_1\xi_2; ...) \\ \psi(r_1\xi_2; r_2\xi_1; ...) \\ \psi(r_2\xi_2; r_1\xi_1; ...)\end{array}\right.$$

---

[1] P. A. M. Dirac, *Proc. Roy. Soc.*, **112A**: 661 (1926).

[2] W. Heisenberg, *Z. Physik*, **38**: 441 (1926).

[3] Cf. Blatt and Weisskopf, *Theoretical Nuclear Physics*, Wiley, New York, 1952, p. 136. Note that the operator $\mathscr{P}^B$ was invented by Dirac, *Proc. Roy. Soc.*, **123A**: 714 (1929).

where r_1, r_2 are the spatial and ξ_1, ξ_2 the spin coordinates of two electrons. Clearly,

$$\mathscr{P}^H = \mathscr{P}^M \mathscr{P}^B$$

and later we shall see that on the set of wavefunctions allowable to electrons, $\mathscr{P}^H$ always has eigenvalue $\equiv -1$, so that $\mathscr{P}^M$ and $\mathscr{P}^B$ are effectively inverses of one another. Let us construct the simpler one, $\mathscr{P}^B$, out of the spin one-half operators at our disposal. It must be invariant under (physically meaningless) rotations in spin space and have eigenvalue $+1$ in triplet states and -1 in singlet states. These requirements finally lead to the unique choice:

$$\mathscr{P}^B = \tfrac{1}{2}(1 + 4\mathbf{S}_1 \cdot \mathbf{S}_2) \tag{1}$$

Assuming there is an energy $-J_{12}$ associated with the exchange, this leads to an effective Hamiltonian $\propto -J_{12}\mathbf{S}_1 \cdot \mathbf{S}_2$ (omitting the uninteresting constant part). It is also interesting to remember that just such an effective Hamiltonian had been postulated in the "vector model" of the atom, before the invention of wave mechanics, and that it is in effect a sort of semiempirical rule. We shall later see how it correlated with Hund's rules of atomic structure. In the present chapter we shall be more interested in obtaining a qualitative understanding of the meaning of exchange, of its limitations and of its successes in laying the groundwork of a theoretical understanding of magnetism.

The work of Dirac, Heisenberg, and others, and particularly the book of Van Vleck[4] first focused attention on an elementary interaction of the type in Eq. (1) as the fundamental object of study of the theory of magnetism. It may be supposed that this is the reason the Heisenberg exchange Hamiltonian (also called the vector model, the Heisenberg-Dirac-Van Vleck (HDVV) Hamiltonian)

$$\boxed{\mathscr{H}_{\text{Heis}} = -\sum_{i,\,j} J_{ij}\mathbf{S}_i \cdot \mathbf{S}_j} \tag{2}$$

occupied so many theorists over the span of a generation. They calculated its energy levels and eigenfunctions and the statistical mechanics which flowed therefrom. No less effort went into calculating the magnitudes of the exchange constants J_{ij} from atomistic considerations.

In spite of all this effort, and perhaps because of what it revealed, it was *not* possible to elevate exchange to the rank of a universal principle, to make of it a force of nature such as Coulomb's law or Newton's laws. For example, even though the explanation of Hund's rules by the vector model was one of the earliest successes of the theory, it turned out that the idealized Hamiltonian of Eq. (2) was only semiquantitatively accurate in complicated atoms and that a more exact Hamiltonian had to be solved in a higher approximation than the one in which exchange is well defined. And in general, notions of electronic correlations and other effects not directly related to the Pauli principle came to cloud the naïve picture.

Even today, many difficulties, both in principle and in practice, still plague those who would derive Eq. (2) from first principles. This will be made evident in the present

---

[4] J. H. Van Vleck, *The Theory of Electric and Magnetic Susceptibilities*, Oxford, 1932.

chapter as well as in succeeding ones. As Henry Wadsworth Longfellow once wrote, "So nature deals with us and takes away our playthings one by one."

EXCHANGE EQUALS OVERLAP

In order for exchange to occur, the paths of the interacting electrons must inevitably and inextricably overlap. Let us prove this, with the aid of a model in which electrons are confined to nonoverlapping regions.[5] Consider N electrons, with arbitrary interactions, and divide coordinate space into N separate boxes such that electron

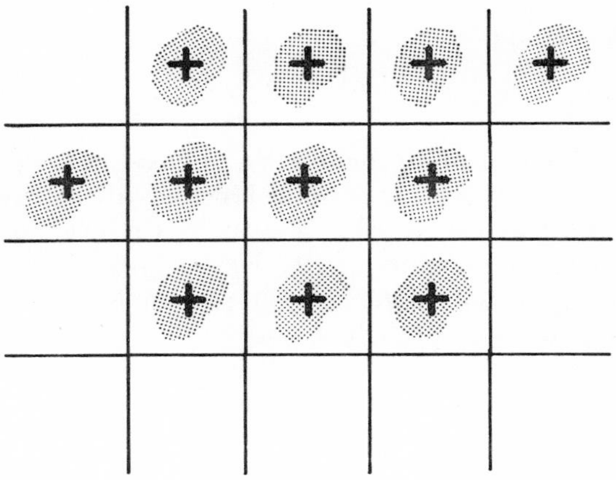

FIG. 2.1. Crosses indicate protons; shading, electrons. The wavefunction is constrained to vanish on the potential barriers indicated by solid lines, i.e., the nodal surfaces are imposed.

number 1 is confined to box number 1, electron number 2 to the second box, etc. The wavefunction is thus subject to the boundary condition that it vanish whenever a particle reaches the surface of the volume assigned to it. We illustrate a reasonable choice of boundary conditions in the case of N electrons + N fixed protons in Fig. 2.1. Subject to the boundary condition we have specified, the spatial eigenfunctions obey the Schrödinger equation

$$\mathscr{H}\varphi = \sum_i \mathscr{H}(r_i)\varphi + \sum_{i,j} V(r_i, r_j)\varphi = E\varphi \tag{3}$$

in which the Hamiltonian is generally invariant under any permutation of the coordinates of the indistinguishable particles, but is otherwise quite arbitrary.

If the electrons were truly noninteracting, an arbitrary solution of Eq. (3) could be written as a product function,

$$\varphi = f_1(r_1)f_2(r_2) \ldots \tag{4}$$

the Hartree product wavefunction. In effect, $f_i(r_j)$ would be the one-particle wavefunction of the jth electron, when constrained to the ith box. But before discussing the product wavefunction, it must be stressed that it is *not* an eigenfunction of $\mathscr{H}$. For even though the particles are constrained to remain in separate compartments, they do

---

[5] E. Lieb and D. Mattis, unpublished work.

interact, and their correlated motion cannot in general be factored. Therefore if we do not wish to sacrifice generality, we must write the true eigenfunction φ as,

$$\varphi = \varphi(1/2/.../N) \tag{5}$$

indicating by this notation that particle number 1 is in box number 1, etc. Because of the symmetry of the Hamiltonian under permutations, we can transpose particles 1 and 2, and the wavefunction

$$\mathscr{P}^M_{1,2}\varphi = \varphi(2/1/.../N)$$

will also be an eigenfunction of the Hamiltonian, Eq. (3), as indeed are any of the $N!$ permutations

$$\mathscr{P}_\rho\varphi \equiv \varphi_\rho \qquad \rho = 1, 2, \ldots, N! \tag{6}$$

of the N electrons amongst themselves, in the original wavefunction of Eq. (5). It is trivial to check that all these functions are orthogonal to one another, as the particles are constrained to be in separate boxes. Every energy level of the many-body Hamiltonian is therefore intrinsically $N!$-fold degenerate for the boundary conditions specified. But all $N!$ are not admissible: for example, the totally symmetric linear combination of functions φ_ρ,

$$\Psi_{\text{sym}} \equiv \sum_{\rho=1}^{N!} \varphi_\rho \tag{7}$$

while it might serve in the theory of a system of similar Bosons, is never suitable for $N \geq 3$ Fermi-Dirac particles. This is but one of the consequences of the Pauli exclusion principle.

Rules for constructing totally antisymmetric wavefunctions of space and spin are given in Chapter 4. What is most important in the present analysis, is that there are two spin degrees of freedom for each electron, therefore 2^N orthonormal spin functions which may be combined with the $N!$ space functions, to give *precisely 2^N wavefunctions of space and spin obeying the Pauli principle, for every eigenvalue E*. If N is even (odd) the resultant total spin ranges in magnitude from $S_{\text{tot}} = 0$ ($\frac{1}{2}$) to a maximum of $\frac{1}{2}N$.

We may anticipate the chapter on statistical mechanics, to state that even at finite temperature and in an applied external magnetic field H, the free energies of the electronic and spin degrees of freedom remain additive, in the sense that $F = F_{\text{el}} + F_{\text{sp}}$. In particular, the free energy of the spins is

$$F_{\text{sp}} = -kTN \ln \cosh \frac{g\mu_B H}{2kT}$$

identically that of noninteracting spins studied on p. 223. Even if we neglect the dia-magnetism of F_{el} (p. 183), the spins respond only paramagnetically to the field and *not* ferromagnetically. Therefore, in the present model ferromagnetism is impossible.

When the fictitious potential barrier which separates the electrons is removed, this 2^N-fold degeneracy of each eigenvalue E is lifted, as depicted in Fig. 2.2, where

E_0 is the ground state, E_1 the first excited state, etc. The manner in which E_0 fans out is perhaps the most crucial: if the exchange Hamiltonian is capable of reproducing the true spectrum of E_0, we shall have achieved a significant simplification of the problem. Even if there is considerable overlap between the spectrum of E_0 and that of the higher E_j, $j = 1, 2, \ldots$, the wavefunctions may be physically so different that they can be classified according to whether they represent magnetic degrees of freedom or electronic degrees of freedom, and a whole set of 2^N low-lying states can conceivably be described by the Heisenberg Hamiltonian, i.e., by an "effective" interaction among the spins.

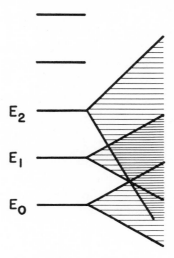

FIG. 2.2. Fanning out of 2^N-fold degenerate levels, when potential barriers are removed. Note that levels may cross.

E_2

E_1

E_0

   In the chapter on the theory of magnetism in metals, we shall examine at least two instances where this procedure works. When the electrons are allowed to co-mingle, and their interactions are treated in low order of perturbation theory, it is found there that the manner in which the degeneracy of E_0 is lifted *is* precisely described by the Heisenberg Hamiltonian. This is the case both in certain insulators, and in those metals regulated by the indirect exchange mechanism. However, we are anticipating too far ahead, and it is important to develop the plot gradually.

   Suffice it to say that there is in general no guarantee that the levels will fan out in the desired manner, and in many substances they do not do so and therefore defy simple-minded descriptions. Hopefully, a detailed analysis based on physically admissible approximations to the Schrödinger equation will give us some sharper criteria. It is to this task that we turn our attention in this chapter and in Chapters 4 and 7.

HYDROGEN MOLECULE

We study molecules first to appreciate some of the difficulties which are absent in our subsequent study of the atom. But these are by now almost classical subjects on which many books have been written. The actual treatment will therefore be addressed to the students who are yet unacquainted with or have forgotten atomic and molecular physics (or quantum chemistry, as it is now known). The more experienced reader can omit all but a few remarks towards the end of the chapter concerning subjects with which he might be less familiar. The method with which we break ground was invented by Heitler and London[6] shortly after the discoveries of Schrödinger, Heisenberg[7] and Dirac[8] gave impetus to the quantitative study of the many-body problem in quantum theory. It is still the simplest approach to the problems of molecular binding and interatomic exchange.

Assume nuclei fixed at $\mathbf{R}_a$ and $\mathbf{R}_b$, with interatomic spacing R_{ab} = several atomic radii. (We set the mass of the proton = ∞ so as to be able to localize it. Taking the finite mass into account does not change the results much, but leads to an interesting exchange effect: the existence of two species of H_2, ortho- and parahydrogen. It is caused by overlap between the proton wavefunctions rotating about a common axis, the overlap due to vibrational motion being negligible. So when the molecule is hindered in its rotation, e.g., by a crystal field, the splitting between ortho- and parahydrogen must disappear.) To a first approximation each neutral atom exerts no force on the other, and each electron "sees" only the central force field of its own proton. According to this hypothesis, we simplify the two-particle Schrödinger equation,

$$\mathscr{H}\Psi_I = E\Psi_I$$

with
$$\mathscr{H} = \left(\frac{p_1^2}{2m} - \frac{e^2}{r_{1a}} + \frac{p_2^2}{2m} - \frac{e^2}{r_{2b}}\right) + \left(\frac{e^2}{R_{ab}} + \frac{e^2}{r_{12}} - \frac{e^2}{r_{1b}} - \frac{e^2}{r_{2a}}\right)$$

(8)

by choosing $\Psi_I(\mathbf{r}_1, \mathbf{r}_2)$ to be a product function $\varphi_a(\mathbf{r}_1)\varphi_b(\mathbf{r}_2)$, where each factor obeys the one-particle Schrödinger equation, (there should be no confusion between the eigenvalue e and the charge of the electron)

$$\left(\frac{p_1^2}{2m} - \frac{e^2}{r_{1a}}\right)\varphi_a(\mathbf{r}_1) = e\varphi_a(\mathbf{r}_1)$$

and
$$\left(\frac{p_2^2}{2m} - \frac{e^2}{r_{2b}}\right)\varphi_b(\mathbf{r}_2) = e\varphi_b(\mathbf{r}_2)$$

(9)

As the total Hamiltonian is invariant under the interchange of the two coordinates $\mathbf{r}_1$ and $\mathbf{r}_2$, an equally good choice must be $\Psi_{II} = \varphi_a(\mathbf{r}_2)\varphi_b(\mathbf{r}_1)$. Therefore, let us diagonalize the Hamiltonian of Eq. (8) within the subspace of these two simple functions. Assume the atomic orbitals $\varphi(\mathbf{r})$ to be normalized, and define various overlap integrals as follows:

$$1 = \int d_3r|\varphi_a(\mathbf{r})|^2 = \int d_3r|\varphi_b(\mathbf{r})|^2 \qquad l \equiv \int d_3r\varphi_a^*(\mathbf{r})\varphi_b(\mathbf{r})$$

$$V \equiv \int d_3r_1 \, d_3r_2|\Psi_I|^2\left(\frac{e^2}{R_{ab}} + \frac{e^2}{r_{12}} - \frac{e^2}{r_{1b}} - \frac{e^2}{r_{2a}}\right)$$

$$= \int d_3r_1 \, d_3r_2|\Psi_{II}|^2\left(\frac{e^2}{R_{ab}} + \frac{e^2}{r_{12}} - \frac{e^2}{r_{1a}} - \frac{e^2}{r_{2b}}\right)$$

and
$$U \equiv \int d_3r_1 \, d_3r_2\Psi_I^*\Psi_{II}\left(\frac{e^2}{R_{ab}} + \frac{e^2}{r_{12}} - \frac{e^2}{r_{1b}} - \frac{e^2}{r_{2a}}\right)$$

(10)

[6] W. Heitler and F. London, Z. Physik, 44: 455 (1927), or any good text on molecular physics or chemistry (see the Bibliography).
[7] Op. cit.
[8] Op. cit.

Let us take a variational wavefunction

$$\psi = c_I \psi_I + c_{II} \psi_{II} \qquad (11)$$

and determine the coefficients c_I and c_{II} so as to make the variational energy stationary:

$$E_{var} = \frac{\int d_3 r_1 \, d_3 r_2 \, \psi^* \mathcal{H} \psi}{\int d_3 r_1 \, d_3 r_2 \, \psi^* \psi} \qquad \frac{dE_{var}}{dc_{I,\,II}} = 0 \qquad (12)$$

The solutions to this are best expressed in matrix notation. Let ψ_I correspond to the vector (1, 0) and ψ_{II} to the vector (0, 1). In this notation, the variational wavefunction ψ is merely (c_I, c_{II}), and the variational equations can be expressed in compact matrix form:

$$\begin{vmatrix} V & U \\ U^* & V \end{vmatrix} \begin{vmatrix} c_I \\ c_{II} \end{vmatrix} = (E - 2e) \begin{vmatrix} 1 & l^2 \\ l^{2*} & 1 \end{vmatrix} \begin{vmatrix} c_I \\ c_{II} \end{vmatrix} \qquad (13)$$

As in fact all functions under consideration are (or can be made) real, we shall henceforth omit the asterisk. It is not difficult to guess that the solutions to this equation are the symmetric and antisymmetric functions corresponding to

$$c_I = \pm c_{II} \qquad (14)$$

and that the respective eigenvalues are

$$E_\pm = 2e + \frac{V \pm U}{1 \pm l^2} \qquad (15)$$

The space symmetric (+) solution calls for the (antisymmetric) "spin-singlet" function, and the space antisymmetric function (−) for any of the (symmetric) "spin-triplet" functions. The triplet–singlet separation is

$$\Delta E = E_- - E_+ = 2 \frac{Vl^2 - U}{1 - l^4} \qquad (16)$$

and can be used to define an effective exchange force in the Heisenberg Hamiltonian. For the energy levels of

$$\mathcal{H}_{Heis} = -J_{12} \mathbf{S}_1 \cdot \mathbf{S}_2 = -J_{12} \left[\frac{(\mathbf{S}_1 + \mathbf{S}_2)^2}{2} - \frac{3}{4} \right] \qquad (17)$$

are $-\frac{1}{4}J_{12}$ in the triplet states, and $+\frac{3}{4}J_{12}$ in the singlet state. $[(\mathbf{S}_1 + \mathbf{S}_2)^2$ has eigenvalues $\mathbf{S}_{tot}(\mathbf{S}_{tot} + 1)$, where $\mathbf{S}_{tot} = 0$ or 1, the two possible spin values for two spins 1/2. The triplet state $\mathbf{S}_{tot} = 1$ is so called because of the three possible projections, $M = -1, 0, +1$, of the magnetic quantum number. The singlet state $\mathbf{S}_{tot} = 0$ has $M = 0$ only. This will become clearer subsequently; see also chapter on angular momentum.] By comparison with Eq. (16), the exchange constant is deduced to be

$$J_{12} = -2 \frac{Vl^2 - U}{1 - l^4} \tag{18}$$

Typically, the integral $U \propto O(l^2)$, but it is possible to construct cases with $l = 0$ but $U \neq 0$. Ferromagnetism, of an embryonic molecular sort, would occur if the exchange constant J_{12} turned out positive. Antiferromagnetism would be the consequence of an antiferromagnetic bond $J_{12} < 0$. What the actual sign turns out to be depends on the relative magnitudes of the "Coulomb integral" V, the "overlap integral" l, and the "exchange integral" U. In the primitive calculation of Heitler and London unperturbed hydrogen $1s$ orbitals were used in the calculation of these various integrals—yielding results in satisfactory agreement both with experiment and more accurate modern calculations (see Problem 1, below). The exchange constant turned

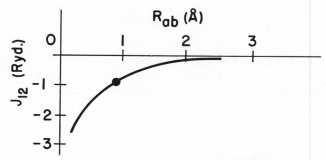

FIG. 2.3.   Exchange parameter J_{12} as function of internuclear distance R_{ab} in hydrogen molecule (H_2). Dot shows equilibrium value.

out *negative*, corresponding to a singlet (i.e., embryonic antiferromagnetic) ground state, and varied with internuclear distance R_{ab} as shown in Fig. 2.3. The triplet state was found, correctly, to be *unbound*, to have energy greater than the energy of two separate atoms, $2e$.

A second method for treating the H_2 molecule owes its origin to the work of F. Hund and R. S. Mulliken,[9,10] and is known as the method of molecular orbitals (M-O). The one-electron functions are chosen, in this method, to be eigenfunctions of some of the symmetry operations which leave an appropriately defined zeroth order Hamiltonian invariant. In this case, the eigenstates of the H_2^{+1} could be chosen to be the molecular orbitals. These fall into two classes, the even ones and the odd ones. A further refinement would be to take for the one-electron functions the solutions of a Hamiltonian in which the ionic potentials are screened in a self-consistent way. But even the following crude choice gives reasonable agreement with the exact solution, at the equilibrium value of R_{ab}. Let

$$\varphi_g = \frac{\varphi_a(\mathbf{r}) + \varphi_b(\mathbf{r})}{\sqrt{2(1 + l)}} \tag{19}$$

[9] See, for example, R. S. Mulliken, *Phys. Rev.*, **43**: 279 (1933).
[10] See also J. C. Slater, *Quantum Theory of Molecules and Solids*, McGraw-Hill. New York, 1963.

and
$$\varphi_u = \frac{\varphi_a(r) - \varphi_b(r)}{\sqrt{2(1 - l)}} \tag{19A}$$

approximating the even and odd (gerade, ungerade, in the time-honored notation g, u) eigenfunctions of H_2^{+1} by linear combinations of the atomic orbitals. This generates a subspace of four functions in which to diagonalize the Hamiltonian,

$$\varphi_g(\mathbf{r}_1) \cdot \varphi_g(\mathbf{r}_2), \qquad \varphi_g(\mathbf{r}_1) \cdot \varphi_u(\mathbf{r}_2), \qquad \varphi_u(\mathbf{r}_1) \cdot \varphi_g(\mathbf{r}_2), \qquad \varphi_u(\mathbf{r}_1) \cdot \varphi_u(\mathbf{r}_2) \tag{19B}$$

That is, the M-O method generates four eigenvalues starting with the raw atomic orbitals, twice as many as either the H-L scheme or the Heisenberg Hamiltonian. (The molecular orbitals are known as Bloch functions in solid-state theory and are further discussed on p. 175.) There is another linear combination, more perspicuous than the above, which leads to orthogonal functions with the property of reducing to the atomic orbitals in the limit of large separation, i.e., $l \to 0$. These functions are,

$$\psi_a = \frac{\varphi_a - g\varphi_b}{\sqrt{1 + g^2 - 2gl}} \tag{20}$$

and
$$\psi_b = \frac{\varphi_b - g\varphi_a}{\sqrt{1 + g^2 - 2gl}} \tag{20A}$$

with
$$g = \frac{1}{l}(1 - \sqrt{1 - l^2})$$

to ensure orthogonality. (The localized orthogonalized orbitals are the Fourier transforms of the Bloch functions in solid-state theory and are known as Wannier functions; see p. 176.) The eigenvalues of the Hamiltonian can be found within the subspace of the four orthonormal functions,

$$F_1 = \psi_a(\mathbf{r}_1) \cdot \psi_a(\mathbf{r}_2) \qquad F_2 = \psi_a(\mathbf{r}_1) \cdot \psi_b(\mathbf{r}_2)$$
$$F_3 = \psi_b(\mathbf{r}_1) \cdot \psi_b(\mathbf{r}_2) \qquad F_4 = \psi_b(\mathbf{r}_1) \cdot \psi_a(\mathbf{r}_2) \tag{20B}$$

As these functions span the same "function space" as the four M-O functions Eq. (19B), the four eigenvalues will be the same as if we worked with molecular orbitals. F_2 and F_4 correspond approximately to Ψ_I and Ψ_{II} for the nonorthogonal orbitals, F_1 and F_3 to "ionized configurations." The two lowest eigenvalues will correspond to $E_\pm$ of Eq. (15); see Problem 1.

Problem 1: Find the eigenvectors and eigenvalues of the 4×4 matrix

$$\mathscr{H}_{ij} = \int F_i \mathscr{H} F_j \, d_3 r_1 \, d_3 r_2$$

In addition to the definitions in Eq. (10), this requires the definition of additional integrals W and X, etc. Define them.

(a) Show that there is one triplet (space antisymmetric) eigenfunction, with energy $E_- = \mathscr{H}_{22} - \mathscr{H}_{24} =$ identically as given in Eq. (15). Find the lowest of the three space symmetric, singlet, solutions. Prove that it has energy *lower* than E_+, the H-L ground state.

(b) Second-order perturbation theory can also be used to calculate the singlet ground state energy,

$$E_+ \sim \mathscr{H}_{22} + \mathscr{H}_{24} - \frac{(\mathscr{H}_{12} + \mathscr{H}_{14})^2}{\mathscr{H}_{11} - \mathscr{H}_{22} - \mathscr{H}_{24}}$$

Express this formula in terms of U, V, W, X, and l, and by comparison with the exact result found in part (a) determine the physical region of approximate validity of the perturbation theory.

The importance of this calculation is that it shows that the Heisenberg-Hamiltonian can be derived on the basis of first- and second-order perturbation theory, using orthogonalized orbitals; and therefore many of the results of the theory (exchange constant, spin waves, existence of Curie temperature, etc.) are valid even when H-L theory is not.

THREE HYDROGEN ATOMS

The total Hamiltonian is separated into terms appropriate to individual hydrogen atoms + the interaction terms,

$$\mathscr{H} = \left[\left(\frac{p_1^2}{2m} - \frac{e^2}{r_{1a}} \right) + \left(\frac{p_2^2}{2m} - \frac{e^2}{r_{2b}} \right) + \left(\frac{p_3^2}{2m} - \frac{e^2}{r_{3c}} \right) \right]$$

$$+ e^2 \left[\left(\frac{1}{R_{ab}} + \frac{1}{R_{bc}} + \frac{1}{R_{ac}} \right) + \left(\frac{1}{r_{12}} + \frac{1}{r_{23}} + \frac{1}{r_{13}} \right) - \left(\frac{1}{r_{1b}} + \frac{1}{r_{1c}} \right) \right.$$

$$\left. - \left(\frac{1}{r_{2a}} + \frac{1}{r_{2c}} \right) - \left(\frac{1}{r_{3a}} + \frac{1}{r_{3b}} \right) \right]$$

$$= \{\mathscr{H}_0\} + \{\mathscr{H}'\} \tag{21}$$

and as before, we use products of the nonorthogonal atomic functions of Eq. (9) of which there are $3! = 6$ in total. Let us label them according to the following table:

$$\psi_1 = \varphi_a(1)\varphi_b(2)\varphi_c(3)$$
$$\psi_2 = \varphi_a(2)\varphi_b(1)\varphi_c(3)$$
$$\psi_3 = \varphi_a(3)\varphi_b(2)\varphi_c(1)$$
$$\psi_4 = \varphi_a(1)\varphi_b(3)\varphi_c(2) \tag{22}$$
$$\psi_5 = \varphi_a(2)\varphi_b(3)\varphi_c(1)$$
$$\psi_6 = \varphi_a(3)\varphi_b(1)\varphi_c(2)$$

How are these related to each other under the permutations of various particles? For typographical simplicity, let us omit the Greek symbols, and write ψ_1 as 1, ψ_2 as 2, etc. Then we can draw up simple tables (showing into which functions any of the six transform) under transpositions (permutations of two particles):

$$
\begin{aligned}
1 &\rightarrow 2, 3, \quad \text{or} \quad 4 \\
2 &\rightarrow 1, 5, \quad \text{or} \quad 6 \\
3 &\rightarrow 1, 5, \quad \text{or} \quad 6 \\
4 &\rightarrow 1, 5, \quad \text{or} \quad 6 \\
5 &\rightarrow 2, 3, \quad \text{or} \quad 4 \\
6 &\rightarrow 2, 3, \quad \text{or} \quad 4
\end{aligned}
\tag{23}
$$

and under nontrivial permutations of all *three* particles:

$$
\begin{aligned}
1 &\rightarrow 5, 6 \\
2 &\rightarrow 3, 4 \\
3 &\rightarrow 2, 4 \\
4 &\rightarrow 2, 3 \\
5 &\rightarrow 1, 6 \\
6 &\rightarrow 1, 5
\end{aligned}
\tag{24}
$$

Thus, for equidistant atoms at the vertices of an equilateral triangle, Fig. 2.4,

$$
\int \psi_1^* \psi_2 \, d\tau = \int \psi_1^* \psi_3 \, d\tau = \int \psi_1^* \psi_4 \, d\tau = l^2 = \int \psi_2^* \psi_5 \, d\tau, \quad \text{etc.}
\tag{25}
$$

and

$$
\int \psi_1^* \psi_5 \, d\tau = \int \psi_1^* \psi_6 \, d\tau = l^3 = \int \psi_2^* \psi_3 \, d\tau
\tag{26}
$$

etc. Or in general if we use these integrals to define an overlap matrix Ω

$$
\Omega_{ij} = \int \psi_i^* \psi_j \, d\tau
\tag{27}
$$

then we have simply,

$$
\Omega = \begin{vmatrix}
1 & l^2 & l^2 & l^2 & l^3 & l^3 \\
l^2 & 1 & l^3 & l^3 & l^2 & l^2 \\
l^2 & l^3 & 1 & l^3 & l^2 & l^2 \\
l^2 & l^3 & l^3 & 1 & l^2 & l^2 \\
l^3 & l^2 & l^2 & l^2 & 1 & l^3 \\
l^3 & l^2 & l^2 & l^2 & l^3 & 1
\end{vmatrix}
\tag{28}
$$

a real symmetric, matrix. And as for the matrix elements of the Hamiltonian, we do not have to examine all 36 possibilities, but in fact just 6:

$$\int \Psi_1^* \mathcal{H} \Psi_i d\tau = H_{1,i} \quad , \quad i = 1, 2, \ldots, 6 \tag{29}$$

for we can obtain all the others by appropriate permutations. And of these only three are independent. They are,

$$H_{1,1} = 3e + H'_{1,1} \tag{30A}$$

$$H_{1,2} = H_{1,3} = H_{1,4} = 3el^2 + H'_{1,2} \tag{30B}$$

$$H_{1,5} = H_{1,6} = 3el^3 + H'_{1,5} \tag{30C}$$

From (30A) we also get $H_{2,2} = H_{3,3} = \cdots = H_{1,1}$. From (30B) we get the matrix elements of $\mathcal{H}$ between any function in Eq. (23) and its transform, for example, $H_{2,5} = H_{1,2}$, etc.; and (30C) gives the archetype matrix element between functions of Eq. (24) and their transform. A slight change of notation will greatly simplify the appearance of the interaction matrix. We define A, b, and c by

$$A = H'_{1,1}, \qquad bl^2 \cdot A = H'_{1,2} \quad \text{and} \quad cl^3 \cdot A = H'_{1,5} \tag{31}$$

This replaces the matrix elements as parameters by A, b, c, and the previously defined overlap integral l [cf. Eq. (10)]. The Hamiltonian matrix is then particularly convenient to derive: $3e$ times the overlap matrix, plus A times an interaction matrix (which can be derived from the overlap matrix merely by replacing l^2 by bl^2 and l^3 by cl^3 in the latter), so that the eigenvalue equation now reads:

$$A \begin{vmatrix} 1 & bl^2 & bl^2 & bl^2 & cl^3 & cl^3 \\ bl^2 & 1 & cl^3 & cl^3 & bl^2 & bl^2 \\ bl^2 & cl^3 & 1 & cl^3 & bl^2 & bl^2 \\ bl^2 & cl^3 & cl^3 & 1 & bl^2 & bl^2 \\ cl^3 & bl^2 & bl^2 & bl^2 & 1 & cl^3 \\ cl^3 & bl^2 & bl^2 & bl^2 & cl^3 & 1 \end{vmatrix} \cdot \mathbf{v} = (E - 3e) \begin{vmatrix} 1 & l^2 & l^2 & l^2 & l^3 & l^3 \\ l^2 & 1 & l^3 & l^3 & l^2 & l^2 \\ l^2 & l^3 & 1 & l^3 & l^2 & l^2 \\ l^2 & l^3 & l^3 & 1 & l^2 & l^2 \\ l^3 & l^2 & l^2 & l^2 & 1 & l^3 \\ l^3 & l^2 & l^2 & l^2 & l^3 & 1 \end{vmatrix} \cdot \mathbf{v} \tag{32}$$

We denote eigenvectors by $\mathbf{v}$. We construct the six distinct eigenvectors by use of the permutation tables given just previously. One starts with ψ_1, or

$$\begin{vmatrix} 1 \\ 0 \\ 0 \\ 0 \\ 0 \\ 0 \end{vmatrix} \tag{33}$$

in the vector notation. A totally symmetric function is constructed by adding to this vector all the vectors obtained by permutations of the particles; for example,

$$\mathbf{v}_{\text{sym}} = (1, 1, 1, 1, 1, 1) \tag{34}$$

(For typographical reasons, we write the vectors as row vectors. Technically, therefore, they are *left* eigenvectors.) For the totally antisymmetric function, we again start with ψ_1, subtract all the odd permutations, which are given in Eq. (23), and add the even permutations, given in Eq. (24):

$$\mathbf{v}_{a\text{-}s} = (1, -1, -1, -1, +1, +1) \tag{35}$$

We then seek vectors antisymmetric in particles 2 and 3, but not totally antisymmetric, that is, orthogonal to $\mathbf{v}_{a\text{-}s}$. We find:

$$\mathbf{v}_{23} = (1, \tfrac{1}{2}, \tfrac{1}{2}, -1, -\tfrac{1}{2}, -\tfrac{1}{2}) \quad \text{and} \quad \mathbf{v}'_{23} = (0, 1, -1, 0, +1, -1) \tag{36}$$

Next, we look for vectors symmetric in particles 2 and 3, but orthogonal to $\mathbf{v}_{\text{sym}}$:

$$\mathbf{v}_{23\text{sym}} = (1, -\tfrac{1}{2}, -\tfrac{1}{2}, 1, -\tfrac{1}{2}, -\tfrac{1}{2}) \quad \text{and} \quad \mathbf{v}'_{23\text{sym}} = (0, 1, -1, 0, -1, +1) \tag{37}$$

but these choices are not unambiguous. The important point is that because of the invariance of the Hamiltonian under the permutation group, functions of different symmetries do not mix. The totally symmetric and the totally antisymmetric function both stand alone in their own symmetry class and therefore must be eigenvectors. The remaining four eigenvalues are obtained by diagonalizing the matrices of the eigenvalue equation Eq. (32), in the 2×2 subspaces of the functions of Eqs. (36) and (37) respectively. This rudimentary group theory saves us from the tedium of diagonalizing 6×6 matrices: the importance of the permutation operators should be already abundantly clear.

In the present problem, hidden symmetries simplify the eigenvalue equation further. For it happens that each of the last four vectors is simultaneously an eigenvector of both the overlap and the interaction matrices, and are all degenerate. The eigenvalues can be found almost by inspection now.

$$E_{\text{sym}} = 3e + A\,\frac{1 + 3bl^2 + 2cl^3}{1 + 3l^2 + 2l^3} \tag{38}$$

$$E_{a\text{-}s} = 3e + A\,\frac{1 - 3bl^2 + 2cl^3}{1 - 3l^2 + 2l^3} \tag{39}$$

and the four-fold degenerate eigenvalue,

$$E_{23} = 3e + A\,\frac{1 - cl^3}{1 - l^3} \tag{40}$$

Elsewhere we discuss how to combine space with spin to obtain wavefunctions of space and spin, obeying the Pauli principle. At present we need only the following information which the reader must accept on faith: $\mathbf{v}_{\text{sym}}$ is not an allowable eigenfunction for electrons; $\mathbf{v}_{a\text{-}s}$ will be used to construct the function of spin three-halves and $\mathbf{v}_{23}$ the function of spin one-half, known as quartet and doublet states, respectively. No other values of total spin angular momentum can be obtained with three electrons.

How do these results compare with the solutions of the Heisenberg Hamiltonian?

To the two-spin Hamiltonian of Eq. (17) which corresponded to the hydrogen molecule, $-J_{12}\mathbf{S}_1\cdot\mathbf{S}_2$, we now must add two more equal bonds to connect all sides of the equilateral triangle, as shown in Fig. 2.4. That is,

$$\mathscr{H}_{\text{Heis}} = -J_{12}^{\ddagger}(\mathbf{S}_1\cdot\mathbf{S}_2 + \mathbf{S}_2\cdot\mathbf{S}_3 + \mathbf{S}_3\cdot\mathbf{S}_1) \tag{41}$$

We use a superscript ($\ddagger$), however, to warn that the exchange "constant" might be rather more variable than its name suggests, and that the value we shall find in the present calculation may not agree with the result previously obtained for two atoms.

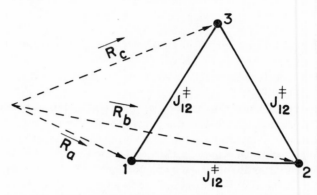

FIG. 2.4.   Three-atom molecule, or three-equivalent Heisenberg spins, with solid lines indicating bonds.

The distinct eigenvalues of the above Heisenberg Hamiltonian can be calculated by diagonalizing $\mathscr{H}_{\text{Heis}}$ in the subspace of the three functions belonging to $M = +\frac{1}{2}$. Because of the rotational symmetry, it is found moreover that the two solutions belonging to $M = S = \frac{1}{2}$ are degenerate. The quartet solution is of course unique and, therefore, automatically an eigenfunction of the Hamiltonian. The reader is encouraged to construct these states, starting with a basis

$$\chi_1 \equiv \uparrow\downarrow\downarrow \qquad \chi_2 \equiv \downarrow\uparrow\downarrow \qquad \chi_3 \equiv \downarrow\downarrow\uparrow \tag{42}$$

in an obvious notation. One can also obtain the eigenvalues more simply by completing the square in Eq. (41). Either way, he finds for the solutions of Eq. (41):

$$E_{\text{quart}} - E_{\text{doubl}} = -\tfrac{3}{2}J_{12}^{\ddagger} \tag{43}$$

Now this must be set equal to

$$E_{a\text{-}s} - E_{23} = A\left(\frac{1 - 3bl^2 + 2cl^3}{1 - 3l^2 + 2l^3} - \frac{1 - cl^3}{1 - l^3}\right) = -\tfrac{3}{2}J_{12}^{\ddagger} \tag{44}$$

the calculated level separation, so as to obtain finally a value for the exchange parameter:

$$J_{12}^{\ddagger} = -2Al^2\frac{(1 - b) + (l + l^2)(c - b)}{(1 - l^3)(1 + l - 2l^2)} \tag{45}$$

Unless the overlap is very small, this expression has terms in l^3, etc., and is in no way comparable to the formula of Eq. (18) which we obtained previously. However, there is no reason to take the H-L scheme seriously if the overlap is that great. [Note that if the atoms are exceedingly close, then the eigenfunctions of atomic lithium are a better zeroth-order set than the three hydrogen atomic functions, whereas those of helium best approximate the solution of the H_2 molecule. In vain can we expect the H-L picture to describe these physical systems when $l \sim 1$. In solids, the H-L picture breaks down completely once l exceeds $1/z$ in magnitude, where z = number of nearest neighbors of each atom ($z = 6$ for simple cubic structure, etc.) because Ω becomes a singular matrix. That is, the wavefunctions cannot be normalized unless $l < 1/z$; see ahead.]

For the reasons above, in a microscopic derivation of the Heisenberg Hamiltonian and of the exchange constant, we must assume that R_{ab} = many atomic units, and calculate only to lowest order in the overlap, l. One is powerless to define interatomic exchange more accurately (although once again in the atom, for *intra*-atomic exchange, the situation is more favorable, as we shall see subsequently).

In accordance with these arguments, we now calculate the exchange parameters *to lowest order in the overlap*: From Eq. (18),

$$\tfrac{1}{2}J_{12} \doteq -Vl^2 + J = -l^2 \int d_3r_1 \, d_3r_2 \varphi_a^2(\mathbf{r}_1)\varphi_b^2(\mathbf{r}_2)\left(\frac{e^2}{R_{ab}} + \frac{e^2}{r_{12}} - \frac{e^2}{r_{1b}} - \frac{e^2}{r_{2a}}\right)$$

$$+ \int d_3r_1 \, d_3r_2 \varphi_a(\mathbf{r}_1)\varphi_b(\mathbf{r}_1)\varphi_a(\mathbf{r}_2)\varphi_b(\mathbf{r}_2)\left(\frac{e^2}{R_{ab}} + \frac{e^2}{r_{12}} - \frac{e^2}{r_{1b}} - \frac{e^2}{r_{2a}}\right) \quad (46)$$

and the calculation of Eq. (45) giving

$$\tfrac{1}{2}J_{12}^{\ddagger} \doteq -Al^2 + Al^2b = -H'_{1,1}l^2 + H'_{1,2}$$

$$= -l^2 \int d_3r_1 \, d_3r_2 \, d_3r_3 \varphi_a^2(\mathbf{r}_1)\varphi_b^2(\mathbf{r}_2)\varphi_c^2(\mathbf{r}_3)\left[\left(\frac{e^2}{R_{ab}} + \frac{e^2}{R_{ac}} + \frac{e^2}{R_{bc}}\right)\right.$$

$$\left. + \left(\frac{e^2}{r_{12}} + \frac{e^2}{r_{13}} + \frac{e^2}{r_{23}}\right) - \left(\frac{e^2}{r_{1b}} + \frac{e^2}{r_{1c}} + \frac{e^2}{r_{2a}} + \frac{e^2}{r_{2c}} + \frac{e^2}{r_{3a}} + \frac{e^2}{r_{3b}}\right)\right]$$

$$+ \int d_3r_1 \, d_3r_2 \, d_3r_3 \varphi_a(\mathbf{r}_1)\varphi_b(\mathbf{r}_1)\varphi_a(\mathbf{r}_2)\varphi_b(\mathbf{r}_2)\varphi_c^2(\mathbf{r}_3)\left[\left(\frac{e^2}{R_{ab}} + \frac{e^2}{R_{ac}} + \frac{e^2}{R_{bc}}\right)\right.$$

$$\left. + \left(\frac{e^2}{r_{12}} + \frac{e^2}{r_{13}} + \frac{e^2}{r_{23}}\right) - \left(\frac{e^2}{r_{1b}} + \frac{e^2}{r_{1c}} + \frac{e^2}{r_{2a}} + \frac{e^2}{r_{2c}} + \frac{e^2}{r_{3a}} + \frac{e^2}{r_{3b}}\right)\right] \quad (47)$$

recalling the definition of the various parameters in Eq. (31), and assuming also for simplicity that all the atomic functions are real, and normalized.

Let us try to reduce the second calculation to some of the integrals in the first, so that we may effect a comparison. First, Eq. (46): The terms in R_{ab} cancel exactly, and the remainder can be put in the form

$$\tfrac{1}{2}J_{12} = \int d_3r_1 \, d_3r_2 \left(\frac{2e^2}{r_{1b}} - \frac{e^2}{r_{12}}\right)(\rho_{12}l^2 - \rho_{12\mathrm{ex}}) \quad (48)$$

defining ρ_{12} to be the ordinary electron density $\varphi_a^2(\mathbf{r}_1)\varphi_b^2(\mathbf{r}_2)$ and ρ_{12ex} to be the "exchange density" $\varphi_a(\mathbf{r}_1)\varphi_b(\mathbf{r}_1)\varphi_a(\mathbf{r}_2)\varphi_b(\mathbf{r}_2)$, in an obvious notation.

Some simple manipulations of the terms in the integrals for $J_{12}^{\ddagger}$ enable us to reach, finally, the desired result:

$$J_{12}^{\ddagger} = J_{12} + 4le^2 \int d_3r_1\, d_3r_2 \varphi_b^2(\mathbf{r}_2)\cdot[\varphi_a(\mathbf{r}_1)\varphi_c(\mathbf{r}_1) - l\varphi_a^2(\mathbf{r}_1)]\left(\frac{1}{r_{12}} - \frac{1}{r_{1b}}\right) \quad (49)$$

The correction term is not necessarily negligible compared to the exchange parameter itself (see Problem 2).

Problem 2: $\varphi_a(r)$ is the unperturbed $1s$ atomic ground-state wavefunction of an electron belonging to a hydrogen atom at R_a, and φ_b is defined correspondingly. Calculate $l(R_{ab})$ and $J_{12}(l)$, $J_{12}^{\ddagger}(l)$. Is the exchange parameter increased or decreased by the presence of the third atom? (Assume $R_{ab} \to \infty$.) See also Eq. (6) of Ref. 13.

The presence of the third atom at R_c modifies the exchange bond, as we have defined it, between spins at R_a and R_b. If atoms a and b were imbedded in a solid, the exchange interaction between them would be further modified, and the molecular exchange constant J_{12} or $J_{12}^{\ddagger}$ would be of little quantitative use. Those who would calculate exchange parameters must heed the following warning: It is futile to imagine that exchange, even between similar atoms, can be characterized by a universal parameter $J_{12}(R_{12})$ which one might calculate on a molecular model, no matter how refined. It should be regarded as a parameter which depends on all the other environing atoms as well, even to lowest order. When the Heisenberg Hamiltonian [Eq. (1)] is not applicable, the exchange parameter loses, of course, even this meaning, and exchange vanishes into the limbo of ill-defined concepts and ideas.

[Herring[11] points out that the H-L scheme per se is in fact asymptotically wrong for $R_{ab} >$ some 50 atomic distances, where it predicts a ferromagnetic exchange parameter, albeit an exponentially small one. Thus even if the Heisenberg Hamiltonian is applicable, and even if an exchange parameter can be defined and the overlap is small, it still seems a tricky matter to calculate the exchange parameter properly! Herring's interesting remedy is a method of calculating the exchange parameters as *surface* integrals, of something akin to the Wronskians, rather than as volume overlap integrals; for an explanation of which we refer the reader to his original article.]

NONORTHOGONALITY CATASTROPHE

In the many-body problem, when one unwittingly expands e^{gN} in a Taylor series,

$$e^{gN} = 1 + gN + \tfrac{1}{2}(gN)^2 + \cdots \quad (50)$$

and tries to take the limit $N \to \infty$, he is overtaken by what is mildly termed a catastrophe. Because of the use of nonorthogonal orbitals in the H-L scheme, just such a nonorthogonality catastrophe occurs when we try to apply the methods which were used in the two- and three-body problems, to the N-body problem of an infinite chain

---

[11] C. Herring, "Critique of the Heitler-London Method of Calculating Spin Couplings at Large Distances," *Rev. Mod. Phys.*, **34**: 631 (1962). For another approach, see p. 193.

or infinite three-dimensional solid. This difficulty, first pointed out by Slater[12] and Inglis[13] (the catastrophe is now known by their names), has for many years been resolved in principle. Nevertheless it adds considerably to the confusion and difficulties of the problem and to the headaches of those who seek to understand exchange.

The overlap matrix and the interaction matrix will both be $N! \times N!$, although as we have mentioned not all the eigenfunctions will be admissible, and only 2^N will survive the process of antisymmetrization. A row in the overlap matrix may include one 1, N terms in l^2, N^2 terms in l^3, etc., and the question will no longer be, "can we neglect l^2 compared to 1, or l^3 compared to l^2?" but rather, "can we neglect Nl^2 compared to 1? Or $N^2 l^3$ compared to Nl^2?" The answer is an emphatic "No!" no matter how small the overlap. In the present section we give a preliminary qualitative, intuitive analysis resulting in an approximate derivation of the Heisenberg Hamiltonian.

It is not practicable to set down either the overlap or interaction matrices in the explicit form we have previously used, and an operator formalism is required. We expand both as series in permutation operators, decomposed into simple transposition operators and their products, and then take advantage of the Pauli principle to express these in the form of spin exchange operators.

Assume, for example, that the atomic functions are truncated slightly so that there is overlap only with nearest neighbors, in a regular geometric array of N atoms.

$$\int |\varphi_n(r)|^2 \, d_3 r = 1 \qquad \int \varphi_n^*(r)\varphi_m(r) \, d_3 r = \begin{cases} l \text{ if } n, m = \text{nearest neighb} \\ 0 \text{ otherwise} \end{cases} \tag{51}$$

Then with the normally ordered function as the standard, the $N!$ functions can be obtained by various permutations of the particle coordinates:

$$\psi_1 = \varphi_1(r_1)\varphi_2(r_2) \cdots \varphi_N(r_N)$$

$$\mathscr{P}_{12}\psi_1 = \varphi_1(r_2)\varphi_2(r_1) \cdots \varphi_N(r_N) \tag{52}$$

$$\mathscr{P}_{12}\mathscr{P}_{2N}\psi_1 = \varphi_1(r_2)\varphi_2(r_N) \cdots \varphi_N(r_1)$$

etc. The great advantage of the operator formalism is that the eigenvalues of the matrices we obtain are independent of the choice of the particular function ψ_1. We can almost guess:

$$\mathbf{\Omega} = 1 + \mathbf{h}l^2 + \tfrac{1}{2}\mathbf{h}^2 l^4 + \cdots = e^{\mathbf{h}l^2} + \cdots \tag{53}$$

with

$$\mathbf{h} \equiv \sum_{n, m = \text{nearest neighb}} \mathscr{P}_{nm} \tag{54}$$

and dots ($\cdots$) to hide the real difficulties. There are two types of correction: "Kinematical" are those due to counting errors, because a product of x factors of $\mathscr{P}_{nm}$ does not always describe a permutation of x pairs of coordinates. For example, terms of the type

$$\mathscr{P}_{12}\mathscr{P}_{12} = 1 \tag{55}$$

[12] J. C. Slater, *Phys. Rev.*, **35**: 509 (1930).
[13] D. R. Inglis, *Phys. Rev.*, **46**: 135 (1934).

should be subtracted from $\frac{1}{2}\mathbf{h}^2 l^4$, so that the first kinematical correction is

$$-\tfrac{1}{4}Nzl^4 \tag{56}$$

where z is the number of nearest neighbors of each atom (for example, $z = 2$ in the linear chain, and $z = 6$ in the simple cubic lattice). The next constant correction is

$$-\tfrac{1}{16}N^2z^2l^8 \tag{57}$$

neglecting terms of order Nl^8 which are smaller than Eq. (56), not to speak of Eq. (57). The fact is, that the principal corrections enter with ever-increasing powers of N, to form an apparently divergent series. If we add the largest contributions in $\mathbf{h}$, $\mathbf{h}^2$, etc., the overlap matrix can be resummed as

$$\mathbf{\Omega} = Re^{\mathbf{h}l^2} + \cdots \tag{58}$$

with R representing a nonconvergent (that is, N-dependent) series

$$R = \sum_{n=0}^{N} \left(\frac{Nzl^4}{4}\right)^n C_n \tag{59}$$

and the ellipsis ($\cdots$) higher-order neglected terms.

Among further corrections are the "dynamical corrections," which we shall now define. These are concerned with the nature of the particular law assumed for the overlap, Eq. (51) in the present case. Unlike the terms in R, the dynamical corrections would be subject to change if we assumed a next-nearest-neighbor overlap, or some other law. They also depend on geometrical niceties, such as: Can an atom have nearest neighbors which are nearest neighbors of each other? If the answer is negative (as in the simple cubic lattice) the first dynamical correction to the overlap occurs in the third term of Eq. (53), from which we must subtract

$$\tfrac{1}{2}l^4 \sum_{n \neq n'} \mathscr{P}_{nm}\mathscr{P}_{mn'} \tag{60}$$

in order to eliminate what amounts to an effective next-nearest-neighbor exchange, prohibited by our postulates. Further dynamical corrections consist, in part, of eliminating from the series for $\mathbf{\Omega}$ all the permutations which, incorrectly, remove an electron to a distance further than its nearest neighbors.

An entirely analogous analysis can be made of the interaction matrix. It is important to recall that there is no exchange interaction between nonoverlapping electrons, as was proved in a preceding section; so that the truncation of the atomic functions, cf. Eq. (51) *supra*, leaves only a nearest-neighbor interaction. Even the long-ranged Coulomb force cancels to a large extent because of average electrical neutrality. The problem is most simplified if we take for the zero of energy not N times e, but $\mathscr{H}_{1,1}$. The interaction term, which is the extension to the present problem of the left-hand side of Eq. (32), thus can also be guessed to be a series in powers of h, with corrections of both the kinematical and dynamical sort.

$$\text{Int} = u_1\mathbf{h} + \tfrac{1}{2}u_2\mathbf{h}^2 + \cdots \tag{61}$$

with
$$u_1 = \int d_3r_1 \cdots d_3r_N \psi_1^* \mathcal{H}(\mathcal{P}_{12} - l^2)\psi_1 \tag{62}$$

$$u_2 = 2u_1 l^2, \ldots \qquad u_n = nu_1 l^{2n-2}, \ldots \tag{63}$$

Besides corrections of the same nature as in the overlap matrix, there are additional dynamical corrections to the u_n's, particularly when there are successive interchanges of neighbouring pairs. For example, instead of u_2 as defined above, the coefficient of the particular permutation $\mathcal{P}_{12}\mathcal{P}_{34}$ should be precisely

$$\int d_3r_1 \cdots d_3r_N \psi_1^* \mathcal{H}(\mathcal{P}_{12}\mathcal{P}_{34} - l^4)\psi_1 \tag{64}$$

or else one counts double the nonnegligible interactions among the four particles when they are nearest neighbors. Again leaving this and other corrections to the dots, we find

$$\text{Int} = \mathbf{h}u_1(\text{Re}^{\mathbf{h}l^2} + \cdots) \tag{65}$$

Thus, the eigenvalue equation is

$$\mathbf{h}u_1(\text{Re}^{\mathbf{h}l^2} + \cdots)\varphi = E(\text{Re}^{\mathbf{h}l^2} + \cdots)\varphi \tag{66}$$

with E measured relative to $H_{1,1}$ and φ the appropriate spatial eigenfunction. However, since the latter is eventually to be multiplied by the appropriate spin functions and totally antisymmetrized, it is permissible to replace the Majorana particle permutation operators $\mathcal{P}_{nm}$ by their spin conjugate operators,

$$\mathcal{P}_{nm} \rightarrow -\tfrac{1}{2}(1 + 4\mathbf{S}_n \cdot \mathbf{S}_m) \tag{67}$$

Let us suppose momentarily that the corrections indicated by dots do not diverge as badly as R, or that they are approximately the same on both sides of the above equation. The parentheses can be factored in that case, and making the above substitution into (66) we obtain the HDVV eigenvalue equation

$$-\tfrac{1}{2}u_1 \sum_{(n, m) = \text{nearest neighb}} (1 + 4\mathbf{S}_n \cdot \mathbf{S}_m)\chi = E\chi \tag{68}$$

with χ a spin eigenfunction. Except for the trivial additive constant term, the left-hand side of this eigenvalue equation is the Heisenberg nearest-neighbor exchange Hamiltonian. The exchange parameter is the integral $2u_1$, in the present case, which can be compared to the exchange parameters J_{12} or $J_{12}^{\ddagger}$ which were obtained in the preceding section. Although it is of the same general form, the actual numerical value may differ. Like J_{12}, u_1 may in general be positive or negative. With hydrogen atomic functions and ordinary interatomic spacings, the calculated exchange parameter is normally negative, which leads to an antiferromagnetic ground state. This is in agreement with the observed ground state of N atoms of hydrogen (a molecular nonferromagnetic solid at or near zero absolute temperature).

Although the "catastrophe" has been averted, it has not been shown that the neglect of the dots is justified. Permutations leading to terms quartic or higher-order in spin operators may sometime be found to be of importance.[14] In the following section, we shall discuss a method which has aims somewhat more modest than the construction of a Heisenberg Hamiltonian, but achieves these limited goals quantitatively without uncontrollable approximations. In the chapter on magnetism and magnons in metals, the Heisenberg Hamiltonian will finally be seen to be the incidental consequence of low-order perturbation theory carried out for insulators. The neglect of three-body permutations will be seen as equivalent to the neglect of third- and higher-order perturbation corrections. However before presenting this fairly up-to-date interpretation, many other topics will occupy our interest.

METHOD OF LÖWDIN AND CARR

The nonorthogonality catastrophe in the Heitler-London theory was introduced and discussed qualitatively in the previous section. Here we shall present a constructive method for calculating directly the eigenvalues of the H-L Hamiltonian. For the range of parameters in which this theory gives reasonable results, these solutions are equivalent to finding the energy of the 2^N lowest eigenstates of $\mathcal{H}$, which can then be fitted to a Heisenberg Hamiltonian. If the fit is good, it provides evidence that the procedure of the previous section would work. If the parameters of the Heisenberg Hamiltonian cannot be chosen so as to reproduce the correct eigenvalues, then the evidence is that exchange processes involving three or more spins are important, i.e., the higher-order permutations indicated by dots in the previous section do not factor between the interaction and the overlap, and are of physical importance.

One advantage of the method introduced by Löwdin and discussed by Carr[15] is that it deals with $N \times N$ arrays rather than $N! \times N!$ arrays of the permutation space. We shall here obtain the variational energy of two very important states with it: the ferromagnetic state, for which the spatial function is the totally antisymmetric determinantal function, and the Néel state of alternating spins "up" and "down," which we shall define subsequently. Starting with the ferromagnetic state, the many electron wavefunction is,

$$
\Psi = \frac{1}{\sqrt{N!}}
\begin{vmatrix}
\varphi_1(r_1) & \varphi_2(r_1) & \cdots & \varphi_N(r_1) \\
\varphi_1(r_2) & \varphi_2(r_2) & \cdots & \cdot \\
\cdot & \cdot & & \cdot \\
\cdot & \cdot & & \cdot \\
\cdot & \cdot & & \cdot \\
\varphi_1(r_N) & \cdot & \cdots & \varphi_N(r_N)
\end{vmatrix}
\tag{69}
$$

---

[14] For a systematic analysis of this approach see T. Arai, *Phys. Rev.*, **134**: A824 (1964). For different approaches cf. the next section and Chapter 7. Experimental evidence of higher-order spin-coupling is found in E. Harris and J. Owen, *Phys. Rev. Letters*, **11**: 9 (1963); and also in D. S. Rodbell et al., *ibid.*, 10.

[15] Löwdin's methods for nonorthogonal arrays were applied to the problem of ferromagnetism by W. J. Carr, *Phys. Rev.*, **92**: 28 (1953). A variant method was used by F. Takano, *J. Phys. Soc. Japan*, **14**: 348 (1959).

The energy of this state is simply

$$E_{\text{Ferro}} = \frac{\int \Psi^* \mathcal{H} \Psi \, d_3 r_1 \cdots d_3 r_N}{\int \Psi^* \Psi \, d_3 r_1 \cdots d_3 r_N} \tag{70}$$

The Hamiltonian $\mathcal{H}$ may quite generally be taken of the form,

$$\mathcal{H} = \mathcal{H}_0 + \sum_i U(r_i) + \sum_{i \neq j} \sum V(r_i, r_j) \tag{71}$$

such that the principal diagonal in the determinantal function is an eigenfunction of $\mathcal{H}_0$ with eigenvalue e_0. Without loss of generality, let us pose $e_0 = 0$, which sets the origin of the scale of energy. Thus,

$$E_{\text{Ferro}} = \sum_i \frac{\int |\Psi|^2 U(r_i) \, d_3 r_1 \cdots d_3 r_N}{\text{denominator}} + \sum_{i \neq j} \sum \frac{\int |\Psi|^2 V(r_i, r_j) \, d_3 r_1 \cdots d_3 r_N}{\text{denominator}} \tag{72}$$

The denominator may be manipulated as follows:

$$\text{denominator} = \frac{1}{N!} \int \begin{vmatrix} \varphi_1^*(r_1) & \cdots \\ & \cdot \\ & \cdot \\ & \cdot & \cdots \end{vmatrix} \times \begin{vmatrix} \varphi_1(r_1) & \cdots \\ & \cdot \\ & \cdot \\ & \cdot & \cdots \end{vmatrix} d_3 r_1 \cdots$$

$$= \int \varphi_1^*(r_1) \varphi_2^*(r_2) \cdots \varphi_N^*(r_N) \begin{vmatrix} \varphi_1(r_1) & \cdots \\ & \cdot \\ & \cdot \\ & \cdot & \cdots \end{vmatrix} d_3 r_1 \cdots$$

$$= \int \begin{vmatrix} \varphi_1^*(r_1)\varphi_1(r_1) & \varphi_1^*(r_1)\varphi_2(r_1) & \cdots \\ \varphi_2^*(r_2)\varphi_1(r_2) & \varphi_2^*(r_2)\varphi_2(r_2) & \\ & \cdot & \\ & \cdot & \\ \varphi_N^*(r_N)\varphi_1(r_N) & \cdot & \cdots \end{vmatrix} d_3 r_1 \cdots \tag{73}$$

The second form of "denominator" is obtained by noting that each term in the expansion of the left-hand determinant contributes equally. Using this symmetry, one obtains exactly the same value of the integral by retaining only the principal diagonal and multiplying the result by $N!$ By the standard rules of multiplication of determinants by scalars, each row in the right-hand array can now be multiplied by a function occurring in the principal diagonal of the first array, and this results in the third form of Eq. (73).

The numerators are handled in an analogous manner, although the problem is somewhat trickier. We may not assume that the various terms in the potential energy are invariant with respect to interchange of the particle coordinates. However the total Hamiltonian is invariant under such interchange. We obtain, for one-body potentials:

$$\int |\Psi|^2 \sum_i U(r_i) \, d_3 r_1 \cdots = \sum_{i,j} \int \varphi_i^*(r_i) U(r_i) \varphi_j(r_i) \, d_3 r_i \int D_j^i \, d_3 r_1 \cdots d_3 r_{i-1} \, d_3 r_{i+1} \cdots \tag{74}$$

and for two-body potentials:

$$\int |\Psi|^2 \sum_i \sum_{i \neq j} V(r_i, r_j)\, d_3 r_1 \cdots = \sum_{i,\,j,\,l,\,m} \int \varphi_i^*(r_i)\varphi_j^*(r_j) V(r_i, r_j)\varphi_l(r_i)\varphi_m(r_j)$$

$$\times \int D_{lm}^{ij}\, d_3 r_1 \cdots d_3 r_{i-1}\, d_3 r_{i+1} \cdots d_3 r_{j-1}\, d_3 r_{j+1} \cdots \quad (75)$$

The sum of these terms when divided by denominator, equals the ferromagnetic energy.

The integrands D_j^i and D_{lm}^{ij} are obtained from the third line of Eq. (73) by striking out the ith row and jth column to obtain $D_j^i \times (-1)^{i+j}$; and the ith and jth rows, lth and mth columns, to obtain $D_{lm}^{ij} \times (-1)^{i+j+l+m}$. The functions which have been so stricken are explicitly taken into the energy integrals. Now all these determinants can be easily evaluated, by expanding, integrating, and recollecting terms. One finds first:

$$\text{Denominator} = \det|L_{ij}| \quad \text{where} \quad L_{ij} \equiv \int \varphi_i^*(r)\varphi_j(r)\, d_3 r \quad (76)$$

The integral of D_j^i is seen to be merely the *cofactor* of L_{ij} in this determinant. And by the usual theory of determinants, we have

$$\frac{\int D_j^i\, d_3 r_1 \cdots}{\text{denominator}} = (L^{-1})_{ij} \quad (77)$$

And similarly,

$$\frac{\int D_{lm}^{ij}\, d_3 r_1 \cdots}{\text{denominator}} = (L^{-1})_{li}(L^{-1})_{mj} - (L^{-1})_{lj}(L^{-1})_{mi} \quad (78)$$

Here L^{-1} indicates the matrix inverse to L, the latter being defined as the square matrix array with elements L_{ij}. In solids which possess translational invariance, these are cyclic matrices and can easily be inverted.[16]

For example, consider a one-dimensional chain with nearest-neighbor overlap only. Thus, $L_{ii} = 1$ and $L_{i,\,i\pm 1} \equiv l$, and all other matrix elements vanish. To make the matrix cyclic, we set $N + 1 = 1$, which is equivalent to periodic boundary conditions. The eigenvectors of L are the plane waves,

$$e^{ikn} \quad \text{with} \quad k = \pm 2\pi \frac{\text{integer}}{N} \quad (79)$$

and the eigenvalues

$$L_k = 1 + 2l \cos k \quad (80)$$

Thus, it may be verified that $L_{nm} = 1/N \sum_k e^{ik(n-m)} L_k$, and more importantly, that the

---

[16] The problem of inversion of the overlap matrix is discussed further in Löwdin et al., *J. Math. Phys.*, **1**: 461 (1960), T. L. Gilbert, *ibid.*, **3**: 107 (1962), and J. Calais and K. Appel, *ibid.*, **5**: 1001 (1964).

matrix elements of the inverse matrix are

$$(L^{-1})_{nm} = \frac{1}{N} \sum_k e^{ik(n-m)} \frac{1}{L_k}$$

$$= \frac{1}{2\pi} \int_{-\pi}^{\pi} d\theta \frac{\cos \theta (n-m)}{1 - 2l \cos \theta} = d^{|n-m|} \frac{1+d^2}{1-d^2} \qquad (81)$$

where $\quad l = \dfrac{-d}{1+d^2} \quad$ that is $\quad d = \dfrac{-1}{2l}(1 - \sqrt{1-4l^2}) \approx -l$

In the second line the sum over $\mathbf{k}$ was replaced by the integral appropriate in the limit $N \to \infty$. It is seen that the elements of the inverse matrix decrease exponentially with distance $|n - m|$. Therefore if l is sufficiently small, only $|n - m| = 0$ will survive, which corresponds (as we shall see) to a Heisenberg nearest-neighbor interaction. Let us illustrate this in three dimensions, in the simple cubic structure.

Using Eq. (72) and those following, we find that the energy of the ferromagnetic state in the three-dimensional array is

$$E_{\text{Ferro}} = \sum_i \sum_j (L^{-1})_{ij} \int \varphi_i^*(r) U(r) \varphi_j(r) \, d_3 r$$

$$+ \sum_i \sum_j \sum_l \sum_m (L^{-1})_{li}(L^{-1})_{mj} \int [\varphi_i^*(r)\varphi_j^*(r') - \varphi_i^*(r')\varphi_j^*(r)]$$

$$\times V(r, r')\varphi_l(r)\varphi_m(r') \, d_3 r \, d_3 r' \qquad (82)$$

Let $\quad \mathbf{R}_{il} \equiv a\mathbf{n} = a(n_1, n_2, n_3) \quad$ and $\quad \mathbf{R}_{mj} \equiv a\mathbf{n}' = a(n_1', n_2', n_3') \qquad (83)$

define $\qquad U_{\mathbf{k}} = \sum_i e^{-i\mathbf{k}\cdot\mathbf{R}_{ij}} \int \varphi_i^*(r) U(r) \varphi_j(r) \, d_3 r \qquad (84)$

and $\qquad L_{\mathbf{k}} = \sum_i e^{-i\mathbf{k}\cdot\mathbf{R}_{ij}} L_{ij} = 1 + 2l(\cos k_x a + \cos k_y a + \cos k_z a) \qquad (85)$

Thus, *unless* $l < \frac{1}{6}$, some $L_{\mathbf{k}}$ vanishes and L_{ij} *does not have an inverse*. Using the identity $l/f = \int_0^\infty ds\, e^{-sf}$ and the definition of $I_n(z)$, the Bessel function of imaginary argument [Eq. (99), p. 246], we readily find

$$(L^{-1})_{mj} = \int_0^\infty ds\, e^{-s} I_{n_1'}(2sl) I_{n_2'}(2sl) I_{n_3'}(2sl)$$

$$= L^{-1}(n_1', n_2', n_3') \qquad (86)$$

indicating the explicit dependence on distance by the argument (n_1', n_2', n_3') and assuming $l < \frac{1}{6}$. Note that to leading order $L^{-1}(0) = 1 + 6l^2 \doteq 1$; and $L^{-1}(1,0,0) = -l$; $L^{-1}(1, 1, 0)$ and $L^{-1}(2, 0, 0) = O(l^2)$; etc. Finally, the ferromagnetic energy is,

$$E_{\text{Ferro}} = \sum_{\mathbf{k}} \frac{U_{\mathbf{k}}}{L_{\mathbf{k}}} + \sum_{l, m, n, n'} L^{-1}(\mathbf{n}) L^{-1}(\mathbf{n}') \int [\varphi_i^*(r)\varphi_j^*(r') - \varphi_i^*(r')\varphi_j^*(r)]$$

$$\times V(r, r')\varphi_l(r)\varphi_m(r') \, d_3 r \, d_3 r' \qquad (87)$$

with $\mathbf{R}_i = \mathbf{R}_l + a\mathbf{n}$, and $\mathbf{R}_j = \mathbf{R}_m - a\mathbf{n}'$. The $L^{-1}(0)$ terms yield the direct and Heisenberg exchange interactions, denoted V and U respectively in the notation we used for the hydrogen molecule. The $L^{-1}(1, 0, 0)$ terms include integrals reminiscent of the three-atom molecule:

$$L^{-1}(1, 0, 0)L^{-1}(0)\int [\varphi^*_{1+a(1,0,0)}(r)\varphi^*_{m}(r') - \varphi^*_{1+a(1,0,0)}(r')\varphi^*_{m}(r)]V(r, r')$$
$$\times \varphi_1(r)\varphi_m(r')d_3r\, d_3r'$$

These, and successively more complicated terms cannot be associated with simple operators of the form $\mathbf{S}_i \cdot \mathbf{S}_j$, but require such forms as

$$(\mathbf{S}_i \cdot \mathbf{S}_j\, \mathbf{S}_j \cdot \mathbf{S}_m) \qquad \text{or} \qquad (\mathbf{S}_i \cdot \mathbf{S}_j\, \mathbf{S}_n \cdot \mathbf{S}_m) \quad \text{etc.} \qquad (88)$$

in their description. Fortunately, they enter with ever-increasing powers of l, and therefore may be presumed negligible if l is sufficiently small. Note that there is no "catastrophe": l must be small compared to $\frac{1}{6}$, but not to $1/N$, in order that a Heisenberg Hamiltonian, with (at worst) corrections of the type indicated in Eq. (88), describe the energy of the ferromagnetic state.

We turn to another important state, the antiferromagnetic Néel configuration, defined as follows: Every electron of spin "up" is surrounded by neighbors of spin "down." We note that because the spin functions of nearest-neighboring electrons are orthogonal, the one-electron wavefunctions of space and spin are also orthogonal, and therefore lack of orthogonality of the spatial parts is irrelevant. There is then no "exchange" whatever as $U(r)$ and $V(r, r')$ do not involve the spins, and the energy is straightaway,

$$E_{\text{Néel}} = \sum_i \int \varphi^*_i(r)U(r)\varphi_i(r) + \sum_{i, j} \int |\varphi^*_i(r)\varphi_j(r')|^2 V(r, r')\, d_3r\, d_3r' \qquad (89)$$

As we shall see elsewhere (p. 169) the energy of the Néel state is likely within 25 percent of the true ground-state energy of an antiferromagnet in three dimensions. Therefore, within the stated accuracy and restricted range of validity of the H-L scheme, one can determine whether the ground state is ferromagnetic or antiferromagnetic by comparing Eqs. (87) and (89), without in fact any need to calculate exchange constants or to first set up a Heisenberg Hamiltonian.

One often encounters the following statement: "The Heitler-London scheme and the band structure theory coalesce for *filled* bands." As we have an enlightening example of this phenomenon in the present section, it is appropriate to terminate with a brief remark on the subject. Return to the wavefunction given in Eq. (69) and take linear combinations of the columns (this does not affect the value of a determinant) to obtain

$$\Psi = \frac{1}{\sqrt{N!}} \begin{vmatrix} \psi_{k_1}(r_1) & \psi_{k_2}(r_1) & \cdots \\ \psi_{k_1}(r_2) & \psi_{k_2}(r_2) & \cdots \\ \cdot & \cdot & \\ \cdot & \cdot & \\ \cdot & \cdot & \\ \psi_{k_1}(r_N) & \cdot & \end{vmatrix} \qquad (90)$$

where
$$\psi_{\mathbf{k}}(r) = \frac{1}{\sqrt{N}} \sum_i e^{i\mathbf{k}\cdot\mathbf{R}_i}\varphi_i(r) \tag{91}$$

is the desired linear combination. It is exactly the *Bloch* wavefunction for an electron in the tight-binding limit. The set of functions in Eq. (91) is an orthogonal set, albeit an unnormalized one. For,

$$\int \psi_{\mathbf{k}}^*(r)\psi_{\mathbf{k}'}(r)\,d_3r = \frac{1}{N}\sum_i \sum_{R_{ij}} e^{i(\mathbf{k}-\mathbf{k}')\cdot\mathbf{R}_i} e^{i\mathbf{k}'\cdot\mathbf{R}_{ij}} \int \varphi_j^*(r)\varphi_i(r)\,d_3r$$

$$= \delta_{\mathbf{k},\,\mathbf{k}'} \sum_{R_{ij}} e^{i\mathbf{k}\cdot\mathbf{R}_{ij}} L_{ij} \tag{92}$$

from which one may deduce Eq. (80) and other results in the text. This sort of procedure has been used by Takano[17] to examine the theory of spin waves.

Problem 3: Assume a simple cubic structure, quasiconstant electron wavefunctions

$$\phi_j(\mathbf{r}) = +(7a^3)^{-\frac{1}{2}}$$

when $\mathbf{r}$ is within the unit cube (a^3) centered about $\mathbf{R}_j$, or within any of the six nearest-neighbor unit cubes centered about $\mathbf{R}_j \pm (a, 0, 0), \dots, \mathbf{R}_j \pm (0, 0, a)$, and

$$\phi_j(\mathbf{r}) = 0$$

otherwise. Let the potentials be

$$U(\mathbf{r}) = -A$$

that is, constant, and

$$V(\mathbf{r}, \mathbf{r}') = +B\delta(\mathbf{r} - \mathbf{r}')$$

Using these functions to calculate the various quantities in the method of Löwdin and Carr, find the following:

(a) The ferromagnetic and Néel state energies: Determine which lies lower. How does this depend on the magnitude of A? of B?

(b) In the pure Heisenberg model, simple cubic lattice, there are $3N$ bonds and therefore $E_{\text{Néel}} - E_{\text{Ferro}} = \frac{3}{2}NJ_{12}$, where $R_{12} = a =$ near neighb distance and $J_{12} =$ near neighb exchange parameter. Using the energies calculated in part (a), obtain J_{12}. Then use the definition, Eq. (18), to calculate J_{12}. Explain the agreement (or disagreement) between the results of these two alternative calculations.

---

[17] Takano, *op. cit.*

CHAPTER 3

QUANTUM THEORY
OF ANGULAR MOMENTUM

This chapter is an introduction to the quantum theory of angular momentum, and consists of a brief exposition of some severely limited topics. One object is to develop skill in expressing angular momentum operators in terms of Boson and Fermion fields. Another objective is to show that the kinetic angular momentum operators taken alone are inadequate, and so to introduce the Pauli spin matrices. All the material beyond this may be omitted on the first reading, although the operator representation methods are a prerequisite for the two later chapters on the quantum theory of magnons. The angular momentum of a charged particle is proportional to its magnetization; therefore the subject of this chapter is at the core of the theory of magnetism.

KINETIC ANGULAR MOMENTUM

In the absence of any external forces, the classical angular momentum of a point particle has the value

$$\mathbf{L} = \mathbf{r} \times \mathbf{p} \tag{1}$$

and therefore in quantum theory the analogous quantity, which shall be denoted "kinetic angular momentum" is

$$\mathbf{L} = \mathbf{r} \times \frac{\hbar}{i} \nabla \tag{2}$$

according to the usual rule for constructing quantum-mechanical momenta: $p_x = \hbar/i(d/dx)$, etc. *The angular momentum associated with a wavefunction ψ can be easily determined if this function is spherically symmetric* so that it does not depend on the angular coordinates φ and θ, but only on the magnitude of the radius vector r. For in that case we can prove that $\mathbf{L} \equiv 0$ by noting that

$$\nabla \psi(r) = \hat{\mathbf{u}}_r \frac{d}{dr} \psi(r) \tag{3}$$

where $\hat{\mathbf{u}}_r$ = unit vector in the radial direction = $\mathbf{r}/r$, and therefore,

$$\mathbf{L}\psi(r) = \frac{\hbar}{i}(\mathbf{r} \times \hat{\mathbf{u}}_r)\frac{d}{dr}\psi(r) \equiv 0 \tag{4}$$

Functions with *nontrivial* angular dependence have *nonvanishing* kinetic angular momentum, although it is not always so simple to discover its magnitude. For this requires the solution of an eigenvalue problem; and moreover, the three components of $\mathbf{L} = (L_x, L_y, L_z)$ do not commute with one another and therefore cannot be simultaneously specified. Briefly, the reason is this. If A and B are either numbers or diagonal matrices, or diagonal operators of some kind, AB equals BA. However, for the components of $\mathbf{L}$, the *commutator* (conventionally indicated by square brackets) is

$$[L_x, L_y] = L_x L_y - L_y L_x$$

$$= \frac{\hbar}{i}\frac{\hbar}{i}\left\{\left(y\frac{d}{dz} - z\frac{d}{dy}\right)\left(z\frac{d}{dx} - x\frac{d}{dz}\right) - \left(z\frac{d}{dx} - x\frac{d}{dz}\right)\left(y\frac{d}{dz} - z\frac{d}{dy}\right)\right\}$$

$$= \hbar^2\left(x\frac{d}{dy} - y\frac{d}{dx}\right)$$

$$= i\hbar L_z \tag{5}$$

When the other two components are obtained by cyclic permutations of the above, we find a set of relations which can most conveniently be described by the vector cross product, as given by the usual determinantal rule:

$$\mathbf{L} \times \mathbf{L} \equiv \begin{vmatrix} \hat{\mathbf{u}}_x & \hat{\mathbf{u}}_y & \hat{\mathbf{u}}_z \\ L_x & L_y & L_z \\ L_x & L_y & L_z \end{vmatrix} = i\hbar\mathbf{L} \tag{6}$$

While it is true that this rule was obtained by the definition of angular momentum given in Eq. (2), it is in fact more general than that, and there are operators (identified later) which obey Eq. (6) but not Eq. (2). It is therefore important that we define angular momentum as follows: *A vector operator is a genuine angular momentum operator (whether kinetic, spin, or generalized angular momentum) only if it satisfies Eq. (6) or the equivalent equations Eqs. (10) to (16).*

    Example: If $\mathbf{L} = (L_x, L_y, L_z)$ is an angular momentum, then $\mathbf{L}' = (-L_x, -L_y, -L_z)$ is not. This is related to the pseudovector nature of the classical angular momentum $\mathbf{r} \times \mathbf{p}$, and is also directly a consequence of Eq. (6).

Returning to the kinetic angular momentum, if we make use of the explicit operator representation given at the beginning, we may express it in a spherical polar coordinate system in which

$$\mathbf{r} = (r\sin\theta\cos\phi,\ r\sin\theta\sin\phi,\ r\cos\theta)$$

and in which the components of **L** take the form

$$L_z = \frac{\hbar}{i} \frac{\partial}{\partial \phi} \tag{7}$$

$$L^+ = \hbar e^{i\phi}\left(\frac{\partial}{\partial \theta} + i \cot \theta \frac{\partial}{\partial \phi}\right) \tag{8}$$

$$L^- = \hbar e^{-i\phi}\left(-\frac{\partial}{\partial \theta} + i \cot \theta \frac{\partial}{\partial \phi}\right) \tag{9}$$

Here, for future convenience, we introduced the operators

$$L^{\pm} \equiv L_x \pm iL_y \tag{10}$$

But if desired, the Cartesian components may be extracted by (what is equivalent to the last equation):

$$L_x = \tfrac{1}{2}(L^+ + L^-) \quad \text{and} \quad L_y = \frac{1}{2i}(L^+ - L^-) \tag{11}$$

The $\pm$ operators are the more useful, though, and have the names of angular momentum *raising* (+) and *lowering* (−) operators, respectively. The reason for this nomenclature is to be sought in the commutation laws for these operators. Because it is possible to derive these commutators using only Eq. (6), without making use of the actual differential forms for L_z, etc., given above, the following equations are generally valid for any angular momentum:

$$[L_z, L^+] = \hbar L^+ \tag{12}$$

and
$$[L_z, L^-] = -\hbar L^- \tag{13}$$

Given an eigenfunction of L_z with eigenvalue m, that is,

$$L_z \varphi_m = \hbar m \varphi_m$$

let us apply both sides of Eq. (12) to this eigenfunction and after rearranging terms, obtain:

$$L_z(L^+ \varphi_m) = \hbar(m + 1)(L^+ \varphi_m)$$

That is, $L^+ \varphi_m$ is an eigenfunction of L_z belonging to eigenvalue $m + 1$. It is similarly shown that $L^- \varphi_m$ belongs to eigenvalue $m - 1$, whence the terminology of "raising" and "lowering" operators. A final commutation law which can be obtained from Eq. (6) is,

$$[L^+, L^-] = 2i[L_y, L_x] = 2\hbar L_z \tag{14}$$

There is only one important operator which has not yet been introduced; it is the scalar associated with the vector angular momentum, i.e., the square of the latter.

$$L^2 = L_x^2 + L_y^2 + L_z^2 \tag{15A}$$

$$= \tfrac{1}{2}(L^+L^- + L^-L^+) + L_z^2 \tag{15B}$$

$$= L^+L^- + L_z(L_z - \hbar) \tag{15C}$$

$$= L^-L^+ + L_z(L_z + \hbar) \tag{15D}$$

The various alternative forms for L^2 are obtained from each other by means of the commutation relations of Eq. (14), and the definitions (10) and (11). Some will be more useful than others when dealing with eigenfunctions of L_z, for example.

It is trivial to prove that L^2 commutes with all the components of **L**, that is,

$$[L^2, L_z] = [L^2, L_x] = [L^2, L_y] = [L^2, L^\pm] \equiv 0 \tag{16}$$

This is seen by inspection for L_z. The product (L^+L^-) which occurs in Eqs. (15) will not change any eigenfunction of L_z, except to multiply it by a constant; for if L^- lowers the eigenvalue, L^+ raises it back to the initial value, and similarly for the product (L^-L^+). As a consequence, L^2 is simultaneously diagonal with L_z, and therefore they commute. This may be checked, and the validity of the above equation for the other components established, by use of the fundamental commutation relations Eqs. (12) to (14). (However, for kinetic angular momentum the proof is immediate: L^2 does not involve the azimuthal angle ϕ, and therefore must commute with $\dfrac{\partial}{\partial\phi}$. By rotational symmetry, it must therefore commute with all the other components of **L**.)

Because L^2 and L_z commute, they have a complete set of eigenfunctions in common, which can be labeled by the eigenvalue of each of these two operators. Because L_x and L_y (and also $L^\pm$) do not commute with L_z, they cannot be simultaneously diagonalized with the former two operators, and therefore their eigenvalues *cannot* also be specified. But there is no loss of generality in singling out the component L_z, since the z axis can be picked along any arbitrary direction. In the case of kinetic angular momentum, the desired eigenfunctions will be the well-known spherical harmonics, as we shall now discover.

SPHERICAL HARMONICS

Because the radial dependence of the wavefunction plays no role in the determination of angular momentum, we may dispense with it altogether and consider functional dependence on the angles only. The wavefunctions are normalized on the unit sphere,

$$\int_0^{2\pi} d\phi \int_{-\pi}^{\pi} d\theta \, \sin\theta\psi^*(\theta, \phi)\psi(\theta, \phi) = 1 \tag{17}$$

and the two simultaneous eigenvalue equations are

$$L_z\psi \equiv \frac{\hbar}{i}\frac{\partial}{\partial\phi}\psi = \hbar m\psi \tag{18}$$

and
$$L^2\psi = -\hbar^2\left[\frac{1}{\sin\theta}\frac{\partial}{\partial\theta}\left(\sin\theta\frac{\partial}{\partial\theta}\right) + \frac{1}{\sin^2\theta}\frac{\partial^2}{\partial\phi^2}\right]\psi = \hbar^2\lambda\psi \tag{19}$$

with eigenvalues, respectively, of m (the "magnetic quantum number") and λ. We still show the dependence on the quantum-mechanical unit of angular momentum $\hbar$, but eventually it will be most convenient to use units such that $\hbar = 1$, and such units will be assumed throughout most of the book.

The L_z equation can be integrated directly, with the result

$$\psi(\theta, \phi) = e^{im\phi}\psi(\theta, 0) \tag{20}$$

A boundary condition must now be invoked to determine the quantum numbers m, an obvious choice being to require $\psi(\theta, \phi)$ to be single-valued on the unit sphere. Therefore we require

$$e^{im(\phi + 2\pi)} = e^{im\phi} \tag{21}$$

which is satisfied by the choice,

$$m = \text{integer} = 0, \pm 1, \pm 2, ... \tag{22}$$

Although other boundary conditions are possible, they would violate other requirements of quantum theory which we have not yet discussed, which shall be examined in the following section. The same boundary condition of Eq. (21) has also been used by Dirac (see *Note* at end of section) to prove that the electric charge is quantized, in units of a fundamental charge q.

The solution, Eq. (20), may now be introduced into the second differential equation, Eq. (19), which is the eigenvalue equation for L^2. One finds directly

$$\left(\frac{1}{\sin\theta}\frac{\partial}{\partial\theta}\sin\theta\frac{\partial}{\partial\theta} - \frac{m^2}{\sin^2\theta} + \lambda\right)\psi = 0 \tag{23}$$

which is the equation obeyed by the *associated Legendre polynomials*, the properties of which are well established. But if they were not known, the following constructive procedure would solve this eigenvalue equation by elementary means:

Assume that the wavefunction $\psi(\theta, \phi) = e^{im\phi}\psi(\theta, 0)$ is a solution of the following first-order partial differential equation,

$$L^+\psi(\theta, \phi) = 0 \tag{24}$$

Therefore, by Eq. (15D), ψ is an eigenfunction of L^2 with eigenvalue

$$\lambda = m(m + 1) \tag{25}$$

The value of m is a special one, by virtue of the previous equation, $L^+\psi = 0$. *It cannot be stepped up.* It is the maximum value of the azimuthal quantum number for the calculated value of λ. Therefore we shall denote it by the symbol l, defined by

$$\lambda = l(l + 1) \tag{26}$$

and let m continue to represent the azimuthal (or "magnetic") quantum number. For the function which obeys Eq. (24), $l = m$. By repeated application of L^-, we can generate functions always belonging to the same value of λ or l, but with decreasing magnetic quantum numbers $m = l - 1$, $m = l - 2$, ... The series terminates with $m = -l$, by Eq. (15C).

The first eigenfunction, with $m = l$, is obtained explicitly by integrating the linear first-order differential equation Eq. (24). Given

$$\left(\frac{\partial}{\partial \theta} - l \cot \theta\right)\psi = 0 \tag{27}$$

divide by $(\cos \theta) \cdot (\psi)$, and integrate to obtain:

$$\psi = (\sin^l \theta)(e^{il\phi})\text{const} \tag{28}$$

Except for normalization factors, the remaining functions of the set having the common eigenvalue l are found by repeated applications of the operator L^- to this solution. These functions can be normalized, given standard phases, and are then denoted *spherical harmonics*, $Y_{l,m}$.

$$Y_{l,m}(\theta, \phi) = \frac{(-1)^{l+m}}{2^l l!}\sqrt{\frac{(2l+1)(l-m)!}{4\pi(l+m)!}} \cdot (\sin \theta)^m \left(\frac{\partial}{\partial \cos \theta}\right)^{l+m} (\sin \theta)^{2l} e^{im\phi} \tag{29}$$

These are, then, the associated Legendre polynomials of $(\cos \theta)$, multiplied by $e^{im\phi}$ and suitably normalized over the unit sphere.[1] These functions form a complete, orthonormal set (see Table 3.1).

Note: Dirac assumed the existence, somewhere in the universe, of a magnetic *monopole.* Although such objects have never been found on earth or in astronomical observations, which have so far always indicated that the magnetic dipole is the fundamental source of magnetic fields, the search goes on for this elusive particle,[2] and we may follow Dirac in assuming the existence of at least one such source—of strength μ_0. The magnetic field of such a pole is

$$H = \frac{\mu_0}{r^2}$$

which implies a vector potential (in spherical polar coordinates)

$$\mathbf{A} = (A_r, A_\theta, A_\phi) \quad \text{with } A_r = A_\theta = 0 \quad \text{and} \quad A_\phi = \frac{\mu_0}{r}\tan \tfrac{1}{2}\theta$$

---

[1] The phase $(-1)^{l+m}$ is chosen in conformity with A. R. Edmonds, *Angular Momentum in Quantum Mechanics*, Princeton Univ. Press, N.J., 1957, and E. U. Condon and G. Shortley, *The Theory of Atomic Spectra*, Cambridge, New York, 1935.

[2] Cf. E. Goto et al., "Search for Ferromagnetically Trapped Magnetic Monopoles of Cosmic Ray Origin," *Phys. Rev.* (1963), and other papers.

This may be verified by the relation $\mathbf{V} \times \mathbf{A} = \mathbf{H}$, defining $\mathbf{A}$. As we know, the Hamiltonian, as well as any other dynamical operator of a $\pm$ charged particle, is modified in a magnetic field because of a change in the momentum of the particle:

$$\mathbf{p} \to \mathbf{p} \pm \frac{e}{c} \mathbf{A}$$

with c = speed of light. But notice that $\mathbf{A} \to \infty$ along the line $\theta = \pi$, in just such a way that the integral along a path enclosing this line has a definite value, namely,

$$\oint_{\theta=\pi} \mathbf{A} \cdot d\mathbf{s} = \mu_0 4\pi$$

A particle which in the absence of the monopole had magnetic quantum number m, now has magnetic quantum number

$$m' = m \pm \left(e \oint \mathbf{A} \frac{d\mathbf{s}}{2\pi\hbar c} \right) = m \pm \frac{e}{2\pi\hbar c} \mu_0 4\pi$$

The wavefunction must still be single-valued, hence m' must be an integer, from which it follows that $\pm e$ must be an integer multiple of the "fundamental charge"

$$q = \frac{\hbar c}{2\mu_0} \qquad \text{Q.E.D.}$$

By showing that there is no fundamental unit of length associated with the magnetic monopole, Dirac proved moreover, that there could not be any bound states of a charged particle in the field H, so that the main physical effect of the monopole is the quantization of charge.[3]

REASON FOR INTEGER *l* AND *m*

It is a straightforward matter to show that l and m are all integers, or all half-odd integers. The choice between these two sets is, however, not so simple.

    Let us prove the first statement by recalling the boundary condition, Eq. (21), by which we required the wavefunctions to be single-valued on the unit sphere. This is too strict; in fact, the only physical requirement is that the probability density—a physical *observable*—be single-valued in an arbitrary state. That is, if we take an arbitrary linear combination of wavefunctions $\psi_n(\theta, \phi)$, it is required that

$$\left| \sum_n \psi_n(\theta, \phi + 2\pi) \right|^2 = \left| \sum_n \psi_n(\theta, \phi) \right|^2 \tag{30}$$

Since the dependence on the angle ϕ can be factored as $e^{im\phi}$ with different wavefunctions belonging to different values of m, the only way to satisfy this equation in all generality

---

[3] The original article is P.A.M. Dirac, "Quantized Singularities in the Electromagnetic Field," *Proc. Roy. Soc. (London)*, A **CXXXIII**: 60 (1931).

TABLE 3.1

l	*m*	$Y_{l,m}$ (normalized on unit sphere)	
0	0	$\dfrac{1}{2\sqrt{\pi}}$	
1	1	$\dfrac{1}{r}\left[-\sqrt{\dfrac{3}{8\pi}}(x+iy)\right]$	$=-\sqrt{\dfrac{3}{8\pi}}\sin\theta e^{i\varphi}$
	0	$\dfrac{1}{r}\sqrt{\dfrac{3}{4\pi}}z$	$=\sqrt{\dfrac{3}{4\pi}}\cos\theta$
2	2	$\dfrac{1}{r^2}\left[\sqrt{\dfrac{15}{32\pi}}(x+iy)^2\right]$	$=\sqrt{\dfrac{15}{32\pi}}\sin^2\theta e^{2i\varphi}$
	1	$\dfrac{1}{r^2}\left[-\sqrt{\dfrac{15}{8\pi}}z(x+iy)\right]$	$=-\sqrt{\dfrac{15}{8\pi}}\cos\theta\sin\theta e^{i\varphi}$
	0	$\dfrac{1}{r^2}\left[\sqrt{\dfrac{5}{16\pi}}(3z^2-r^2)\right]$	$=\sqrt{\dfrac{5}{16\pi}}(2\cos^2\theta-\sin^2\theta)$
3	3	$\dfrac{1}{r^3}\left[-\sqrt{\dfrac{35}{64\pi}}(x+iy)^3\right]$	$=-\sqrt{\dfrac{35}{64\pi}}\sin^3\theta e^{3i\varphi}$
	2	$\dfrac{1}{r^3}\left[\sqrt{\dfrac{105}{32\pi}}z(x+iy)^2\right]$	$=\sqrt{\dfrac{105}{32\pi}}\cos\theta\sin^2\theta e^{2i\varphi}$
	1	$\dfrac{1}{r^3}\left[-\sqrt{\dfrac{21}{64\pi}}(5z^2-r^2)(x+iy)\right]$	$=-\sqrt{\dfrac{21}{64\pi}}(4\cos^2\theta\sin\theta-\sin^3\theta)e^{i\varphi}$
	0	$\dfrac{1}{r^3}\left[\sqrt{\dfrac{7}{16\pi}}(5z^2-3r^2)z\right]$	$=\sqrt{\dfrac{7}{16\pi}}(2\cos^3\theta-3\cos\theta\sin^2\theta)$
4	4	$\dfrac{1}{r^4}\left[\dfrac{3}{16}\sqrt{\dfrac{35}{2\pi}}(x+iy)^4\right]$	$=\dfrac{3}{16}\sqrt{\dfrac{35}{2\pi}}\sin^4\theta e^{4i\varphi}$
	3	$\dfrac{1}{r^4}\left[-\dfrac{3}{8}\sqrt{\dfrac{35}{\pi}}z(x+iy)^3\right]$	$=-\dfrac{3}{8}\sqrt{\dfrac{35}{\pi}}\sin^3\theta\cos\theta e^{3i\varphi}$
	2	$\dfrac{1}{r^4}\left[\dfrac{3}{8}\sqrt{\dfrac{5}{2\pi}}(7z^2-r^2)(x+iy)^2\right]$	$=\dfrac{3}{8}\sqrt{\dfrac{5}{2\pi}}(6\sin^2\theta\cos^2\theta-\sin^4\theta)e^{2i\varphi}$
	1	$\dfrac{1}{r^4}\left[-\sqrt{\dfrac{45}{64\pi}}(7z^2-3r^2)z(x+iy)\right]$	$=-\sqrt{\dfrac{45}{64\pi}}(4\sin\theta\cos^3\theta-3\cos\theta\sin^3\theta)e^{i\varphi}$
	0	$\dfrac{1}{r^4}\left[\dfrac{3}{16\sqrt{\pi}}(35z^4-30r^2z^2+3r^4)\right]$	$=\dfrac{3}{16\sqrt{\pi}}(8\cos^4\theta+3\sin^4\theta-24\sin^2\theta\cos^2\theta)$

NOTE: $\dfrac{1}{r^4}\left(x^4+y^4+z^4-\dfrac{3}{5}r^4\right)=\dfrac{4\sqrt{\pi}}{15}\left[Y_{4,0}+\sqrt{\dfrac{5}{14}}\left(Y_{4,4}+Y_{4,-4}\right)\right]$

$Y_{l,-m}=(-1)^m Y^*_{l,m}$

is to choose all the *m*'s integers, *or* all the *m*'s half-odd integers. It is a simple exercise to verify that if both are admitted, or other choices of *m* are made, then some probability densities can be constructed which violate this equation.

The choice between the integers and half-integers is now made on the basis of the following reasoning. Physical quantities must be independent of the choice of coordinate system (whether Cartesian, spherical, or whatever) and of the origin of that coordinate system. For example, even when particles are not undergoing circular motion, the complete set of eigenfunctions of angular momentum, or linear combinations of them, must be adequate to describe the angular part of the motion. And conversely, purely spherical motion must be describable in terms of other complete sets of wavefunctions, such as the plane-wave states. Let us take this for an example. The well-known formula for the expansion of plane waves in spherical harmonics is

$$e^{i\mathbf{k}\cdot\mathbf{r}} = 4\pi \sum_{l=0}^{\infty} \sum_{m=-l}^{+l} i^l j_l(kr) Y_{l,m}(\theta, \phi) Y_{l,m}^*(\Theta, \Phi) \tag{31}$$

where the coefficients

$$j_l(kr) = \sqrt{\frac{\pi}{2kr}} J_{l+\frac{1}{2}}(kr) \tag{32}$$

are spherical Bessel functions, here defined in terms of the ordinary Bessel functions $J_p(z)$. If Θ and Φ are the angles of the $\mathbf{k}$ vector and θ and ϕ are the angles of the coordinate vector $\mathbf{r}$, the expansion formula is further reduced by expressing it in terms of the relative angle ω,

$$\cos \omega \equiv \frac{\mathbf{k}\cdot\mathbf{r}}{kr} = \cos \theta \cos \Theta + \sin \theta \sin \Theta \cos (\phi - \Phi) \tag{33}$$

using the so-called *addition* formula,

$$P_n(\cos \omega) = \frac{4\pi}{2n + 1} \sum_{m=-n}^{+n} Y_{n,m}^*(\theta, \phi) Y_{n,m}(\Theta, \Phi) \tag{34}$$

While we make no attempt to prove Eqs. (31) to (34), they are well established in mathematics and electromagnetic and quantum theory, and may be taken for granted. The Legendre polynomials, for example,

$$P_0(x) = 1 \qquad P_1(x) = x \qquad P_2(x) = \frac{1}{2}(3x^2 - 1) \qquad \dots \tag{35}$$

are particularly well known (almost elementary) functions, forming a complete set of orthonormal polynomials on the interval $-1 \leqslant x \leqslant +1$.

The expansion of the plane waves given above or of any other useful complete set of nonspherical wavefunctions in a complete set of spherical wavefunctions *only* works for the *integer* values of l and m, and this is what finally fixes our choice.

Note that the plane waves are a complete set of states of the infinitesimal translation operator. The half-odd-integer eigenvalues and their related eigenfunctions can well be useful in a fixed spherical coordinate system, where translations are *not* allowed. There is in fact such a space, denoted *spin space*, and we shall return to these considerations shortly.

MATRICES OF ANGULAR MOMENTUM

The spherical harmonics are the orthonormal eigenfunctions of L^2 and L_z, and by using them we can calculate the matrix structure of such operators as L_x and L_y, or $L^{\pm}$. For example, supplementing the relationship we had already derived,

$$L^+ Y_{l,l} = 0$$

we can obtain

$$L^+ Y_{l,m} = \hbar\sqrt{(l-m)(l+m+1)}\ Y_{l,m+1} \tag{36}$$

by operating directly on the spherical harmonics given in Eq. (29). The following relations are also very useful:

$$L^- Y_{l,m} = \hbar\sqrt{(l-m+1)(l+m)}\ Y_{l,m-1} \tag{37}$$

$$L_z Y_{l,m} = \hbar m Y_{l,m} \tag{38}$$

and

$$\begin{aligned}
L^2 Y_{l,m} &= [L_z^2 + \tfrac{1}{2}(L^+ L^- + L^- L^+)]Y_{l,m} \\
&= \hbar^2[m^2 + \tfrac{1}{2}(l-m)(l+m+1) + \tfrac{1}{2}(l-m+1)(l+m)]Y_{l,m} \\
&= \hbar^2 l(l+1)Y_{l,m}
\end{aligned} \tag{39}$$

Note that in this last equation, no property of the spherical harmonics needs be used. The eigenvalue of L^2 can be calculated using the previous three equations, that is, by knowing the matrix structure of $L^\pm$ and L_z. But this matrix structure, also, can be derived without explicit recourse to the spherical harmonics, by using the commutation relations, Eqs. (12) to (14). Thus it would apply also to the half-odd-integer solutions in which we shall soon be interested.

The conventional notation of $L^\pm$, L_z, and L^2, l, and m, will continue to be used when we are dealing with kinetic angular momentum. For general or arbitrary angular momentum, when only the basic commutation relations are invoked but the arguments are not restricted to integer values of l and m, $\mathbf{J}$ will replace $\mathbf{L}$ and j will replace l, although the eigenvalue associated with J_z will still be denoted m. The general matrix structure of the general angular momentum operators can be obtained using only Eqs. (12) to (16) and the construction given in the first section. One obtains the following results:

$$(j'm'|J^+|jm) = \delta_{j,j'}\delta_{m+1,m'}\hbar\sqrt{(j-m)(j+m+1)} \tag{40}$$

$$(j'm'|J^-|jm) = \delta_{j,j'}\delta_{m-1,m'}\hbar\sqrt{(j-m+1)(j+m)} \tag{41}$$

$$(j'm'|J_z|jm) = \delta_{j,j'}\delta_{m,m'}\hbar m \tag{42}$$

$$(j'm'|J^2|jm) = \delta_{j,j'}\delta_{m,m'}\hbar^2 j(j+1) \tag{43}$$

Because of their common factor $\delta_{j,j'}$, the general angular momentum operators can be represented by $(2j+1) \times (2j+1)$ square matrices which act in a subspace of the $2j+1$ linearly independent eigenfunctions of J^2 belonging to a given j value. Such matrices satisfy the basic commutation relations Eq. (6) or Eqs. (12) to (16), *by construction*, and are therefore genuine angular momenta in their own right.

Larger matrices can also be found which are angular momenta, but then they have sub-blocks with the above matrix structure, and are called *reducible representations*.

The most compact matrices having the properties of angular momentum are *irreducible representations* of the angular momentum operators, and they are of foremost interest. For example, the irreducible representation of angular momentum = 1 is

$$\mathscr{L}^+ = \hbar \begin{vmatrix} 0 & \sqrt{2} & 0 \\ 0 & 0 & \sqrt{2} \\ 0 & 0 & 0 \end{vmatrix}$$

$$\mathscr{L}^- = \hbar \begin{vmatrix} 0 & 0 & 0 \\ \sqrt{2} & 0 & 0 \\ 0 & \sqrt{2} & 0 \end{vmatrix} \tag{44}$$

$$\mathscr{L}_z = \hbar \begin{vmatrix} 1 & 0 & 0 \\ 0 & 0 & 0 \\ 0 & 0 & -1 \end{vmatrix}$$

We omit writing $\mathscr{L}^2$, which is just $\hbar^2 \times 2 \times$ unit matrix of this 3×3 subspace.

For angular momentum = 2 there are 5×5 matrices, for angular momentum = 3 there are 7×7, etc. It is a striking fact, however, that all the *even*-dimensional representations are missing from the list if we insist on the integer values of angular momentum possessed by the spherical harmonics. The missing matrices, the even-dimensional ones, are the spin angular momentum operators for $j, m =$ half-odd integers, and by including these, the series is made complete.

PAULI SPIN MATRICES

Here we shall discuss the smallest of the even-dimensional irreducible representations of angular momentum, the matrices of *spin one-half*. They are very similar to the 2×2 Pauli matrices, which were invented precisely for the purpose of describing the intrinsic spin angular momentum of the electron.

In this smallest subspace, the spin operators are, according to Eqs. (40)–(43),

$$S^+ = \hbar \begin{vmatrix} 0 & 1 \\ 0 & 0 \end{vmatrix} \qquad S^- = \hbar \begin{vmatrix} 0 & 0 \\ 1 & 0 \end{vmatrix} \tag{45}$$

and
$$S_z = \hbar \begin{vmatrix} \tfrac{1}{2} & 0 \\ 0 & -\tfrac{1}{2} \end{vmatrix}$$

and
$$S^2 = \hbar^2 \tfrac{3}{4} \begin{vmatrix} 1 & 0 \\ 0 & 1 \end{vmatrix} \tag{46}$$

The Pauli spin matrices are obtained from S_z, $S_x = \tfrac{1}{2}(S^+ + S^-)$, and $S_y = (S^+ - S^-)/2i$ by

$$\mathbf{S} = \tfrac{1}{2}\hbar\boldsymbol{\sigma} = \tfrac{1}{2}\hbar(\sigma_x, \sigma_y, \sigma_z) \tag{47}$$

and so are explicitly

$$\sigma_x = \begin{vmatrix} 0 & 1 \\ 1 & 0 \end{vmatrix} \quad \sigma_y = i \begin{vmatrix} 0 & -1 \\ 1 & 0 \end{vmatrix} \quad \sigma_z = \begin{vmatrix} 1 & 0 \\ 0 & -1 \end{vmatrix} \quad \text{and} \quad \mathbb{1} = \begin{vmatrix} 1 & 0 \\ 0 & 1 \end{vmatrix} \quad (48)$$

The eigenvectors of S_z and σ_z are the two-component *spinors*

$$\chi_+ = \begin{vmatrix} 1 \\ 0 \end{vmatrix} \quad \text{and} \quad \chi_- = \begin{vmatrix} 0 \\ 1 \end{vmatrix} \quad (49)$$

corresponding to $m = \pm\frac{1}{2}$, respectively. Conventionally, $\sigma^\pm$ are defined by $\sigma^\pm = S^\pm$.

The higher-dimensional even matrices, 4×4, 6×6, etc., can be similarly constructed using the general set of rules for the matrix elements given in Eqs. (40) to (43) and will represent the higher spins 3/2, 5/2, etc. There is no need to give these explicitly, particularly because matrices become unwieldy with increasing size, and because we shall find far more convenient operator representations.

COMPOUNDING ANGULAR MOMENTUM

It is frequently necessary to compound constituent angular momenta into a total angular momentum operator and, conversely, to decompose and simplify operators with complex structure. Let us go into this matter briefly and directly, even at the expense of omitting formal proofs.

Given two angular momenta $\mathbf{J}_1$ and $\mathbf{J}_2$, it seems certain (intuitively) that $\mathbf{J} = \mathbf{J}_1 + \mathbf{J}_2$ will be an allowable angular momentum, obeying the commutation laws of Eqs. (6) and those following. But no other linear combination of $\mathbf{J}_1$ and $\mathbf{J}_2$ will do (cf. Problem 1).

Problem 1: Given angular momenta $\mathbf{J}_1$ and $\mathbf{J}_2$, show that $a\mathbf{J}_1 + b\mathbf{J}_2$ is itself an angular momentum only if $a = b = 1$; or $a = 1$, $b = 0$; or $a = 0$, $b = 1$.

How does one express the eigenfunctions of $\mathbf{J}_1$ and $\mathbf{J}_2$ in terms of the eigenfunctions of $\mathbf{J}$, and vice versa?

Supposing we start by knowing a complete set of angular momenta eigenfunctions of $\mathbf{J}_1$ and $\mathbf{J}_2$, whether spinors or spherical harmonics, or whatever, which we label by the two sets of quantum numbers:

$$|j_1 m_1 j_2 m_2) \quad (50)$$

For fixed j_1 and j_2 there are $(2j_1 + 1) \cdot (2j_2 + 1)$ orthonormal eigenfunctions of this type corresponding to the various choices of m_1 and m_2. Each one is, therefore, also an eigenfunction of J^z, with eigenvalue $m = m_1 + m_2$. (Henceforth, subscripts will label individual angular momenta, and superscripts their components; for example, J_i^x.) This has a maximum value $j_1 + j_2$, therefore it is the maximum value of m, which is by definition j, the quantum number of J^2 [recall Eqs. (24) to (26)]. By repeated applications of the operator $J^- = J_1^- + J_2^-$ to this state of maximal m, we generate a total of $2(j_1 + j_2) + 1$ orthogonal states all belonging to the same j value, but with $m = j_1 + j_2, j_1 + j_2 - 1, \dots, -j_1 - j_2$. (Note that j is not changed, because J^- commutes with J^2.) Only *one* of these states has $m = j_1 + j_2 - 1$, for, indeed, every m value occurs only once in this list. But there are *two* of the original states which belong to this eigenvalue of J^z: $|j_1 j_1 - 1 j_2 j_2)$ and $|j_1 j_1 j_2 j_2 - 1)$. The function which has been included is in fact the *sum* of these two functions,

$$|j_1 j_1 - 1 j_2 j_2) + |j_1 j_1 j_2 j_2 - 1) \tag{51}$$

because $J^- = J_1^- + J_2^-$. This leaves us free to consider the difference of the two:

$$|j_1 j_1 - 1 j_2 j_2) - |j_1 j_1 j_2 j_2 - 1) \tag{52}$$

This function is orthogonal to the previous one, it belongs to the same m value, and when $J^+ = J_1^+ + J_2^+$ is applied to it the result vanishes. Therefore the m value to which it belongs must be maximal, and Eq. (52) must be an eigenfunction belonging to $j = j_1 + j_2 - 1$. Repeated applications of J^- to this function, Eq. (52), results indeed in $2(j_1 + j_2 - 1) + 1$ orthogonal functions, corresponding to all the attainable m values.

Two of the three states belonging to $m = j_1 + j_2 - 2$ are thus accounted for, and the third can now be used to construct the set of functions belonging to $j = j_1 + j_2 - 2$. This procedure may be continued until all $(2j_1 + 1) \cdot (2j_2 + 1)$ initial states are exhausted. Such a stage is reached when $j = |j_1 - j_2|$, which is therefore the *minimum* magnitude of the compound angular momentum, just as $j_1 + j_2$ is the *maximum* magnitude. The proof is given in Problem 2 and by an operator method in Eqs. (75) and (76). j obeys the so-called "triangle inequality."

Problem 2: Show that the procedure indicated in the text does in fact use every one of the initial functions, by proving the identity

$$\sum_{j=|j_1-j_2|}^{j_1+j_2} (2j+1) = (2j_1 + 1) \cdot (2j_2 + 1)$$

Having constructed the complete set of eigenfunctions of J^2 and J^z from the set of eigenfunctions of J_1^z and J_2^z, one may formalize this procedure somewhat. The two sets of orthonormal states are related by a canonical (unitary) transformation, that is, we can express the new wavefunctions $|j_1 j_2 jm)$ in terms of the old by

$$|j_1 j_2 jm) = \sum_{m_1, m_2} |j_1 m_1 j_2 m_2)(j_1 m_1 j_2 m_2 | j_1 j_2 jm) \tag{53}$$

where the matrix elements of the transformation operator

$$(j_1 m_1 j_2 m_2 | j_1 j_2 jm) \tag{54}$$

are the vector-coupling, or *Clebsch-Gordan coefficients*. A somewhat symmetric form for these coefficients was derived first by Wigner using group-theoretical methods, and later by Racah and by Schwinger.[4] (Later in this chapter there is an introduction to

---

[4] For references to Wigner's and other work, and for detailed formulas, see Edmonds, *op. cit.*

Schwinger's operator technique in angular momentum.) We quote the result:

$$(j_1 m_1 j_2 m_2 | j_1 j_2 jm) = \delta_{m_1+m_2, m}$$

$$\cdot \left[\frac{(2j+1)(j_1+j_2-j)!(j_1-j_2+j)!(-j_1+j_2+j)!(j_1+m_1)!(j_1-m_1)!(j_2+m_2)!}{(j_1+j_2+j+1)!} \right.$$

$$\left. \cdot (j_2-m_2)!(j+m)!(j-m)! \right]^{1/2}$$

$$\cdot \sum_z (-1)^z [z!(j_1+j_2-j-z)!(j_1-m_1-z)!(j_2+m_2-z)!$$

$$(j-j_2+m_1+z)!(j-j_1-m_2+z)!]^{-1} \tag{55}$$

This unwieldy formula is evaluated in a form useful in problems involving angular momenta $\tfrac{1}{2}$ or 1 in Table 3.2.

TABLE 3.2
Nonvanishing Clebsch-Gordan Coefficients for $j_2 = \tfrac{1}{2}$ and 1

$(j_1 m_1 \tfrac{1}{2} m_2 \| j_1 \tfrac{1}{2} jm)$		
	$m_2 = \tfrac{1}{2}$	$m_2 = -\tfrac{1}{2}$
$j = j_1 + \tfrac{1}{2}$	$+\sqrt{\dfrac{j_1+m+\tfrac{1}{2}}{2j_1+1}}$	$+\sqrt{\dfrac{j_1-m+\tfrac{1}{2}}{2j_1+1}}$
$j = j_1 - \tfrac{1}{2}$	$-\sqrt{\dfrac{j_1-m+\tfrac{1}{2}}{2j_1+1}}$	$+\sqrt{\dfrac{j_1+m+\tfrac{1}{2}}{2j_1+1}}$

$(j_1 m_1 1 m_2 \| j_1 1 jm)$			
j	$m_2 = 1$	$m_2 = 0$	$m_2 = -1$
$j_1 + 1$	$+\sqrt{\dfrac{(j_1+m)(j_1+m+1)}{(2j_1+1)(2j_1+2)}}$	$+\sqrt{\dfrac{(j_1-m+1)(j_1+m+1)}{(2j_1+1)(j_1+1)}}$	$+\sqrt{\dfrac{(j_1-m)(j_1-m+1)}{(2j_1+1)(2j_1+2)}}$
j_1	$-\sqrt{\dfrac{(j_1+m)(j_1-m+1)}{2j_1(j_1+1)}}$	$+\dfrac{m}{\sqrt{j_1(j_1+1)}}$	$+\sqrt{\dfrac{(j_1-m)(j_1+m+1)}{2j_1(j_1+1)}}$
$j_1 - 1$	$+\sqrt{\dfrac{(j_1-m)(j_1-m+1)}{2j_1(2j_1+1)}}$	$-\sqrt{\dfrac{(j_1-m)(j_1+m)}{j_1(2j_1+1)}}$	$+\sqrt{\dfrac{(j_1+m+1)(j_1+m)}{2j_1(2j_1+1)}}$

For the purposes of nuclear and atomic physics, a symmetrized form of these coefficients, the *Wigner 3-j symbols*, is simpler to manipulate. However, it does not serve any purpose to introduce them here, and we refer the reader to Edmonds' book.

We shall return to the subject of compound angular momentum, after introducing an operator technique for expressing the angular momenta.

COUPLED-BOSON REPRESENTATION

In semiclassical theories of magnetism it is common to approximate the unwieldy spin operators or matrices by harmonic-oscillator operators, for the general matrix structure of the spins, Eqs. (40) to (43), resembles in many respects the matrix structure of harmonic oscillator operators. That this is no coincidence has been proved by Schwinger in his theory of angular momentum[5] based on coupled harmonic-oscillator fields.

As is well known, one may take linear combinations of momentum and coordinate operators, to obtain harmonic-oscillator "raising" and "lowering" operators a^* and a; for example,

$$a^* = \frac{1}{\sqrt{2\hbar}}\left(\frac{\hbar}{i}\frac{\partial}{\partial x} + ix\right) \qquad a = \frac{1}{\sqrt{2\hbar}}\left(\frac{\hbar}{i}\frac{\partial}{\partial x} - ix\right)$$

Let us make clear the reason for this terminology. The commutation relations which may be derived for the operators a, a^* are those of *Bosons*

$$[a_i, a_j] = [a_i^*, a_j^*] = 0 \qquad [a_i, a_j^*] = \delta_{ij} \tag{56}$$

with i, j referring to different particles, from which we deduce also:

$$[\mathfrak{n}_i, a_j^*] = \delta_{ij} \qquad [\mathfrak{n}_i, a_j] = -\delta_{ij} \tag{57}$$

introducing $\mathfrak{n}_i = a_i^* a_i = $ *occupation-number operator*, referring to the degree of excitation (occupation) of the ith harmonic oscillator. One may construct a complete set of states, labeled by their eigenvalues, by first introducing a "vacuum." This is the ground state of all the harmonic oscillators, the no-particle state, denoted $|0)$, which is annihilated by every lowering operator:

$$a_i|0) \equiv 0 \qquad \text{for all } i \tag{58}$$

The one-particle states are clearly

$$a_i^*|0)$$

and the (normalized) two-particle states are

$$a_1^* a_2^*|0) \qquad \text{or} \qquad \frac{(a_1^*)^2}{\sqrt{2}}|0)$$

etc. The general formula for the many-particle, normalized state is

$$\frac{(a_1^*)^{n_1}(a_2^*)^{n_2}\ldots}{\sqrt{n_1!n_2!\ldots}}|0) \tag{59}$$

---

[5] Julian Schwinger, "On Angular Momentum," U.S. Atomic Energy Commission, NYO-3071 (1952), unpublished report.

as proved in Problem 3. In these states, the occupation-number operators n_i are diagonal, with positive integer eigenvalues $n_i = 0, 1, 2, \ldots$. The total occupation of a state is given by the sum of the eigenvalues,

$$\sum n_i$$

Problem 3: Prove that the state in Eq. (59) is normalized by evaluating $(0| \ldots (a_2)^{n_2}(a_1)^{n_1}(a_1^*)^{n_1}(a_2^*)^{n_2} \ldots |0)$, using only the definition of the vacuum, Eq. (58), and the commutation relations of Eqs. (56) and (57). Show that n_i is the eigenvalue of n_i.

Schwinger showed that with the aid of only two harmonic oscillators the entire matrix structure of a single angular momentum, as summarized in Eqs. (40) to (43), could be exactly reproduced. The advantages are great, even if no new results were obtained, most especially for large values of j for which the angular-momentum matrices are large and unwieldy. New features can also be studied with Schwinger's approach, due to the great understanding which has been achieved concerning the harmonic-oscillator fields as compared to the more obscure angular momentum-operators. Labeling the two oscillators by subscripts 1 and 2, let us introduce the Schwinger *spinor operators*:

$$\mathbf{a}^+ = (a_1^*, a_2^*) \qquad \text{and} \qquad \mathbf{a} = \begin{pmatrix} a_1 \\ a_2 \end{pmatrix} \tag{60}$$

which are merely two-component vectors with operator components. If, moreover, we contract these operators with the Pauli spin matrices, we obtain the desired representation. That is, let

$$J^z = \frac{\hbar}{2}\, \mathbf{a}^+ \cdot \mathbf{\sigma}_z \cdot \mathbf{a} = \frac{\hbar}{2}\,(a_1^* a_1 - a_2^* a_2) = \frac{\hbar}{2}\,(n_1 - n_2)$$

and similarly for the other components, with the following compact result:

$$\boxed{\mathbf{J} = \frac{\hbar}{2}\, \mathbf{a}^+ \cdot \mathbf{\sigma} \cdot \mathbf{a}} \tag{61}$$

One-half times the contraction with the unit operator will be denoted the j operator:

$$\mathbf{j} = \tfrac{1}{2}\mathbf{a}^+ \cdot \mathbf{a} = \tfrac{1}{2}(a_1^* a_1 + a_2^* a_2) = \tfrac{1}{2}n_1 + \tfrac{1}{2}n_2 \tag{62}$$

It may be verified that the eigenvalue of this operator is indeed $j = 0, \tfrac{1}{2}, 1, \tfrac{3}{2}, \ldots$, where $\mathbf{J}^2$ has eigenvalue $\hbar^2 j(j + 1)$.

Problem 4: Show that $J^+ = \hbar a_1^* a_2$ and $J^- = \hbar a_2^* a_1$. (These formulas and the ones in the text may be remembered by associating a change $\Delta m = +\tfrac{1}{2}$ with each type-1 particle, and $\Delta m = -\tfrac{1}{2}$ with each type-2 particle.)

Problem 5: Prove the operator identity

$$\mathbf{J}^2 = \hbar^2 \mathbf{j}(\mathbf{j} + 1)$$

Problem 6: Quantization of the electric and magnetic fields of light waves is the first step in quantum electrodynamic theory. Assuming these are harmonic-oscillator fields, let subscript 1 refer to the electric field and subscript 2 to the magnetic field in operators a_1, a_1^* and a_2, a_2^* (e.g., for a particular plane-wave mode). Use the fact that half the total energy must be contained in each field to prove that the eigenvalues j can only take on integer values, thus showing that the photon has quantized spin of unity. Compare with Eqs. (100) and (101).

Normalized eigenfunctions of a single angular momentum, possessing definite m and j eigenvalues shall be denoted $|jm)$, and are simply

$$|jm) = \frac{(a_1^*)^{j+m}(a_2^*)^{j-m}}{\sqrt{(j+m)!(j-m)!}} \, |0) \tag{63}$$

The coupled-Boson operators have more flexibility than the original angular-momentum operators. For example, we can make use of the extra degrees of freedom to construct the so-called *hyperbolic operators* which conserve m, but *raise* or *lower* j:

$$K^+ = \hbar a_1^* a_2^* \qquad K^- = \hbar a_2 a_1 \qquad \text{and} \qquad K^z = \frac{\hbar}{2}(n_1 + n_2 + 1) \tag{64}$$

They obey the commutation relations,

$$[K^z, K^+] = \hbar K^+ \qquad [K^z, K^-] = -\hbar K^-$$

and

$$[K^+, K^-] = -2\hbar K^z \tag{65}$$

Only the last of these differs, by a sign, from the commutation relations of the angular-momentum operators. The following equations may also be verified:

$$(J^z)^2 - \tfrac{1}{4}\hbar^2 = (K^z)^2 - \tfrac{1}{2}(K^+K^- + K^-K^+) \tag{66A}$$

$$= K^z(K^z - \hbar) - K^+K^- \tag{66B}$$

$$= K^z(K^z + \hbar) - K^-K^+ \tag{66C}$$

ROTATIONS

The study of rotations of coordinate systems and of particles is intimately tied in with the theory of angular momentum. For example, given an arbitrary function $f(\phi)$ of the azimuthal angle ϕ, its argument may be rotated through an angle α by applying a differential operator:

$$e^{\alpha(d/d\phi)} f(\phi) = f(\phi + \alpha)$$

This formula may be checked by a Taylor series expansion of both sides, in powers of α. The operator which is exponentiated will be recognized as proportional to L^z, and is just one of the three differential operators, or linear combinations thereof, which may be exponentiated to effect desired rotations in the coordinate system. The most general rotation is expressible in terms of the three Euler angles α, β, and γ, and takes the form of the unitary operator

$$D(\alpha\beta\gamma) = e^{i(\alpha/\hbar)J^z}e^{i(\beta/\hbar)J^y}e^{i(\gamma/\hbar)J^z} = (D^\dagger)^{-1} \tag{67}$$

One writes $\mathbf{J}$ instead of $\mathbf{L}$ because the rotations are not limited to the integer angular momenta. Of course, the three-Euler-angle formula is equivalent to a single rotation about a suitably chosen axis, with its direction along a unit vector $\hat{\mathbf{u}}$, and so

$$D(\alpha\beta\gamma) = e^{i\alpha'\hat{\mathbf{u}}\cdot\mathbf{J}} \tag{68}$$

for a suitable angle α'. Thus, two or more successive rotations can be expressed by a single one. One of the practical consequences of this equality, after the rotations are expressed in terms of a complete set of spherical harmonics (for integer angular momentum), is a very useful formula for expressing *products* of spherical harmonics as a *linear* combination of spherical harmonics, viz.,

$$Y_{l_1 m_1}(\theta, \phi)Y_{l_2 m_2}(\theta, \phi) = \sum_{l,m} Y_{l,m}(\theta, \phi)\sqrt{\frac{(2l_1+1)(2l_2+1)}{4\pi(2l+1)}}$$

$$\cdot(l_1 m_1 l_2 m_2 | l_1 l_2 lm)(l_1 0 l_2 0 | l_1 l_2 l0) \tag{69}$$

We shall not prove this formula here, but proceed instead to show in what way the rotations are related to the unitary transformations of Boson operators. The transformation which takes a operators into a linear combination of each other is a unitary canonical transformation if it preserves the Boson commutation relations, and the Hermitean nature of Hermitean operators. If it also preserves the eigenvalue j (that is, commutes with $\mathbf{j}$), it corresponds precisely to a rotation. In particular,

$$\begin{aligned}
a_1^* &\to [e^{+(i/2)(\alpha+\gamma)}\cos\tfrac{1}{2}\beta]a_1^* + [e^{(i/2)(\gamma-\alpha)}\sin\tfrac{1}{2}\beta]a_2^* \\
a_2^* &\to -[e^{(i/2)(\alpha-\gamma)}\sin\tfrac{1}{2}\beta]a_1^* + [e^{(i/2)(\alpha+\gamma)}\cos\tfrac{1}{2}\beta]a_2^* \\
a_1 &\to [e^{-(i/2)(\alpha+\gamma)}\cos\tfrac{1}{2}\beta]a_1 + [e^{-(i/2)(\gamma-\alpha)}\sin\tfrac{1}{2}\beta]a_2 \\
a_2 &\to [e^{-(i/2)(\alpha-\gamma)}\sin\tfrac{1}{2}\beta]a_1 + [e^{-(i/2)(\alpha+\gamma)}\cos\tfrac{1}{2}\beta]a_2
\end{aligned} \tag{70}$$

is the transformation which results if in Eq. (67) we express the components of $\mathbf{J}$ in the coupled-Boson representation, and calculate

$$a_i \to D(\alpha\beta\gamma)a_i D^{-1}(\alpha\beta\gamma)$$

For complex angles, this is no longer a unitary but a *similarity* transformation, which preserves the commutation relations but not Hermiticity. One may also imagine unitary or similarity transformations which do not conserve j, and which mix the a operators with a^* operators. Such transformations mix the angular-momentum operators with the hyperbolic ones and are generated by including the components of $\mathbf{K}$ as well as of $\mathbf{J}$ in D.

MORE ON COMPOUND ANGULAR MOMENTUM

The addition of the spin of an electron to its mechanical angular momentum, the addition of the angular momenta or spins of two distinct electrons, and in general the coupling of two or more angular momenta of various origins, require mathematical techniques beyond the simple formulation given so far. Here we shall show some of the machinery established by Schwinger for handling these problems, without, however, entering into the details. We shall study the coupling of two angular momenta, and it might appear that by induction one may use this theory to couple an arbitrary number of angular momenta. However, in practice this is not quite so, and even for three angular momenta certain additional simplifications must be sought if the problem is to remain manageable.

Two angular momenta require four Bose particles for their description. But with four Boson operators, far more than the components of $\mathbf{J}_1$ and $\mathbf{J}_2$ can be constructed: we can obtain $\mathbf{J} = \mathbf{J}_1 + \mathbf{J}_2$, and also all the relevant hyperbolic operators. The Clebsch-Gordan coefficients, rotations in one or the other angular-momentum space, and all the other possible subjects of interest also may be investigated by studying the Bose operators and their eigenfunctions.

Let the Bose operators referring to angular momentum 1 be labeled a_1 and a_2, and those referring to angular momentum 2 be labeled b_1 and b_2. Any a operator commutes with any b operator. The notation and terminology will be that introduced in Eqs. (56) to (63). This takes care of the usual operators, the components of $\mathbf{J}_i$, and J_i^2. In addition, the following new ones are required:

$$I^+ = \hbar \mathbf{a}^+\mathbf{b} \qquad I^- = \hbar \mathbf{b}^+\mathbf{a} \qquad I^z = \hbar(\mathbf{j}_1 - \mathbf{j}_2) \tag{71}$$

where
$$\mathbf{a}^+\mathbf{b} = a_1^* b_1 + a_2^* b_2 \tag{72}$$

etc., in the spinor notation, and

$$K^+ = \hbar(a_1^* b_2^* - a_2^* b_1^*) \qquad K^- = \hbar(a_1 b_2 - a_2 b_1) \qquad K^z = \hbar(\mathbf{j}_1 + \mathbf{j}_2 + 1) \tag{73}$$

The following relations may be verified by substituting the definitions given above:

$$J^2 = J_x^2 + J_y^2 + J_z^2$$

$$= I^z(I^z - \hbar) + I^+ I^- \tag{74A}$$

$$= I^z(I^z + \hbar) + I^- I^+ \tag{74B}$$

$$= K^z(K^z - \hbar) - K^+ K^- \tag{74C}$$

$$= K^z(K^z + \hbar) - K^- K^+ \tag{74D}$$

Using the definition of I^z [Eq. (71)], and the fact that $I^+ I^-$ in Eq. (74A) is a positive semidefinite operator (so is $I^- I^+$), one proves directly that $j(j+1) \geqslant (j_1 - j_2)(j_1 - j_2 - 1)$. The choice $j_2 \geqslant j_1$ [if $j_2 < j_1$, then use Eq. (74B)] establishes

$$j \geqslant |j_2 - j_1| \tag{75}$$

Similarly, the two equations involving K can be used to prove

$$j \leqslant (j_1 + j_2) \tag{76}$$

and thus to establish the "triangle inequality" first introduced in the discussion following Eq. (52) and in Problem 2.

A state of definite eigenvalues $j_1 m_1$ and $j_2 m_2$ is

$$|j_1 m_1 j_2 m_2) = \frac{(a_1^*)^{j_1+m_1}(a_2^*)^{j_1-m_1}(b_1^*)^{j_2+m_2}(b_2^*)^{j_2-m_2}}{\sqrt{(j_1+m_1)!(j_1-m_1)!(j_2+m_2)!(j_2-m_2)!}} |0) \tag{77}$$

A state of definite j, m, j_1 and j_2 may equally well be labeled j, m, μ, and v, where

$$\mu = j_1 - j_2 \quad \text{and} \quad v = j_1 + j_2 + 1 \tag{78}$$

and denoted

$$|jm\mu v\rangle \tag{79}$$

where $\mu \leqslant j$ and $v \geqslant j + 1$. For $m = j$ and $v = j + 1$, the appropriate state is

$$|jj\mu j + 1\rangle = \frac{(a_1^*)^{j+\mu}(b_1^*)^{j-\mu}}{\sqrt{(j+\mu)!(j-\mu)!}} |0) \tag{80}$$

Application of the spin-lowering operator yields the states $|jm\mu j + 1\rangle$, and finally, arbitrary states are given by

$$|jm\mu v\rangle = \sqrt{\frac{(2j+1)!}{(v+j)!(v-j-1)!}} (K^+)^{v-j-1}|jm\mu j + 1\rangle \tag{81}$$

The inner product of these wavefunctions with the $|j_1 m_1 j_2 m_2)$ of Eq. (77) yields the Clebsch-Gordan coefficients by Schwinger's method.

The Bose operator method may be extended in various directions to recover well-known results (e.g., for the spherical harmonics) or to discover new ones. A connection with the continuous representations may be made using the operator identity

$$a_i F(a_i^*)|0) = \frac{\partial}{\partial a_i^*} F(a_i^*)|0) \tag{82}$$

which may be used to construct generating functions for various sets of orthogonal polynomials. But this subject is properly outside the scope of the present elementary treatment.

OTHER REPRESENTATIONS

The first formal justification of the Bloch theory of spin waves may be found in the work of Holstein and Primakoff.[6] Bloch had naturally assumed that spin waves

---

[6] F. Holstein and H. Primakoff, *Phys. Rev.*, **58**: 1048 (1940).

obey Bose-Einstein statistics, but these authors showed how spin operators could be expressed in terms of true Bose fields, much as we shall show it in the chapter on spin-wave theory. The Holstein-Primakoff representation is best understood as a special case of the Schwinger coupled-Boson representation, that is, as an irreducible representation of the latter in a subspace of fixed j. Recall Eq. (62), which we rewrite as

$$a_2^* a_2 = \sqrt{2\mathbf{j} - \mathfrak{n}_1} \cdot \sqrt{2\mathbf{j} - \mathfrak{n}_1} \tag{83}$$

In a subspace of fixed eigenvalue j, this equation is solved by treating a_2 and its conjugate as two diagonal operators,

$$a_2 = a_2^* = (2j)^{1/2} \sqrt{1 - \frac{\mathfrak{n}}{2j}} \tag{84}$$

hence, $$J^+ = \hbar a^*(2j)^{1/2} \sqrt{1 - \frac{\mathfrak{n}}{2j}} \qquad J^- = \hbar(2j)^{1/2} \sqrt{1 - \frac{\mathfrak{n}}{2j}}\, a$$

and $$J^z = \hbar(\mathfrak{n} - j) \tag{85}$$

omitting the subscript $(_1)$ on a and $\mathfrak{n}$. The formalism is incorrect whenever n exceeds $2j$, but within the allowed range, it may be verified that the basic commutation relations Eqs. (12) to (16) are correctly obeyed. (The rationalization of the square root is discussed, following Eq. (98) in the section on "spins one.")

If all that one requires is the satisfaction of these commutation laws, and if one relaxes the requirement that J^+ and J^- be Hermitean conjugate operators, then he may perform the so-called Maléev similarity transformation to a new set of operators:

$$J^+ = a^*(2j)^{1/2}\left(1 - \frac{\mathfrak{n}}{2j}\right)\hbar \qquad J^- = (2j)^{1/2} a \hbar \qquad \text{and} \qquad J^z = (\mathfrak{n} - j)\hbar \tag{86}$$

The obvious advantage, the rationalization of the square root, is somewhat offset by the complications introduced by the nonunitary transformation.

Either of these forms, Eq. (85) or (86), may be transformed without any difficulty by *rotations* of the coordinate system, for this conserves j. The improper rotations, such as generated by the hyperbolic operators K, are not allowed for they would mix in states outside the physically meaningful range.

Either of these representations is useful particularly when j is very large. In connection with this "correspondence limit," we may quote a result by Edmonds,[7] the asymptotic form of the spherical harmonics in the limit of very large l. He obtains by a WKB-type solution of Eq. (23),

$$Y_{lm}(\theta, \phi) \propto \frac{A e^{im\phi}}{(a^2 - x^2)^{1/4}}\, e^{\pm (i/\varepsilon) \int^x dt \sqrt{(a^2 - t^2)/(1 - t^2)}} \qquad \text{for } l \gg 1 \tag{87}$$

---

[7] Edmonds, *op. cit.*

where
$$A = \text{const} \qquad a^2 = 1 - \frac{m^2}{l(l+1)}$$

$$\varepsilon = \frac{1}{\sqrt{l(l+1)}} \qquad \text{and} \qquad x = \cos\theta$$

which may also be used to investigate the correspondence limit. The extreme quantum limit, $j = \frac{1}{2}$ or 1 deserves separate investigation, and will be discussed in the following sections.

SPINS ONE-HALF

For spins one-half, $n = 0, 1$ in the preceding equations, the Holstein-Primakoff and Maléev representations are identical within the physically allowed subspace.

Problems involving N interacting spins one-half may be more easily formulated with the aid of one of several Fermion representations. This takes us back almost 40 years, to the historic paper of Jordan and Wigner on second quantization[8] in which the Fermion anticommuting operators were explicitly constructed out of Pauli spin matrices. It is just the inverse procedure which is of present interest.

Fermion operators, which we denote by the letter c, are a set of *anticommuting* operators; for example, for any state $|\Phi\rangle$,

$$c_1^* c_2^* |\Phi\rangle = - c_2^* c_1^* |\Phi\rangle$$

and therefore, care must be taken of the order in which the operators are written. The vacuum is defined, just as for spins, as the state annihilated by all c's,

$$c_i|0\rangle = 0 \qquad \mathfrak{n}_i|0\rangle = 0 \qquad (i = 1, \ldots, N) \tag{88}$$

and is the state in which the particle number operators

$$\mathfrak{n}_i = c_i^* c_i \tag{89}$$

all have zero eigenvalue.

The anticommutation relations are indicated by curly brackets and are

$$c_i c_j + c_j c_i \equiv \{c_i, c_j\} = 0 \qquad \{c_i^*, c_j^*\} = 0 \qquad \{c_i, c_j^*\} = \delta_{ij} \tag{90}$$

Setting $i = j$ in the above equations yields the relations

$$c_i^2 = (c_i^*)^2 = 0 \qquad c_i^* c_i + c_i c_i^* = 1 \tag{91}$$

which are identically the equations obeyed by the Pauli spin matrices $\sigma^\pm$. It is only the fact that Pauli spin matrices referring to different particles ($i \neq j$) *commute* with one another, which differentiates them from the anticommuting Fermion operators

---

[8] P. Jordan and E. Wigner, *Z. Physik*, **47**: 631 (1928).

above. This may be remedied by introducing a set of drone operators d_i and d_i^*, equal in number to the original set of c's, which anticommute with the latter and obey amongst themselves anticommutation relations entirely anologous to Eq. (90). As a consequence,

$$(d_i + d_i^*)^2 \equiv 1 \quad \text{and} \quad \{d_i + d_i^*, d_j + d_j^*\} = 0 \quad \text{for } i \neq j \tag{92}$$

so that finally

$$S_i^+ = \hbar c_i^*(d_i + d_i^*) \qquad S_i^- = \hbar(d_i + d_i^*)c_i \quad \text{and} \quad S_i^z = \hbar(c_i^* c_i - \tfrac{1}{2}) \tag{93}$$

is the desired set of spin one-half operators, which *commute* when $i \neq j$.

Problem 7: Prove that the various representations in this section obey Eqs. (12) to (16), and also that different spins *commute*:

$$[S_i^k, S_j^{k'}] = 0 \qquad \text{for } i \neq j$$

for all components k, $k' = x$, y, z of the spin vectors.

A second useful representation is the exact analogue of the coupled-Boson picture, but replaces the Bosons by Fermions. The paired Fermions, instead of being labeled 1, 2, will be labeled by ↑ and ↓ to make more explicit the role of each operator. Thus,

$$S_i^+ = \hbar c_{i\uparrow}^* c_{i\downarrow} \qquad S_i^- = \hbar c_{i\downarrow}^* c_{i\uparrow} \quad \text{and} \quad S_i^z = \frac{\hbar}{2}(c_{i\uparrow}^* c_{i\uparrow} - c_{i\downarrow}^* c_{i\downarrow}) \tag{94}$$

where the anticommutation relations are

$$\{c_{i,m}, c_{j,m'}\} = \{c_{i,m}^*, c_{j,m'}^*\} = 0 \qquad \{c_{i,m}, c_{j,m'}^*\} = \delta_{i,j}\delta_{m,m'} \qquad (m = \uparrow \text{ or } \downarrow) \tag{95}$$

This is a very important representation, corresponding to the second quantization of electrons *cum* spin, and we shall return to it in Chapter 7.

A final representation of the spins one-half brings us closest to the work of Jordan and Wigner. The technique which we shall discuss has been useful in the solution of one-dimensional problems, and also is used in Chapter 9 to solve the two-dimensional Ising model, an important subject in the statistical mechanics of magnetism. Therefore, last but not least, set

$$S_i^+ = \hbar c_i^* \mathbf{Q}_i \qquad S_i^- = \hbar \mathbf{Q}_i c_i \quad \text{and} \quad S_i^z = \frac{\hbar}{2}(2c_i^* c_i - 1) \tag{96}$$

where
$$\mathbf{Q}_i = \mathbf{Q}_i^* = \mathbf{Q}_i^{-1} = e^{i\pi \sum_{j<i} c_j^* c_j} \tag{97A}$$

$$= e^{i\pi \sum_{j<i} s_j^+ s_j^-} \tag{97B}$$

$$= \prod_{j<i} (c_j^* + c_j)(c_j^* - c_j) \tag{97C}$$

etc. In actual problems, the choice of ordering $i = 1, \ldots, N$ is crucial, because the phase factors $\mathbf{Q}_i$ introduce great complexity into a problem unless means are found to eliminate them. When this is possible, however, then the representation above is the simplest of all, because it is the only one to establish a one-to-one correspondence between spins and Fermions, and their respective eigenstates.

SPINS ONE

There are no special representations for spins one, except for that which deals specifically with vector fields, such as the electromagnetic field. However, the Holstein-Primakoff representation may be used after rationalizing the square root. For, in the physically admissible range $n = 0, 1, 2$, the equation

$$\sqrt{1 - n/2} \equiv 1 - (\tfrac{3}{2} - \sqrt{2})n - \tfrac{1}{2}(\sqrt{2} - 1)n^2 \tag{98}$$

is exact, and only fails for $n \geqslant 3$, which is outside the domain of validity of this particular representation. (In fact for any j, a polynomial of order $2j$ can be found which has the same structure as the Holstein-Primakoff root, but is quite tedious to construct for large j. Moreover, as the Taylor series expansion of the root,

$$\sqrt{1 - \frac{n}{2j}} \doteq 1 - \frac{n}{4j} + \cdots$$

becomes asymptotically correct in the limit $j = \infty$, it is often used in approximate theories.)

We have not dealt with vector fields, except in Problem 6, where it was suggested that the "intrinsic spin" of the photon was unity. There are good reasons why this should be so. When angular momentum generates infinitesimal rotations of the coordinates, it changes not only the arguments of a vector field, as it does a scalar field (e.g., ordinary wavefunctions), but also mixes the various components of the field amongst themselves. The total effect might be described by an operator

$$J^z = \frac{\hbar}{i}\left(\frac{\partial}{\partial \phi} - \hat{\mathbf{u}}_z \times \right) = L^z + S^z \tag{99}$$

of which the first term takes care of arguments, and the second of the rotations of the vector field components. Similar expression for the two other Cartesian components results in an operator $\mathbf{J} = \mathbf{L} + \mathbf{S}$. Recall that $\mathbf{J}$ can be a true angular momentum only if $\mathbf{L}$ and $\mathbf{S}$ each are, in their own right. Therefore, let us investigate this new angular-momentum operator,

$$\mathbf{S} = i\hbar(\hat{\mathbf{u}}_x \times, \hat{\mathbf{u}}_y \times, \hat{\mathbf{u}}_z \times) \tag{100}$$

specifically constructed to operate on vector fields, such as the vector potential $\mathbf{A}(\mathbf{r})$. Calculating $S^2 = S_x^2 + S_y^2 + S_z^2$, we readily find

$$S^2 = \hbar^2(2) \tag{101}$$

and therefore the spin magnitude $s = 1$.

Field amplitudes may then be expanded in eigenfunctions of S^z, the spherical unit eigenvectors,

$$\hat{e}_{\pm 1} = \frac{-1}{2}(i\hat{u}_y \pm \hat{u}_x) \quad \text{and} \quad \hat{e}_0 = \hat{u}_z \tag{102}$$

with eigenvalues,

$$S^z\hat{e}_r = \hbar r\hat{e}_r, \quad r = -1, 0, 1 \tag{103}$$

These are particularly useful in problems with some spherical symmetry, e.g., the field of a radiating atom. Linear combinations of functions having definite J and total azimuthal quantum number M are called *vector* spherical harmonics

$$\mathscr{Y}_{JlM}(\theta, \phi) = \sum_{mr} Y_{lm}(\theta, \phi)\hat{e}_r(lm1r|l1JM) \tag{104}$$

In addition to J and M, only the l of the spherical harmonic need be indicated, for the spherical unit vectors invariably have unit angular momentum, as we have shown.

The vector spherical harmonics form a complete, orthonormal set for the description of vector fields. The normalization integral, including scalar product, is

$$\int_0^{2\pi} d\phi \int_{-\pi}^{\pi} d\theta \sin\theta \mathscr{Y}^*_{Jlm}(\theta, \phi) \cdot \mathscr{Y}_{J'l'M'}(\theta, \phi) = \delta_{JJ'}\delta_{ll'}\delta_{MM'} \tag{105}$$

POSTSCRIPT

This terminates our brief introduction to the theory of angular momentum. As it overlaps very little with standard treatments in books on the subject, or those which appear in texts on group theory, the reader may wish to round out his knowledge of the subject by studying an orthodox text in the subject.[9] He will find special methods for dealing with very complex problems involving a few particles or a few spins. These will not often apply to the idealized models discussed in this book, where the emphasis is on solving the conceptually simplest problems, and where the irreducible difficulties are those of the many-body problem. It is for this reason that we have emphasized operator techniques and second quantization, of which we shall make much use subsequently.

A subject close to the theory of angular momentum is the theory of symmetry functions of the cube, or of other crystalline shapes.[9] References to this subject are included in the Bibliography. An allied subject also relegated to the Bibliography and extra-curricular study is the theory of the Landé g factor, particularly in solids.

---

[9] We particularly recommend B. R. Judd's *Operator Techniques in Atomic Spectroscopy*, McGraw-Hill, New York (1963), which is also a useful reference for the next chapter (Young's tableaux, etc.). Also the English translation of E. Wigner's now classic *Group Theory and its Application to the Quantum Mechanics of Atomic Spectra*, Academic, New York (1959).

CHAPTER 4

MANY-ELECTRON WAVEFUNCTIONS

Although the old quantum theory of Niels Bohr had great success in the interpretation of the line spectra of the hydrogen atom, it did not provide an adequate framework for the interpretation of the complex spectra of the many-electron atoms and molecules. Nevertheless the old theory had many clever proponents, who with a series of particularly shrewd guesses nailed down the structure of the periodic table and the theory of line spectra some time before the new wave mechanics. Notable was the exclusion principle of Wolfgang Pauli, which included a fourth quantum number in addition to the three which are associated with the orbital motion of each electron.[1] This was the key to explaining why there are two electrons in an s shell, 6 in a p shell, etc., and toward a correct theory of the building-up principle of the periodic table. Almost immediately thereafter, Uhlenbeck and Goudsmit published their evidence that the fourth quantum number referred to the spin of the electron,[2] and their concept helped clarify much of the subsequent thinking on the subject. Indeed so much was understood on the basis of the old theory alone, that it might even appear that the 1926 theories of Schrödinger and Heisenberg, far from solving old problems only raised new difficulties. The reason is that it proved so awkward and difficult to introduce *spin* into the new quantum mechanics.

Once it was established that the probability density is equal to $|\Psi|^2$, the square of the wavefunction, then the following paradox imposed itself: The probability function for N indistinguishable particles must be invariant under any permutation of the particles. Moreover, as any permutation can be achieved by a succession of transpositions (permutations of two particles at a time), one need only investigate the effects of transpositions. The wavefunction, it is then found, can be allowed to be *even* or *odd* under a transposition, but no other choice leads to the correct, totally symmetric probability density. (For two electrons, hydrogen molecule or helium atom, it was recognized from the first that odd functions describe triplet states, and even functions the singlet states. The agreement of the calculated energy levels with experiment was extraordinary. On the other hand, the energy levels of the even or odd functions of three or more electrons did not agree with spectroscopic data, or even with elementary notions of how atoms were constituted. Surely doubts must have been raised regarding

---

[1] W. Pauli, *Z. Physik*, **31**: 765 (1925).
[2] G. E. Uhlenbeck and S. Goudsmit, *Naturwiss.*, **13**: 953 (1925).

whether quantum mechanics was applicable to more than two electrons even in principle.) But the experimental spectra of systems of more than two electrons could only be understood in terms of wavefunctions which were *neither* odd *nor* even under arbitrary transpositions, but, rather, which had complicated properties under the various permutations. This was totally incompatible with the notion of a probability density symmetric under the interchange of identical particles. Nor was it obvious to what values of the total spin, i.e., to what multiplicity these complicated space functions were associated. One can readily guess that the totally antisymmetric function corresponds to the state of maximum multiplicity, all spins parallel; but before the invention by Pauli of the spin matrix operators[3] the calculation of general symmetry properties of the space functions corresponding to arbitrary multiplicity posed many such logical and practical problems.

A remedy was provided by Slater, with his invention of the determinantal wavefunction of space and spin.[4] Spin was an observable; therefore, the spin coordinate belonged in the wavefunction on the same footing as the space coordinate. The exclusion principle could now be correctly stated as follows: "A wavefunction of identical electrons must be antisymmetric under the interchange of any two of them; by which is meant, the interchange of the space + spin coordinates of the two electrons."

We shall examine the Slater determinants, insofar as they shed further light on the molecules of two and three hydrogen atoms we have studied so far. We shall then progress in reverse, it might seem, and ask to which functions of space alone, they correspond for the various multiplicities. We shall not now have any difficulty in finding nor in reconciling these with the antisymmetrization principle (*supra*). This is in contrast with the elaborate theory which was developed for this purpose before spin was finally understood.

We then put this knowledge to use, proving a theorem only recently discovered[5] which flatly contradicts Hund's rule for the atom, that states of highest multiplicity lie lowest. Fortunately this paradox is also soon removed, for the theorem and the rule are found to have overlapping domains of applicability. In the reconciliation of opposites, new light is shed on the theory of ferromagnetism. Naturally, this eventually leads us back to the interesting and central subject of "exchange."

It is essential for an understanding of this chapter, that the reader have familiarity with some notation and theorems of angular momentum, such as provided by the first few sections of the previous chapter, or in any text on quantum theory.

SLATER DETERMINANTS

It might be well to clarify the notion of "spin function" by analyzing the Hilbert space of ordinary space functions and bringing out the similarities. The student will not be surprised, then, to see space and spin treated on equal footing in the determinantal wavefunction, and will obtain insight into the possibilities and limitations of the form. For a more precise notion of meaning of spin and spin coordinates, the reader may wish to consult the chapter on angular momentum, particularly the first five sections.[6]

---

[3] W. Pauli, *Z. Physik*, **43**: 601 (1927).
[4] J. C. Slater, *Phys. Rev.*, **34**: 1293 (1929).
[5] E. Lieb and D. Mattis, *Phys. Rev.*, **125**: 164 (1962).
[6] See also W. Pauli, *Z. Phys.*, **43**: 601 (1927).

Consider a complete set of functions, assumed orthonormal,

$$f_1(r), f_2(r), \dots, f_n(r), \dots \tag{1}$$

in which an arbitrary function $g(r)$ can be expanded,

$$g(r) = \sum_n g_n f_n(r) \tag{2}$$

by analogy with a Fourier expansion. The expansion coefficients g_n play the role of Fourier coefficients (or Fourier transform). The function $g(r)$ can be represented as a vector in Hilbert space,

$$\mathbf{g} = (g_1, \dots, g_n, \dots) \tag{3}$$

The overlap integral,

$$C \equiv \int g^*(r) h(r)\, dr \tag{4}$$

is then the scalar dot product between two vectors

$$C = \sum_n g_n^* h_n = \mathbf{g} \cdot \mathbf{h} \tag{5}$$

Further discussion of the analogy between ordinary functions and vectors is best left to mathematical treatises. However, recall that it is just this strong analogy which unites the matrix mechanics of Heisenberg and the wave mechanics of Schrödinger.

In the space of the Pauli spin matrices, the basis vectors are the spinors

$$(1, 0) \quad \text{and} \quad (0, 1) \tag{6}$$

Similarly, in the functional Hilbert space, the basis vectors are

$$(1, 0, \dots, 0, \dots, 0, \dots) \quad (0, 1, 0, \dots, 0, \dots) \tag{7}$$

etc., as we discover by writing the functions of Eq. (1) in the vector notation of Eq. (3). The spaces spanned by Eqs. (6) and (7) may have different dimensionality, but the vector analysis is similar. The apparent difference between continuous and discrete variables has in fact been removed.

But one can equally well reverse the process and associate two orthonormal functions to the two basis vectors of Eq. (6), for example,

$$\chi_+(\xi) \quad \text{to} \quad (1, 0) \quad \text{spin "up"} \tag{8}$$

and

$$\chi_-(\xi) \quad \text{to} \quad (0, 1) \quad \text{spin "down"} \tag{9}$$

The χ's have properties of ordinary functions. And even if we wished ξ to be a discrete two-valued variable, we could allow the two functions to become delta functions in some appropriate way, and still formally preserve the analogy with the functions $f_n(r)$.

If now the $f_n(r)$ functions describe electronic states, a product function describing three particles for instance, might be

$$\Psi(1, 2, 3) = [f_j(r_1)\chi_r(\xi_1)][f_k(r_2)\chi_s(\xi_2)][f_n(r_3)\chi_t(\xi_3)] \tag{10}$$

with each of r, s, t, assuming the value $+$ or $-$. This is not an allowable wavefunction for identical particles since the probability density

$$P(1, 2, 3) \equiv \Psi^*\Psi \tag{11}$$

is not invariant under permutations of the three particles, except if

$$j = k = n \quad \text{and} \quad r = s = t \tag{12}$$

an equality which would not have been allowed for electrons according to the Pauli exclusion principle, in the old quantum theory. In the new quantum theory, moreover, we are supposed to consider not $\Psi(1, 2, 3)$, but the antisymmetrized version,

$$\Psi_A(1, 2, 3) = \Psi(1, 2, 3) + \Psi(2, 3, 1) + \Psi(3, 1, 2)$$
$$- \Psi(1, 3, 2) - \Psi(3, 2, 1) - \Psi(1, 3, 2) \tag{13}$$

If a product function violated the old Pauli principle, such as in Eq. (12), it would also automatically be projected out by the antisymmetrization procedure, as we shall see, and Ψ_A would vanish identically. This shows that in the new mechanics, electrons cannot violate the Pauli principle even in an arbitrary state—let alone an eigenstate described by good quantum numbers.

To extend the procedure to N particles would require writing out $N!$ terms. But following Slater, we recognize in Eq. (13) the rules for writing out a determinant, i.e.,

$$\Psi_A^{\text{Slater}} = \frac{1}{\sqrt{3!}} \det \begin{Vmatrix} f_j(r_1)\chi_r(\xi_1) & \cdots & f_j(r_3)\chi_r(\xi_3) \\ f_k(r_1)\chi_s(\xi_1) & \cdots & \vdots \\ f_n(r_1)\chi_t(\xi_1) & \cdots & f_n(r_3)\chi_t(\xi_3) \end{Vmatrix} \tag{14}$$

The determinant is conventionally divided by $\sqrt{3!}$ for purposes of normalization. This ensures that in addition to being totally symmetric, the probability distribution of Eq. (11) calculated with Slater determinants of Eq. (14) is normalized to unity, if the $f(r)$ and $\chi(\xi)$ functions are members of an orthonormal set.

It is by means of such determinants as Eq. (14) that one forms a complete, ortho-normal set of states for three electrons, and *not* by means of the product functions of Eq. (10). The number of such linearly independent determinants is always far less than the number of product functions, as all states which cannot be antisymmetrized are "excluded."

ANTISYMMETRIZATION

A simple rule may be helpful to understand the process of antisymmetrization called for by the Pauli principle.

Assume a function of N variables and all $N!$ of its permutations:

$$f(1, 2, 3, \ldots, N), \; f(2, 1, \ldots, N), \; f(N, 3, 1, \ldots, 2), \ldots \tag{15}$$

where in the self-evident notation, j is allowed to stand for the jth variable. Supposing we wish to construct a totally antisymmetric function using the f's, the following is a systematic procedure:

Define a function antisymmetric in variables 1, and 2,

$$f(1, 2/3, \ldots) \equiv f(1, 2, 3, \ldots) - f(2, 1, 3, \ldots) \tag{16}$$

with the bar (/) to signify that the function is antisymmetrized with respect to the variables preceding it. Then by induction, we construct a function antisymmetric in variables 1, 2, and 3,

$$f(1, 2, 3/4, \ldots) \equiv f(1, 2/3, \ldots) - f(1, 3/2, \ldots) - f(3, 2/1, \ldots) \tag{17}$$

In general,

$$f(1, \ldots, p/p + 1, \ldots) = f' - \sum_{j=1}^{p-1} \mathscr{E}^{j, p} f' \tag{18}$$

where $$f' \equiv f(1, \ldots, p - 1/p, \ldots)$$

and $\mathscr{P}_{j, p}$ transposes the jth and pth variables. The procedure can be continued until $p = N$ if desired.

By similar procedures totally symmetric functions, suitable for Bosons, can be constructed. It is merely necessary to replace all the minus ($-$) signs above by plus ($+$).

Problem 1: Prove by repeated use of Eq. (18) that the totally antisymmetric function is given by

$$\sum (-1)^P \mathscr{P} f(1, 2, \ldots, N) \equiv f(1, 2, \ldots, N/)$$

the sum being over all $N!$ distinct permutations of the N variables.

By taking other combinations of permutations, it is possible to generate functions with more complicated transformation properties under permutations of the various variables. But fortunately we do not need these; as we have already mentioned, wavefunctions of Fermions must be totally antisymmetric, and wavefunctions of Bosons totally symmetric, provided, of course, that we are sure to include the spin variable as well as any other coordinates (e.g., isotopic spin, band index, or whatever else is required in the complete description of the particle) in the wavefunction.

Starting with a product function of space and spin coordinates of N electrons, say $f(1)g(2) \ldots h(N)$, the antisymmetrization procedure generates $N!$ terms, which have the same sign ($+$ or $-$) as the corresponding terms in the expansion of a determinant in which $f(1)g(2) \ldots$ is the product along the principal diagonal of the array. If the original product function is normalized, then the determinant is conventionally normalized by dividing it by $\sqrt{N!}$. But this does not in fact normalize it *unless* the various permutations are all orthogonal, as when the one-electron functions in the original product are orthogonal. (We previously encountered problems in nonorthogonality in attempting to extend the Heitler–London scheme to the N-body problem.)

STATES OF THREE ELECTRONS

Let us postpone the trivial problem of two electrons, and study three electrons by means of Slater determinants. The most general single determinant is

$$
\left\|
\begin{array}{ccc}
\varphi_a(r_1)\chi_r(\xi_1) & \varphi_a(r_2)\chi_r(\xi_2) & \varphi_a(r_3)\chi_r(\xi_3) \\
\varphi_b(r_1)\chi_s(\xi_1) & \varphi_b(r_2)\chi_s(\xi_2) & \varphi_b(r_3)\chi_s(\xi_3) \\
\varphi_c(r_1)\chi_t(\xi_1) & \varphi_c(r_2)\chi_t(\xi_2) & \varphi_c(r_3)\chi_t(\xi_3)
\end{array}
\right\|
\tag{19}
$$

aside from a normalization constant. For fixed φ_a, φ_b, φ_c, the two possibilities for *each* spin function result in eight distinct determinantal functions in total. If some of the space functions are not linearly independent, then the number of independent determinantal functions could be less than eight, and in the example of Eq. (12), $j = k = n$, $r = s = t$, the number of possible determinantal functions was zero. But in no case does it exceed eight for three particles. Note that if there were no exclusion principle, and no requirement of antisymmetrization, the number of allowed product configurations of the type in Eq. (10) would be $6 \times 6 \times 6 = 216$ in the present case. So, a considerable number of states have been pruned.

There are two instances of all spins "up" or "down" simultaneously,

$$
\left|
\begin{array}{ccc}
\varphi_a(r_1)\chi_r(\xi_1) & \varphi_a(r_2)\chi_r(\xi_2) & \varphi_a(r_3)\chi_r(\xi_3) \\
\varphi_b(r_1)\chi_r(\xi_1) & \varphi_b(r_2)\chi_r(\xi_2) & \varphi_b(r_3)\chi_r(\xi_3) \\
\varphi_c(r_1)\chi_r(\xi_1) & \varphi_c(r_2)\chi_r(\xi_2) & \varphi_c(r_3)\chi_r(\xi_3)
\end{array}
\right|
\tag{20}
$$

$r = +$ or $-$. The remaining six determinants are, in turn,

$$
\left|
\begin{array}{ccc}
\varphi_a(1)\chi_r(1) & \varphi_a(2)\chi_r(2) & \varphi_a(3)\chi_r(3) \\
\varphi_b(1)\chi_s(1) & \varphi_b(2)\chi_s(2) & \varphi_b(3)\chi_s(3) \\
\varphi_c(1)\chi_s(1) & \varphi_c(2)\chi_s(2) & \varphi_c(3)\chi_s(3)
\end{array}
\right|
\tag{21}
$$

with $r = +$ and $s = -$, or the converse; and

$$
\left|
\begin{array}{ccc}
\varphi_a(1)\chi_s(1) & \varphi_a(2)\chi_s(2) & \varphi_a(3)\chi_s(3) \\
\varphi_b(1)\chi_r(1) & \varphi_b(2)\chi_r(2) & \varphi_b(3)\chi_r(3) \\
\varphi_c(1)\chi_s(1) & \varphi_c(2)\chi_s(2) & \varphi_c(3)\chi_s(3)
\end{array}
\right|
\tag{22}
$$

and finally

$$\begin{vmatrix} \varphi_a(1)\chi_s(1) & \varphi_a(2)\chi_s(2) & \varphi_a(3)\chi_s(3) \\ \varphi_b(1)\chi_s(1) & \varphi_b(2)\chi_s(2) & \varphi_b(3)\chi_s(3) \\ \varphi_c(1)\chi_r(1) & \varphi_c(2)\chi_r(2) & \varphi_c(3)\chi_r(3) \end{vmatrix} \tag{23}$$

all with $r = +$ and $s = -$, or the converse, corresponding to one spin up and two down, or the converse. Of all these determinants, the spin functions factor out of only the two quartet states of Eq. (20). Two more quartet states must therefore be intimately mixed in with the two sets of doublet states in the determinants of Eqs. (21) to (23).

We see that the determinantal method does not necessarily generate eigenfunctions of S_{tot}^2, although by construction all determinants are eigenfunctions of S_{tot}^z.

The doublet states can be projected from the states of Eqs. (21) to (23) by means of the obviously constructed projection operator,

$$\mathbf{D} \equiv \tfrac{1}{3}(\tfrac{15}{4} - \mathbf{S}_{tot}^2) = \tfrac{1}{2} - \tfrac{2}{3}(\mathbf{S}_1\cdot\mathbf{S}_2 + \mathbf{S}_2\cdot\mathbf{S}_3 + \mathbf{S}_3\cdot\mathbf{S}_1) \tag{24}$$

which has zero eigenvalue on the quartet states, and eigenvalue unity on the doublet states. These states are not single Slater determinants, but linear combinations of them.

Problem 2: Find the eigenfunctions of the projection operator of Eq. (24) among the set of determinantal functions of Eqs. (20) to (23). Expand them in terms of the space functions $\psi_1, \psi_2, \ldots, \psi_6$ of the three-atom problem on p. 40.

Trial functions to calculate the low-lying eigenvalues of a Hamiltonian for three electrons could be made of linear combination of the eight determinantal functions. Moreover, if $\mathscr{H}$ doesn't involve the spins explicitly, we can always decompose it into noninteracting blocks by using the projection operators D and $1-D$. The "quartet," i.e., fourfold degenerate states, $S_{tot} = \tfrac{3}{2}$, belong to the totally antisymmetric space function. The two sets of doublet states, $S_{tot} = \tfrac{1}{2}$, give rise to two distinct doubly degenerate doublet levels. (In the case of three hydrogen atoms which we analyzed previously, the two doublets were accidentally degenerate, however, and corresponded to the four solutions of type v_{23}. Another space function which we had constructed (by permutations of space coordinates alone) was the totally symmetric function, which is not admissible and does not even enter via the determinantal approach. The sixth function was the totally antisymmetric quartet state.)

Problem 3: Construct the projection operator $\mathbf{R}$ which has zero eigenvalue for triplet states and eigenvalue unity for singlet states of two electrons. Operate with $\mathbf{R}$ on the most general Slater determinant of two electrons, and show that the singlet state is always symmetric under the interchange of the spatial coordinates of the two particles, and the triplet antisymmetric.

EIGENFUNCTIONS OF TOTAL S^2 AND S^z

If a function of space and spin coordinates is totally antisymmetric, we shall denote it a "Pauli function": the Slater determinants are a special case. If in addition it is an eigenfunction of S_{tot}^2 and S_{tot}^z, then there are severe limitations on the type of spin and space functions which can be used to construct such a Pauli function.

Let us assume first that the Pauli function is an eigenfunction of S_{tot}^z, with eigenvalue M, that is,

$$S_{tot}^z \, {}^M\Psi = M \, {}^M\Psi \tag{25}$$

indicating the quantum number explicitly as a superscript. Let us now expand Eq. (25) in a complete set of spin functions, the product functions:

$$\chi_{r_1}(\xi_1)\chi_{r_2}(\xi_2) \cdots \chi_{r_N}(\xi_N) \tag{26}$$

Normally 2^N such functions would be needed, but the restriction to a definite M value means that

$$M + \tfrac{1}{2}N \text{ have spin up } (+) \quad -M + \tfrac{1}{2}N \text{ have spin down } (-) \tag{27}$$

We can take a typical such function, for example:

$$^M\chi(\xi_1, \xi_2, \ldots, \xi_{M+\frac{1}{2}N} | \xi_{M+\frac{1}{2}N+1}, \ldots, \xi_N) \equiv \chi_+(\xi_1) \cdots \chi_+(\xi_{M+\frac{1}{2}N}) \cdots \chi_-(\xi_N) \tag{28}$$

and generate all the others by permutations. The permutations of the spins *up* among themselves do not generate a new function, and neither do permutations of the spins *down* among themselves. We therefore call these the *trivial permutations* of the spin function $^M\chi(\xi_1, \ldots | \ldots, \xi_N)$. This function is totally symmetric under the trivial permutations, those of spin coordinates to the left of the vertical bar amongst themselves, or of the spin coordinates to the right of the bar amongst themselves.

There are, however, $[N!/(\tfrac{1}{2}N + M)!(\tfrac{1}{2}N - M)!] \equiv n_M$ *nontrivial* permutations generating n_M orthogonal spin functions including the original function in Eq. (28), and these comprise the complete set for the expansion of $^M\psi$. Note that

$$\sum_{M=-\frac{1}{2}N}^{+\frac{1}{2}N} n_M = \sum_{M=-\frac{1}{2}N}^{+\frac{1}{2}N} \frac{N!}{(\tfrac{1}{2}N + M)!(\tfrac{1}{2}N - M)!} = 2^N \tag{29}$$

the dimensionality of all the M subspaces adding up to the total correct number 2^N of orthogonal spin functions.

When $^M\psi$ is expanded in these functions, the coefficient of $^M\chi$ in the expansion must be a space function of the type,

$$^Mf(r_1, r_2, \ldots, r_{\frac{1}{2}N+M} | r_{\frac{1}{2}N+M+1}, \ldots, r_N) \tag{30}$$

which is totally antisymmetric under the trivial permutations of coordinates to the left of the bar amongst themselves, or of coordinates to the right of the bar amongst themselves. In general, however, it has complicated transformation properties under the n_M nontrivial permutations (see Problem 4).

Problem 4: In the case of three hydrogen atoms, there were two states for $M = \tfrac{1}{2}$, notably v_{23} and v'_{23}. Express the *nontrivial* permutations of each of these two states in terms of the other, and of the partly symmetric functions v_{23sy} and v'_{23sy}.

If in addition, the Pauli function is an eigenfunction of S_{tot}^2, with eigenvalue S,

$$S_{tot}^2 \, {}^M\Psi^S = S(S+1) \, {}^M\Psi^S \qquad S_{tot}^z \, {}^M\Psi^S = M \, {}^M\Psi^S \tag{31}$$

then we can actually figure out the nontrivial symmetries of the space functions ${}^M f^S$ using only simple notions about angular momentum. We do this systematically, starting with ${}^{-S} f^S$, which is the coefficient of the spin function of Eq. (28) when $M = -S$. Recall that a fundamental property of angular momentum is that $|M| \leqslant S$, and therefore it should be impossible to further decrease M. In more formal terms,

$$S_{\text{tot}}^{-}({}^{-S}\Psi^S) \equiv 0 \tag{32}$$

This requires that there be some linear relationship among the f functions and their nontrivial permutations, and indeed, by use of Eqs. (28), (30), and (32), we find

$$
{}^{-S} f^S(r_1, \dots, r_{\frac{1}{2}N-S} | r_{\frac{1}{2}N-S+1}, \dots, r_N)
$$

$$
- \sum_{j=\frac{1}{2}N-S+1}^{N} \mathscr{P}_{ij} \, {}^{-S} f^S(r_1, \dots, r_{\frac{1}{2}N-S} | r_{\frac{1}{2}N-S+1}, \dots, r_N) = 0 \tag{33}
$$

with $$i = 1, 2, \dots, \quad \text{or} \quad \tfrac{1}{2}N - S$$

and $\mathscr{P}_{ij}$ being the transposition operator for the coordinates of the particles i and j. But this is very reminiscent of Eq. (18) if we interpret the above as an attempt to increase the number of coordinates to the right of the vertical bar (in which f is totally antisymmetric) by the addition of one member. This attempt results in zero: the set to the right cannot be further increased, i.e., the bar cannot be moved to the left.

We can construct the f functions belonging to higher M values, using the ${}^{-S} f^S$ which properly obey the equation above. This is done by repeated applications of the total-spin raising operator,

$$S_{\text{tot}}^{+} \, {}^{-S}\Psi^S = {}^{-S+1}\Psi^S \qquad \text{unnormalized} \tag{34}$$

and leads directly to

$$
{}^{-S+1} f^S(r_1, \dots, r_{\frac{1}{2}N-S+1} | r_{\frac{1}{2}N-S+2}, \dots) = {}^{-S} f^S - \sum_{j=1}^{\frac{1}{2}N-S} \mathscr{P}_{j, \frac{1}{2}N-S+1} \, {}^{-S} f^S \tag{35}
$$

with $$ {}^{-S} f^S = {}^{-S} f^S(r_1, \dots, r_{\frac{1}{2}N-S} | r_{\frac{1}{2}N-S+1}, \dots) \tag{36}$$

a function which obeys Eq. (33).

Thus, the attempt to move the bar to the right does *not* fail. By further application of the spin-raising operator, or of the antisymmetrization rules of Eq. (18), we progressively generate ${}^{-S+2} f^S, \dots$, up to ${}^{+S} f^S$, *all expressed as linear combinations of the original function ${}^{-S} f^S$ and its nontrivial permutations*. Finally, the angular-momentum rule

$$S_{\text{tot}}^{+}({}^{+S}\Psi^S) \equiv 0 \tag{37}$$

gives us an additional set of constraints on the f functions, similar to the first ones we found *supra*. But now, these constraints are that the bar cannot be moved farther to the *right*:

$${}^{S}f^{S}(r_1, \ldots , r_{\frac{1}{2}N+S}|r_{\frac{1}{2}N+S+1}, \ldots , r_N)$$

$$- \sum_{j=1}^{\frac{1}{2}N+S} \mathscr{P}_{1,q} \, {}^{S}f^{S}(r_1, \ldots , r_{\frac{1}{2}N+S}|r_{\frac{1}{2}N+S+1}, \ldots , r_N) = 0 \qquad (38)$$

with $$q = \tfrac{1}{2}N + S + 1, \ldots , N$$

Given an arbitrary space function, it is always a simple matter to generate a function of the type ${}^{M}f$, that is, the space partner of the spin eigenfunction of S_{tot}^{z}. We merely apply the rules of Eq. (18), and antisymmetrize in the first set of $p = \frac{1}{2}N + M$ coordinates, then antisymmetrize in the set of the remaining coordinates. Only those permutations which we have denoted as "trivial" are used in this process, the others being used to raise or lower M, as we have already seen. If for some reason f is unsuitable, the process of antisymmetrization will yield identically *zero* instead of the desired function. For example: if f is of the form ${}^{0}f^{0}$ and we wish to construct a function ${}^{M}f$ $M \neq 0$ with it, we get zero instead (i.e., like trying to antisymmetrize a symmetric function).

There is no correspondingly simple rule for constructing functions of the type ${}^{M}f^{S}$ from an arbitrary function. It is necessary to project out the unwanted components belonging to values of the total spin other than S by repeated use of the spin raising and lowering operators $S_{\text{tot}}^{\pm}$, after first constructing ${}^{M}f$, with $M = \pm S$. But in some special cases this can be done by inspection, as in the following example:

Example: A product wavefunction describes noninteracting particles, and also has its uses in variational approximations, as we have seen. Let us use such a product space function as the raw material in an example where we construct the proper space functions corresponding to definite M and S eigenvalues.

Starting with such a product as

$$\varphi_1(r_1)\, \varphi_2(r_1)\, \ldots \, \varphi_N(r_N) \qquad (39)$$

we can immediately write the ${}^{M}f$ function as a product of two determinants:

$$
{}^{M}f = \det
\begin{vmatrix}
\varphi_1(r_1) & \varphi_1(r_1) & \cdots & \varphi_1(r_{\frac{1}{2}N+M}) \\
\varphi_2(r_1) & & & \\
\vdots & \vdots & & \vdots \\
\varphi_{\frac{1}{2}N+M}(r_1) & & \cdots & \varphi_{\frac{1}{2}N+M}(r_{\frac{1}{2}N+M})
\end{vmatrix}
$$

$$
\times \det
\begin{vmatrix}
\varphi_{\frac{1}{2}N+M+1}(r_{\frac{1}{2}N+M+1}) & \cdots & \varphi_{\frac{1}{2}N+M+1}(r_N) \\
\vdots & \vdots & \vdots \\
\varphi_N(r_{\frac{1}{2}N+M+1}) & \cdots & \varphi_N(r_N)
\end{vmatrix} \qquad (40)
$$

which is explicitly antisymmetric in the two sets of variables. Now assume $M \leqslant 0$. (The case $M > 0$ can be handled by simply interchanging the two determinants.) Thus the first determinant is smaller than the second. Now, if all the functions $\varphi_1, \varphi_2, \ldots , \varphi_{\frac{1}{2}N+M}$ which appear in the smaller determinant are also present in the bigger one, then according to the rules of Eqs. (32) and (33), the antisymmetrization procedure of Eq. (33) will obviously yield *zero*, and therefore the function of Eq. (40) belongs to the definite S value,

$$S = |M| \qquad (41)$$

Of course this requires that the various φ_j not be all distinct functions. When the φ_j are all distinct, the construction of a function of definite S is possible but more tedious, but we shall not further investigate this topic. The various φ_j in *each* determinant must be distinct or else $^M f$ will vanish identically. But these can appear in both determinants, which is merely another expression of Kramers' degeneracy; for the appearance of a φ_j in the first determinant means there is an electron spin "up" in orbital φ_j, whereas its appearance in the second determinant means there is an electron spin "down" in that orbital.

This completes the demonstration, of how the Pauli wavefunction could be totally antisymmetric while the space functions, presumably eigenfunctions of a space Hamiltonian, could have complex transformation properties under the permutation group. We have also shown that these transformation properties are a consequence of the rules concerning total spin angular momentum. We now proceed to specific applications.

GROUND STATE OF TWO ELECTRONS: A THEOREM[5]

In many problems of differential equations, the lowest eigenvalue can be shown to belong to the nodeless solution. Can something analogous be proved in the many electron problem, and if so, does it have any bearing on the problem of ferromagnetism?

The answer to both queries is affirmative. If we first examine the atoms and the periodic table, we find that in helium the ground state is nodeless, and we draw therefrom important consequences. For heavier atoms, conversely, the ground state has a certain number of nodes, so as to satisfy Hund's rules. These nodes result in atomic spin and angular momentum in the ground state which, as we shall see, apparently violate a two-particle theorem. We shall return to the extension of the theorem to N particles and its apparent violation in three dimensions in subsequent sections.

Consider first the helium atom, slightly generalized to arbitrary potential:

$$\mathcal{H} = \frac{1}{2m}(\mathbf{p}_1^2 + \mathbf{p}_2^2) + V(\mathbf{r}_1, \mathbf{r}_2) \tag{42}$$

The Hamiltonian is assumed only to be real, and invariant under the interchange of the two (indistinguishable) particles. The eigenfunctions $f(\mathbf{r}_1, \mathbf{r}_2)$ of Schrödinger's equation,

$$\mathcal{H}f(\mathbf{r}_1, \mathbf{r}_2) = Ef(\mathbf{r}_1, \mathbf{r}_2) \tag{43}$$

are therefore real, and either even or odd under the interchange of the two particles. Because of the simplicity of the problem, it is not necessary to label f with M and S value: recall merely that the even solutions must be associated with odd spin function.

$$\frac{1}{\sqrt{2}}\left[\chi_+(\xi_1)\chi_-(\xi_2) - \chi_+(\xi_2)\chi_-(\xi_1)\right] \tag{44}$$

belonging to $S_{\text{tot}} = 0$, and the odd solutions with one of the even spin functions

$$[\chi_+(\xi_1)\chi_+(\xi_2)] \quad \text{or} \quad [\chi_-(\xi_1)\chi_-(\xi_2)]$$

$$\text{or} \quad \frac{1}{\sqrt{2}}\left[\chi_+(\xi_1)\chi_-(\xi_2) + \chi_+(\xi_2)\chi_-(\xi_1)\right] \tag{45}$$

belonging to $S_{\text{tot}} = 1$, $M = 1$, -1, or 0. Then the product is a proper Pauli wavefunction. We shall make use of the variational theorem, stated in the following terms: The ground-state energy always lies below the variational energy except when an exact ground-state eigenfunction is used as a variational trial wavefunction. Explicitly,

$$E_{\text{grd state}} \underset{\neq}{\leq} E_{\text{var}} \equiv \frac{\int g^*(\mathbf{r}_1, \mathbf{r}_2) \mathscr{H} g(\mathbf{r}_1, \mathbf{r}_2)\, d_3 r_1\, d_3 r_2}{\int |g|^2\, d_3 r_1\, d_3 r_2} \tag{46}$$

and the strict inequality holds *except* if the trial function $g(\mathbf{r}_1, \mathbf{r}_2)$ obeys the differential equation

$$(\mathscr{H} - E_{\text{grd state}})g(\mathbf{r}_1, \mathbf{r}_2) = 0 \tag{47}$$

for all values of $\mathbf{r}_1$ and $\mathbf{r}_2$. In that case only,

$$E_{\text{var}} = E_{\text{grd state}} \tag{48}$$

We need consider only functions g which are real, and either even or odd under the interchange of $\mathbf{r}_1$ and $\mathbf{r}_2$, as in the case of the eigenfunctions f. We can now prove the following:

Theorem: The ground-state eigenfunction is nodeless, *ergo* it belongs to $S_{\text{tot}} = 0$. Moreover, if $V(\mathbf{r}_1, \mathbf{r}_2)$ is invariant under rotation of the coordinate axes, i.e., commutes with the total angular momentum, then in the ground state also $L_{\text{tot}} = 0$. Thus helium in the ground state, for example, has precisely zero total angular momentum and spin and is totally nonmagnetic.

Proof: We shall first assume that the ground-state eigenfunction has nodes (that is, has at least one change of sign), and then show that this hypothesis leads to a contradiction. Let the ground-state eigenfunction with nodes be f_0, belonging to energy eigenvalue E_0. By hypothesis, $E_0 = E_{\text{grd state}}$.

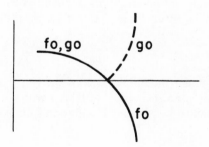

FIG. 4.1. The wavefunction f_0 and its absolute value $g_0 = |f_0|$ plotted along a direction normal to a nodal surface of f_0.

Consider the nodeless function $g_0 \equiv |f_0|$, the absolute value of f_0. Is it an admissible variational wavefunction? If f_0 is constrained to vanish at ∞, or is square integrable, then the same follows for g_0. If f_0 is odd, or if it is even, g_0 is even. Since f_0 is real, so is g_0. Therefore it indeed fulfills all the requirements for a variation trial function.

But g_0 is not itself an eigenfunction, for along the nodal surface $f_0(\mathbf{r}_1, \mathbf{r}_2) = 0$, it has discontinuous normal derivatives. See sketch in Fig. 4.1. Therefore the strict inequality of Eq. (46) is applicable, $E_{\text{var}} > E_{\text{grd state}}$.

The variational energy is calculated by either of two methods with identical results: (1) Observe that g_0 obeys Schrödinger's equation with eigenvalue E_0 everywhere except on the nodal surfaces. Because g_0 itself vanishes on these surfaces, the variational energy is precisely E_0. (2) By partial integration the variational integral in Eq. (46) can be brought into the canonical form, from which Schrödinger initially derived his wave equation:

$$E_{\text{var}} = \frac{\int \left[\frac{\hbar^2}{2m} (|\nabla_1 g_0|^2 + |\nabla_2 g_0|^2) + V|g_0|^2 \right] d_3 r_1 \, d_3 r_2}{\int |g_0|^2 \, d_3 r_1 \, d_3 r_2} \tag{49}$$

But $|g_0|^2 = |f_0|^2$ everywhere, and $|\dot{g}_0|^2 = |\dot{f}_0|^2$ everywhere, letting the dot over the letter stand for any derivative. [In deriving Eq. (49), we have neglected only surface terms at ∞, where both g_0 and f_0 vanish by the boundary condition.] By direct substitution, we now also obtain $E_{\text{var}} = E_0$. Hence $E_0 > E_{\text{grd state}}$.

This result contradicts the hypothesis that $E_0 = E_{\text{grd state}}$, if f_0 has nodes; or the hypothesis that f_0 has nodes, if $E_0 = E_{\text{grd state}}$. Alternatively, if it is assumed that the ground-state wavefunction is nodeless, then its absolute value is just $\pm$ the same function, and there results no such contradiction.

Consequently, *the ground state is nondegenerate*. For if there is more than one eigenfunction belonging to $E_{\text{grd state}}$, the previous arguments indicate that *each* must be nodeless. However, there is only one nodeless eigenfunction of $\mathcal{H}$, because the eigenfunctions of a Hamiltonian form a complete, orthogonal set of functions, and two nodeless functions *cannot be orthogonal*.

If the problem has rotational symmetry, then the eigenfunctions also have definite total angular momentum. The nodeless function must belong to zero eigenvalue, because it is not orthogonal to the constant function 1, itself an eigenfunction of total angular momentum, obviously with *zero* eigenvalue, Q.E.D.

Problem 5: Prove the following unconventional equation for the ground-state energy $E_{\text{grd state}}$ and ground-state wavefunction $f_{\text{grd state}}$ of the helium atom and molecule:

$$E_{\text{grd state}} = \frac{\int e^2 (1/r_{12} - 2/r_1 - 2/r_2) f_{\text{grd state}} \, d_3 r_1 \, d_3 r_2}{\int\int f_{\text{grd state}} \, d_3 r_1 \, d_3 r_2}$$

Find an analogous expression for the ground state of the N-Boson problem.[7] For the ground state of three or more Fermions? Hydrogen atom and molecule?

The actual atomic structures of helium and also of the heavier atoms are just as well understood theoretically[8] as experimentally. The well-known calculations of Hartree and others in the late 1920s and 1930s, and modern high-speed electronic computers have reduced atomic calculations to what is almost an exact science. The present theorem has merely served to show that the well-known ground state properties of helium are not the results of a particular calculation, but are shared by arbitrary two-Fermion systems subject to local, but otherwise arbitrary spatial potentials.

---

[7] E. Lieb, *Phys. Rev.*, **130**: 2518 (1963).

[8] Even in the old quantum theory; cf. F. Hund, *Linienspektren und periodisches System der Elemente*, Berlin, 1927, or any more modern text on atomic structure or quantum mechanics.

HUND'S RULES

The Hartree-Fock procedure[9] allows one to solve the many-electron Schrödinger equation approximately by supposing each electron to move in a self-consistent, averaged potential. Numerical solution of the effective one-body Schrödinger equations is still required, as the self-consistent potentials are not strictly Coulombic so that the eigenfunctions are not obtainable in terms of polynomials of any kind. Still, the one-electron angular momentum is useful to organize the electrons into shells, and the periodic structure of the atomic table is understood to be the consequence of the filling up of successive shells.

We have already examined the first closed shell, that of helium and found that without net spin or angular momentum, it was magnetically inert. Let us add two more electrons, to make *Be*. It may be thought the outer shell obeys an effective two-electron Hamiltonian, the solutions of which must be orthogonalized to the core (helium) states. If the theorem of the preceding section holds for the two new electrons, then the total spin and angular momentum of *Be* must also vanish, which is the case.

Next, we add two more electrons to form *C*, and we find the first surprise. Carbon has $S_{tot} = 1$, and $L_{tot} = 1$, and the theorem fails completely for the third pair of electrons! Indeed, if we look further, of the first eighteen elements to have an even number of electrons (which takes us up to krypton, $Z = 36$), only eight have no spin or angular momentum in the ground state; and of these, half are inert gases. Why does the argument go awry? One might argue that the theorem breaks down for the following mathematical reason: that orthogonality to core states is equivalent to non-local potential forces, for which the theorem is inapplicable. But there are more convincing physical explanations. How can one predict the magnetic properties of an atom in the ground state?

The answers are given by Hund's rules. These laws, originally based on the abundant spectroscopic evidence, were of course confirmed by complete atomic calculations.[9] Fortunately, there exists a less exhaustive explanation of Hund's rules in terms of exchange, or the vector model, of which we shall give some examples.

First Rule: Electrons fill up the $2 \times (2l + 1)$ states of a shell in such a manner as to maximize the total spin. This may determine the configuration uniquely. When it does not, then one appeals to the second rule.

Second Rule: Any ambiguities in the first rule are resolved in favor of the highest value of L_{tot}. But the second rule is not always a unique prescription either, although these two rules are adequate to describe *grosso modo* the magnetic properties of the atom. Other rules determine whether the spin and angular momenta are parallel or not, but it is not necessary for us to become too involved with atomic structure. For with the exception of the rare earths, angular momentum is most always quenched in the process of chemical binding or in the solid state, and only the spin and Hund's first rule survive.

Qualitatively, both Hund's rules follow from degenerate-state perturbation theory. Electrons in the outer shells move in the spherical potential of the nucleus and of the filled inert-gas configurations. To a first approximation, all the configurations within the outer shell are degenerate. It is the Coulomb repulsion between these electrons which lifts the degeneracy. Now if any two electrons are in the same orbital

---

[9] This variational extension of Hartree's calculations by V. Fock, *Z. Physik*, **61**: 126 (1930), and J. C. Slater, *Phys. Rev.*, **35**: 210 (1930), has proved capable of very high accuracy in atomic-structure theory.

state, the Coulomb repulsion is maximal. These configurations should be avoided, just as the ionized configurations were avoided in the Heitler-London theory.

Therefore, in a first crude attempt to "prove" Hund's rules, or rather to make them more plausible without too much work, only those configurations of the outer shell electrons need be considered in which every electron occupies a different orbital state. This would imply that whenever a shell contains $2l + 1$ electrons, all the degenerate orbital states in that shell are occupied: for each ml there is a $-ml$; and therefore presumably $L_{tot} = 0$.

The validity of this simple guess is striking: there appear to be no exceptions in the periodic table. For example, the elements with a half-filled p shell are N, P, As, Sb, Bi, and all have vanishing orbital angular momentum; the elements with half-filled d shell, Cr, Mn, Mo, etc., also obey this rule, etc.

For shells less than half-filled, one speaks of electrons, whereas for shells more than half-filled, one commonly speaks of "holes." There is indeed a great similarity between the ground terms of elements on either side of half-filled shells in the periodic table: with a general exception that the total J value (spin *plus* orbital angular momenta) equals $|S - L|$ for electrons and $S + L$ for holes. This difference is caused by spin-orbit coupling, a relatively small energy responsible for the phenomenon of "magnetic anisotropy" in the solid state.

To understand Hund's rules, the vector model, and particularly their physical origins, it is important to work out some examples. This is done in the following sections, but only for illustrative purposes, and the reader who wishes to become proficient in the true art of atomic calculation and quantum chemistry is referred to specialized treatises and review articles.

Hund's rules give only the ground state of the atom. The methods of atomic calculation which we shall illustrate give the (very important) low-lying excited states as well, together with their energy, spin, and angular-momentum quantum numbers. These results are central to the theory of magnetism, for it is impossible to understand magnetic solids without understanding the magnetic atoms and the magnetic molecules first.

Now we can return to our earlier question: why doesn't the two-particle theorem hold for the valence electrons of carbon? Are Hund's rules contradictory to the theorem? The answer, briefly, is this. The orbital states, in atoms heavier than helium, must be orthogonal to the (inert) core, and therefore cannot be nodeless. The theorem, particularly the method of proof we used, just does not apply to these "excited state" orbitals. On the contrary; if the functions are already required to suffer a number of nodes, and to pay the ensuing price in kinetic energy, it is then advantageous for the potential energy to be minimized *in exactly the manner predicted by Hund's rules*, as we shall now see by actual calculation.

p³ CONFIGURATION

First, recall that four atomic quantum numbers specify each electron: the principal quantum number $n = 1, 2, \ldots$, the orbital angular momentum $l \leqslant n - 1$, the magnetic quantum number $m_l = -l, \ldots, +l$, and the spin eigenvalue $m_s = \pm \frac{1}{2}$. But in the description of an electron, instead of giving $l = 0, 1, 2, 3, \ldots$, it is conventional to use the letters $s(l = 0), p(l = 1), d(l = 2), f(l = 3), g(l = 4)$, and thence in alphabetical sequence. Therefore, $n = 2$ and $l = 0$ *is a 2s electron*. One does not indicate m_l or m_s, and the number of particles with given n and l is shown as a superscript. For example, two electrons with $n = 3$, $l = 2$ are denoted $3d^2$; three such electrons by $3d^3$. The m values not being specified, there are many possible wavefunctions for a given configuration. With the total angular momentum of the configuration indicated by a capital letter, for example, S, P, D, F, ... for $L = 0$, 1, 2, 3, and the total spin S_{tot} *via* an exponent: $2S_{tot} + 1 = $ multiplicity, the various configurations are indicated in Table 4.3.

Consider nitrogen: outside the helium core, two electrons are in the $2s$ shell, and three in the $2p$ shell. The s electrons have no angular momentum or spin, and we ignore them in zeroth order. The important particles are the three $2p$ electrons (the $2p^3$ configuration, in atomic notation). If such is the case, the ground-state and low-lying terms of any atom or ion with a p^3 configuration outside of closed shells must be similar. Figure 4.2 and Table 4.1 confirm this, and show the good agreement between theory and experiment.

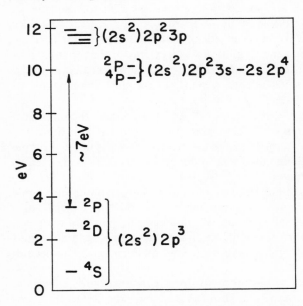

Fig. 4.2. Energy-level diagram of nitrogen (N). Vector model applies to lowest three levels only; but note that they are well below the other levels.

We first tackle this problem by the same technique used in the study of three hydrogen atoms. The more conventional approach is harder, and is discussed in the next section. First we write out the spatial basis functions. Instead of atoms a, b, c, with which to associate the electrons, there are now the three p states specified by the quantum numbers $m_l = -1$, 0, $+1$. We allow each to be occupied just once: this reduces both the Coulomb repulsion, and the number of spatial configurations necessary to consider.

The $3! = 6$ spatial configurations are

$$\psi_1 = \varphi_1(r_1) \quad \varphi_0(r_2) \quad \varphi_{-1}(r_3)$$

$$\psi_2 = \varphi_1(r_2) \quad \varphi_0(r_1) \quad \varphi_{-1}(r_3)$$

$$\psi_3 = \varphi_1(r_3) \quad \varphi_0(r_2) \quad \varphi_{-1}(r_1)$$

$$\psi_4 = \varphi_1(r_1) \quad \varphi_0(r_3) \quad \varphi_{-1}(r_2)$$

$$\psi_5 = \varphi_1(r_2) \quad \varphi_0(r_3) \quad \varphi_{-1}(r_1)$$

$$\psi_6 = \varphi_1(r_3) \quad \varphi_0(r_1) \quad \varphi_{-1}(r_2)$$

(50)

The subscripts on the one-particle functions refer to m_l^i, the eigenvalue of the one-electron operators L_i^z. There are only two major differences between these functions and those in the three-atom case: the present functions are orthonormal, and they are not all three equivalent. The significance of this will become immediately clear.

The functions $\varphi_{m_l}(r)$ are by definition solutions of the best possible self-consistent one-particle Hamiltonian, $\mathscr{H}_0$. As $\mathscr{H}_0$ usually turns out to be spherically symmetric, we shall assume this to be the case here, and factor the functions as follows:

$$\varphi_{m_l}(r) = Y_{l,m}(\theta, \phi)R(r) \tag{51}$$

Fortunately, everything is known about the angular part of the wavefunction, the spherical harmonics, $Y_{l,m}$, and moreover, the (unknown) common radial function will be eliminated from the problem.

The perturbation is

$$\mathscr{H}' = e^2\left(\frac{1}{r_{12}} + \frac{1}{r_{23}} + \frac{1}{r_{31}}\right) \tag{52}$$

We may write down an eigenvalue equation for the energies in terms of the matrix elements of $\mathscr{H}'$ between the six basis states, and the overlap matrix. The justification for this was given in the chapter on exchange, in terms of making the energies stationary, or diagonalizing $\mathscr{H}'$ within the restricted subspace. The overlap matrix is in the present case just the unit matrix, by orthonormality. It might be thought that the $\mathscr{H}'$ matrix could be obtained from our earlier result also by setting the overlap integral $= 0$, but that doesn't quite work as

$$\mathscr{H}'_{1,2} \neq \mathscr{H}'_{1,3} \tag{53}$$

because permuting functions with $|\Delta m_l| = 1$ is not quite the same as when $|\Delta m_l| = 2$. Otherwise, we proceed much as before. We define the diagonal term as

$$A \equiv \mathscr{H}'_{1,1} = \cdots = \mathscr{H}'_{6,6} > 0 \tag{54}$$

and nondiagonal elements $B_1 A$ by

$$B_1 A \equiv \mathscr{H}'_{1,2} = \mathscr{H}'_{1,4} = \cdots = \mathscr{H}'_{4,6}$$

$$= \int \frac{e^2}{r_{12}} [\phi_1^*(r_1)\phi_0(r_1)\phi_0^*(r_2)\phi_1(r_2)] \, d_3r_1 \, d_3r_2 \tag{55}$$

Other nondiagonal elements $B_2 A$ are defined as,

$$B_2 A \equiv \mathscr{H}'_{1,3} = \cdots = \mathscr{H}'_{6,2}$$

$$= \int \frac{e^2}{r_{13}} [\phi_1^*(r_1)\phi_{-1}(r_1)\phi_{-1}^*(r_3)\phi_1(r_3)] \, d_3r_1 \, d_3r_3 \tag{56}$$

All matrix elements are proportional to the same constant A, also all turn out to be real or can be made real. We have made use of the orthonormality of the one-electron functions to eliminate all the irrelevant terms in $\mathscr{H}'$ from these expressions, and have indicated the difference between the two types of exchange integrals by the subscript B_1 or B_2. The third type of matrix element, for example, $\mathscr{H}'_{1,5}$, automatically vanishes. One finds this out either by setting the overlap integral $= 0$ in the previous problem, or by noticing directly that the exchange between functions differing by more than a simple transposition must vanish in the case of two-body forces and ortho-normal basis functions. Finally, we obtain the eigenvalue equation,

$$\mathscr{H}' \cdot \mathbf{v} = A \begin{vmatrix} 1 & B_1 & B_2 & B_1 & 0 & 0 \\ B_1 & 1 & 0 & 0 & B_1 & B_2 \\ B_2 & 0 & 1 & 0 & B_1 & B_1 \\ B_1 & 0 & 0 & 1 & B_2 & B_1 \\ 0 & B_1 & B_1 & B_2 & 1 & 0 \\ 0 & B_2 & B_1 & B_1 & 0 & 1 \end{vmatrix} \cdot \mathbf{v} = E\mathbf{v} \tag{57}$$

Recall that there was a useless totally symmetric eigenvector, and a totally antisym-metric eigenvector which we identified as the space partner of the quartet state, $S_{\text{tot}} = \frac{3}{2}$. Then there were two doublet states; these are no longer degenerate, and we must find the proper linear combination to diagonalize $\mathscr{H}'$. Let us examine the two states $\mathbf{v}_{23}$ and $\mathbf{v}'_{23}$ which were antisymmetric in particles 2 and 3. (They cannot mix with the two functions which are symmetric in those particles, $\mathbf{v}_{23sy}$, and $\mathbf{v}'_{23sy}$). One finds by construction, the new eigenvectors:

$$\mathbf{w}_{23} = \tfrac{2}{3}\mathbf{v}_{23} + \mathbf{v}'_{23} \tag{58}$$

and

$$\mathbf{w}'_{23} = -2\mathbf{v}_{23} + \mathbf{v}'_{23} \tag{59}$$

Problem 6: Find the proper linear combinations of v_{23sy} and v'_{23sy} which are eigenvectors of $\mathscr{H}'$.

There is an additional operator of which we should like to know the eigenvalues, that is L^2_{tot}:

$$L^2_{\text{tot}} = L^2_1 + L^2_2 + L^2_3 + 2(L^z_1 L^z_2 + L^z_2 L^z_3 + L^z_3 L^z_1)$$
$$+ (L^+_1 L^-_2 + L^+_2 L^-_3 + L^+_3 L^-_1 + \text{H.c.}) \tag{60}$$

All that is required to calculate the matrix elements of this operator on our set of states is such information as (cf. Eq. (44))

$$L^2_i = 1(1 + 1) = 2 \tag{61}$$

and

$$(m_i + 1|L^+_i|m_i) = \sqrt{2}(\delta_{m_i, -1} + \delta_{m_i, 0}) \tag{62}$$

for angular momentum 1. Thus in the diagonal matrix element $(L^2_{\text{tot}})_{1,1}$ there enter three contributions of the form of Eq. (61), making 6, minus 2 from $2L^z_1 L^z_3$, for a total of 4. The other matrix elements are just as easily found, and finally,

$$L^2_{\text{tot}} = \begin{vmatrix} 4 & 2 & 0 & 2 & 0 & 0 \\ 2 & 4 & 0 & 0 & 2 & 0 \\ 0 & 0 & 4 & 0 & 2 & 2 \\ 2 & 0 & 0 & 4 & 0 & 2 \\ 0 & 2 & 2 & 0 & 4 & 0 \\ 0 & 0 & 2 & 2 & 0 & 4 \end{vmatrix} \tag{63}$$

It is now a simple exercise (for the reader) to write the eigenvalues E as functions of A, B_1, and B_2 and calculate the value of the angular momentum to which they belong, with the eigenvectors already given. The spin of these same states has already been discussed and given several times.

The following fact may be extricated from Condon and Shortley,[10] or proved directly by an expansion of $(r_{12})^{-1}$ in spherical harmonics (see Problem 8):

$$B_2 = 2B_1 \tag{64}$$

It simplifies the results even more for the actual problem. Finally one finds for the eigenvalues

$$E(^2P) = A(1 + B_1) \tag{65}$$

$$E(^2D) = A(1 - B_1) \tag{66}$$

$$E(^4S) = A(1 - 4B_1) \tag{67}$$

In the usual spectroscopic notation, the multiplicity $(2S_{tot} + 1)$ has been written as a prefixed exponent to the angular momentum $S, P, D, F, G, \dots$ ($L_{tot} = 0, 1, 2, 3, 4, \dots$). From these equations, we find for the level spacings,

$$\frac{E(^2P) - E(^2D)}{E(^2D) - E(^4S)} = \frac{2}{3} \tag{68}$$

a ratio independent of A and B_1, or of the integrals involving the radial parts of the wavefunctions.

The agreement with experiment is pleasant. Not only are all p^3 configurations found to possess low-lying terms of the type discussed, and ordered in energy as we have found them, but the ratio of Eq. (68) is experimentally well obeyed within our self-imposed limits of accuracy. In Fig. 4.2 is reproduced the term level scheme of nitrogen, together with the electronic configurations giving rise to the various terms. In Table 4.1 is given the experimentally observed ratio of Eq. (68) for various substances.

TABLE 4.1

Configuration and Ratio of Term Splittings in Various Atoms and Ions, and Theory

	Theory	Experimental			
		N	O⁺	S⁺	As
Configuration	np^3	$2p^3$	$2p^3$	$3p^3$	$4p^3$
Ratio*	.667	.500	.509	.651	.751

* See Eq. 68.
SOURCE: Condon and Shortley.[10]

[10] E. U. Cordon and G. Shortley, *The Theory of Atomic Spectra*, Cambridge, New York, 1935, pp. 174–179.

Because each one-electron state is occupied, there is no difficulty in principle to the construction of an equivalent Heisenberg, or *vector model*, Hamiltonian for spins one-half. This is illustrated in Fig. 4.3.

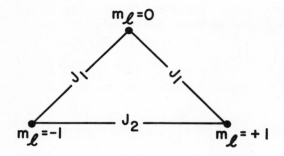

FIG. 4.3. Labels (m_l) and bonds in vector model of N.

From previous experience, we may almost guess that in $\mathscr{H}_{\text{Heis}}$

$$\mathscr{H}_{\text{Heis}} = -J_1(\mathbf{S}_{-1}\cdot\mathbf{S}_0 + \mathbf{S}_0\cdot\mathbf{S}_{+1}) - J_2(\mathbf{S}_{-1}\cdot\mathbf{S}_{+1}) \tag{69}$$

the proper choice of exchange constants is,

$$J_1 = 2B_1A \quad \text{and} \quad J_2 = 2B_2A \tag{70}$$

which are defined in Eqs. (55) and (56). The solutions are given as Problem 7.

Problem 7: Find the eigenvalues of the Heisenberg Hamiltonian for spins one-half, Eq. (69). Use the Pauli principle, and space inversion symmetry considerations (on the true Pauli wavefunction of space and spin) to classify the solutions of this exchange Hamiltonian according to L_{tot} as well as S_{tot}. Find the ratio $[E(^2P) - E(^2D)]/[E(^2D) - E(^4S)]$ and verify that it equals $\frac{2}{3}$ when $J_2 = 2J_1$. Hint: define $\mathbf{T} = \mathbf{S}_{-1} + \mathbf{S}_1$, express $\mathscr{H}_{\text{Heis}}$ in terms of $\mathbf{T}$ and $\mathbf{T} + \mathbf{S}_0$.

p^2 and p^4 CONFIGURATIONS

Carbon, silicon, germanium, tin all have two electrons in the p shell. Oxygen, sulphur, selenium, and others have two holes in the p shell. All have ^3P ground states. (The term level scheme for carbon, which is representative, is given in Fig. 4.4.) Can we show this theoretically, and find the low-lying terms as well?

This is an exercise in Hund's second rule, which has not come into play before. Also, here is a problem in which the Heisenberg Hamiltonian is of dubious validity since there are only *two* particles, with *three* orbital states in which to put them. This configuration is studied in lieu of the complex transition series atoms, or rare-earth series, which are of greatest interest in magnetism. For it is not intended to take the reader into involved computations, regardless of their relevancy, but only to provide him with a minimal introduction to the theory of atomic structure. (The application to magnetic atoms is the subject of some of the books in the Bibliography.)

It is essential to reduce the number of configurations that one has to consider to a manageable few. In the L–S coupling scheme (so-called) states which can be obtained from each other by repeated applications of $S_{\text{tot}}^{\pm}$, or $L_{\text{tot}}^{\pm}$, are equivalent except for the splitting due to spin-orbit coupling, (which is usually treated separately). So, it is only necessary to consider the largest attainable value of M_S and M_L for each term, viz.,

$$M_S = S_{\text{tot}} \qquad \text{and} \qquad M_L = L_{\text{tot}}, \tag{71}$$

and in order to determine S_{tot} and L_{tot} and the associated energy eigenvalues, to remain in the subspace of $M_S = 0, 1$ and $M_L = 0, 1, 2$.

$M_L = 2$: The space function must be

$$\varphi_1(\mathbf{r}_1)\varphi_1(\mathbf{r}_2) \tag{72}$$

in which $M_L = m_{l1} + m_{l2} = 1 + 1 = 2$. As this is symmetric under interchange of the spatial coordinates, the Pauli principle requires an antisymmetric spin function, the singlet state

$$\frac{1}{\sqrt{2}} \left[\chi_+(\xi_1)\chi_-(\xi_2) - \chi_+(\xi_2)\chi_-(\xi_1) \right] \tag{73}$$

Thus, $L_{\text{tot}} = 2$ and $S_{\text{tot}} = 0$, and this is the ${}^1D$ state. The energy will be computed subsequently, but now we continue the classification.

$M_L = 1$: The space function of interest must be

$$\frac{1}{\sqrt{2}} \left[\varphi_1(\mathbf{r}_1)\varphi_0(\mathbf{r}_2) - \varphi_1(\mathbf{r}_2)\varphi_0(\mathbf{r}_1) \right] \tag{74}$$

since the other possibility, the linear combination with $+$ sign, is symmetric under the interchange of the spatial coordinates and is therefore the $M_L = 1$ projection of the $L_{\text{tot}} = 2$ state derived above. If the space part is antisymmetric, the spin part must be symmetric (the spin-triplet) $\chi_+(\xi_1)\chi_+(\xi_2)$, or $\chi_-(\xi_1)\chi_-(\xi_2)$, or Eq. (73) with $+$ replacing $-$); thus $L_{\text{tot}} = 1$ and $S_{\text{tot}} = 1$, and this is the ${}^3P$ configuration.

$M_L = 0$: The three functions with $M_L = 0$ have $m_{l1} = m_{l2} = 0$, or $m_{l1} = -m_{l2} = \pm 1$. Two linear combinations of these must be the $M_L = 0$ projections of the two states found above, Eqs. (72) and (74). The linear combination orthogonal to both of these is the new function of interest,

$$\frac{1}{\sqrt{3}} \left[\varphi_0(\mathbf{r}_1)\varphi_0(\mathbf{r}_2) - \varphi_{-1}(\mathbf{r}_1)\varphi_1(\mathbf{r}_2) - \varphi_{-1}(\mathbf{r}_2)\varphi_1(\mathbf{r}_1) \right] \tag{75}$$

$L_{\text{tot}}^{\pm}$ applied to this state yields identically zero, and it follows that this is the ${}^1S$ configuration, and the list is now complete (see Table 4.3).

The perturbation is

$$\mathcal{H}' = \frac{e^2}{r_{12}} \tag{76}$$

which we expand in Legendre polynomials,

$$\frac{1}{r_{12}} = \sum_{n=0}^{\infty} \frac{r_<^n}{r_>^{n+1}} P_n(\cos \omega) \qquad \text{where} \qquad \cos \omega = \frac{\mathbf{r}_1 \cdot \mathbf{r}_2}{r_1 r_2} \tag{77}$$

in which $r_<$ is the lesser, and $r_>$ is the greater of r_1 and r_2, and ω is the angle between the two vectors. Because one takes expectation values using p functions, only terms with $n = 0$ and $n = 2$ can survive the integration.

The atomic functions have normalized angular factors (cf. Table 3.1):

$$\Phi_0 = (3/4\pi)^{1/2} \cos \theta \tag{78}$$

and

$$\Phi_{\pm 1} = \mp (3/8\pi)^{1/2} \sin \theta e^{\pm i\varphi} \tag{79}$$

as well as a common (unknown) radial factor $R(r)$.

The term energies are the expectation values of the perturbation in the various states listed previously. The leading term in the expansion, corresponding to $n = 0$, is

$$\frac{1}{r_>} \tag{80}$$

which does not depend on angles and is therefore the same in all three states. This can be eliminated by a simple shift in the zero of energy.

The next term in the expansion, $n = 1$,

$$\frac{r_<}{r_>^2} P_1(\cos \omega) \tag{81}$$

vanishes by inversion symmetry, but finally $n = 2$,

$$\frac{r_<^2}{r_>^3} P_2(\cos \omega) \tag{82}$$

contributes differently in all three states. The radial factor is common to all three. It is readily seen or it can be proved by the triangle inequality (of p. 75) that all succeeding terms in the expansion in Legendre polynomials will not contribute. So that apart from an additive constant arising from Eq. (80), all the energies will be proportional to the same, albeit unknown, radial integral. And it remains a straightforward exercise in manipulating trigonometric identities to show that

$$\frac{E(^1S) - E(^1D)}{E(^1D) - E(^3P)} = \frac{3}{2} \tag{83}$$

This relationship is of course independent of the additive energy shift from Eq. (80), or of the common radial integral. Its validity depends only on the validity of the Hartree-Fock procedure and on the validity of our neglect of states outside the p shell. In Table 4.2 we compare the theory with experiment.

Problem 8:   Using the procedure indicated in the text, derive Eq. (83). Hint: no integrals need be evaluated to establish this result, but various integrals need to be compared. This can be done solely by use of the mathematical identity,

$$\int d\varphi_1 \int d\theta_1 \sin \theta_1 P_2(\cos \omega) \cos^2 \theta_1 = -\int d\varphi_1 \int d\theta_1 \sin \theta_1 P_2(\cos \omega) \sin^2 \theta_1$$

The agreement is *not* always as perfect as for the atoms in Table 4.2. For example, the failure of one or another of the hypotheses gives for La^+ the ratio 18.43, which differs from theory by an order of magnitude. In such instances more terms must be taken into account, and the calculation which eventually leads to agreement with

TABLE 4.2

Configurations and Ratio of Term Splittings in Various Atoms versus Theory

	Theory	Experimental				
		C	Si	Ge	Sn	O
Configuration	$np^{3\pm1}$	$2p^2$	$3p^2$	$4p^2$	$5p^2$	$2p^4$
Ratio*	1.50	1.13	1.48	1.50	1.39	1.14

* See Eq. 83.
SOURCE: Condon and Shortley.[10]

experiment may become very involved. But at present the ultimate validity of the many-body Schrödinger equation for the atoms is not in dispute, and even the remarkably simple truncation, such as the organization into atomic shells, gives reasonably accurate results with minimum calculation.

Thus, atomic magnetism which is the consequence of Hund's rule, is documented by experiment, explained by elementary theory, and confirmed by elaborate calculations.

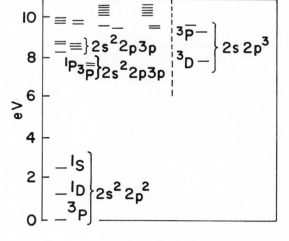

FIG. 4.4. Energy-level diagram of carbon (C), as example of Hund's two rules.

In Fig. 4.4, we show the spectrum of carbon. It is to be noted that as in N, the terms *not* described by the simple theory lie several volts above the ^1S term. As a consequence, theories of carbon in the solid state probably need take only the lowest three terms into account, which in the atom are adequately described by the sort of first-order perturbation theory just expounded.

Finally, in Table 4.3, there is given a list of possible terms (configurations) which can be constructed out of a specified number of equivalent electrons. The lowest, according to Hund's rule, is given in boldface.

TABLE 4.3

Possible Terms for a Number of Equivalent Electrons

s		^2S		
s^2	^1S			
p or p^5		$^2\mathbf{P}$		
p^2 or p^4	^1SD		$^3\mathbf{P}$	
p^3		^2PD		$^4\mathbf{S}$
d or d^9		$^2\mathbf{D}$		
d^2 or d^8	^1SDG		$^3\mathbf{PF}$	
d^3 or d^7		^2PDFGH 2	$^4\mathbf{PF}$	
d^4 or d^6	^1SDFGI 2 2 2		^3PDFGH 2 2	$^5\mathbf{D}$
d^5		$^2SPDFGHI$ 3 2 2	^4PDFG	$^6\mathbf{S}$
f or f^{13}		$^2\mathbf{F}$		
f^2 or f^{12}	^1SDGI		$^3PF\mathbf{H}$	
f^3 or f^{11}		$^2PDFGHIKL$ 2 2 2 2	$^4SDFG\mathbf{I}$	
f^4 or f^{10}	$^1SDFGHIKLN$ 2 4 4 2 3 2		$^3PDFGHIKLM$ 3 2 4 3 4 2 2	$^5SDFG\mathbf{I}$
f^5 or f^9		$^2PDFGHIKLMNO$ 4 5 7 6 7 5 5 3 2	$^4SPDFGHIKLM$ 2 3 4 4 3 3 2	$^6PF\mathbf{H}$
f^6 or f^8	$^1SPDFGHIKLMNQ$ 4 6 4 8 4 7 3 4 2 2	$^3PDFGHIKLMNO$ 6 5 9 7 9 6 6 3 3	$^5SPDFGHIKL$ 3 2 3 2 2	$^7\mathbf{F}$
f^7		$^2SPDFGHIKLMNOQ$ 2 5 7 10 10 9 9 7 5 4 2	$^4SPDFGHIKLMN$ 2 2 6 5 7 5 5 3 3	^6PDFGHI $^8\mathbf{S}$

NOTE: A number under a term symbol indicates the number of different levels of this type. The lowest level is normally that with the highest L of the highest multiplicity (Hund's rule). It is indicated in bold type.

SOURCE: *American Institute of Physics Handbook*, 2nd ed., McGraw-Hill, New York, 1963, pp. 7–21. Reprinted by permission.

Practically all known magnetic substances involve d- or f-shell electrons, the study of which would take us well beyond the scope of an introductory work. The interested reader will readily find specialized treatises on this subject.[11]

INDEPENDENT ELECTRONS

It is possible to refine the study of atomic structure far beyond the short introduction provided in the preceding pages. Moreover, we have not yet approached the subject of magnetic elements. Usually magnetic substances are those composed of rare-earth or transition-series elements, with incomplete (magnetic) f shell or d shell as the case may be. Because magnetism is a phenomenon that occurs in the solid state,

[11] For example, J. S. Griffith, *The Theory of Transition-Metal Ions*, Cambridge, New York, 1961, 455 pp.

it is fitting however to interrupt the discussion of atomic properties, at the point where it begins to become complicated, and turn to the idealized model of electrons in the solid state: the independent particle model.

In this section we shall consider independent electrons in solids from a somewhat special point of view, ordering the ground state and elementary excited states according to their multiplicity, and proving some results which later will apply to a theorem about interacting electrons. What we shall now observe is that the degeneracies (which in the atom were lifted by interactions among the valence electrons, resulting in Hund's rules) will in solids be lifted in a different manner, without the need for any interactions; and that these *noninteracting* electrons will be *nonmagnetic*, except for second-order para- and diamagnetic effects which are discussed elsewhere.

Previously (see the section on overlap exchange) we had proved that interacting electrons are not ferromagnetic without overlap; here we shall show that overlapping electrons are not ferromagnetic if they do not interact.

The Hamiltonian for N independent electrons (for simplicity assume $N =$ even) is of the form

$$\mathcal{H} = \sum_{i=1}^{N} h(\mathbf{r}_i) \tag{84}$$

It is not useful to specify further the one-particle Hamiltonian $h(\mathbf{r})$, which may include interactions with other electrons on the average, with the periodic array of atoms comprising the solid, with the surfaces and other external forces or impurities. In addition to these forces and the kinetic energy of the particle, we may allow any other potentials into $h(\mathbf{r})$, except those which involve the spin of the particle explicitly, and still arrive at the desired results. First, solve the eigenvalue equation,

$$h(\mathbf{r})f_n(\mathbf{r}) = e_n f_n(\mathbf{r}) \tag{85}$$

for the one-particle wavefunctions and eigenvalues f_n and e_n, arranging the eigenvalues in ascending order:

$$e_1 \leqslant e_2 \leqslant \cdots \tag{86}$$

etc. [It should be noted that the density of levels increases with the volume of the box; for a finite but arbitrarily large box, the levels can always be enumerated as in Eq. (86).] The many-electron wavefunctions are Slater determinants of space and spin functions. By the completeness of the set of f_n, the Slater determinants form a complete set of admissible Pauli wavefunctions for the many-electron system. However, we recall that they are not automatically eigenfunctions of S_{tot}^2, although they are always good eigenfunctions of S_{tot}^z with eigenvalue M. Recall also the results of Eqs. (30) and those following: the spin function may be projected out of the Pauli function of definite M, leaving just the space partner

$$^M F(\mathbf{r}_1, \ldots, \mathbf{r}_{\frac{1}{2}N+M}| \ldots, \mathbf{r}_N) \tag{87}$$

which for independent particles is the product of two determinants. Because the one-electron functions may occur once in each determinant, the lowest energy belongs to a function of this type where the lowest possible e_n's are represented twice:

$$^0F = \frac{1}{(\frac{1}{2}N)!} \det \|f_1(\mathbf{r}_1) \cdots f_{\frac{1}{2}N}(\mathbf{r}_{\frac{1}{2}N})\| \det \|f_1(\mathbf{r}_{\frac{1}{2}N+1}) \cdots f_{N\frac{1}{2}}(\mathbf{r}_N)\| \qquad (88)$$

This is automatically an eigenstate belonging to $M = 0$, with energy

$$E_0 = 2 \sum_{n=1}^{\frac{1}{2}N} e_n \qquad (89)$$

The factor of 2 comes ultimately from Kramers' degeneracy.

The function ^0F chosen in this manner has also the important property that it is an eigenfunction of S_{tot}^2 with *zero* eigenvalue (compare p. 90). Therefore, it should be labeled $^0F^0$ according to the notation previously introduced. It is the absolute ground state, unless there is degeneracy, in which case it is among the ground states.

If next we inquire about the ground state in the $M = 1$ subspace, we must first eliminate $^0F^0$ which cannot be raised. But by reasoning similar to the above, the optimum second choice is found to be

$$^1F = \frac{1}{\sqrt{(\frac{1}{2}N+1)!(\frac{1}{2}N-1)!}} \det \|f_1(\mathbf{r}_1) \cdots f_{\frac{1}{2}N+1}(\mathbf{r}_{\frac{1}{2}N+1})\|$$

$$\times \det \|f_1(\mathbf{r}_{\frac{1}{2}N+2}) \cdots f_{\frac{1}{2}N-1}(\mathbf{r}_N)\| \qquad (90)$$

The energy of this state is given in Eq. (91). Now it is trivial to construct functions of the type ^0F and ^{-1}F starting with this new function; but the functions of type $^{\pm 2}F$, which we might attempt to construct with ^1F and its permutations, vanish identically. This proves in fact that we have found $^1F^1$, an eigenfunction of S_{tot}^2 with the indicated eigenvalue. The energy E_1,

$$E_1 = E_0 + e_{\frac{1}{2}N+1} - e_{\frac{1}{2}N} \geqslant E_0 \qquad (91)$$

is the absolute ground-state energy in the subspace of eigenfunctions belonging to $S_{\text{tot}} \geqslant 1$, although it is greater than E_0.

One proceeds systematically through all the higher M subspaces, establishing always that the function of lowest energy of type ^MF is in fact $^MF^M$; and the concomitant result for the energy can be summarized most compactly as

$$\boxed{E_0(S) \leqslant E_0(S+1)} \qquad (92)$$

defining $E_0(S)$ to be the lowest among all the energy eigenvalues $E(S)$ of the determinantal functions or linear combinations thereof, $^MF^S$.

We next examine the possible degeneracies. If $h(\mathbf{r})$ is real and one of the f_n is complex, then by complex conjugation of both sides of Eq. (85) we see that f_n^* is also an eigenfunction, with the same eigenvalue e_n. This is the only degeneracy possible in all generality. For consider an empty box, with dimensions L_x, L_y and L_z and a Hamiltonian

$$h(\mathbf{r}) = -\frac{\hbar^2}{2m} \nabla^2 \qquad (93)$$

(kinetic energy only) which has eigenfunctions $e^{i\mathbf{k}\cdot\mathbf{r}}$ and eigenvalues

$$e_{\mathbf{k}} = \frac{\hbar^2 \mathbf{k}^2}{2m} \qquad \mathbf{k} = 2\pi\left(\frac{n_1}{L_x}, \frac{n_2}{L_y}, \frac{n_3}{L_z}\right) \tag{94}$$

We see that if $L_x \neq L_y \neq L_z$ there is in fact no additional degeneracy; so that in the presence of potentials any added degeneracy would be "accidental" and could be eliminated by distorting the box a little bit, or by some other artifice.

For convenience N is now chosen to be a multiple of 4, which guarantees E_0 to be nondegenerate; for

$$e_{\frac{1}{2}N+1} \underset{\neq}{>} e_{\frac{1}{2}N} \qquad \text{and therefore} \qquad E_1 \underset{\neq}{>} E_0 \tag{95}$$

What is more, the eigenfunction $^0F^0$ of Eq. (88) is real; for it is both possible and necessary in the ground state that for every complex f_n the conjugate f_n^* also be present in each determinant. And even more compelling, is the argument that a complex $^0F^0$ would lead to a degenerate ground state, in violation of Eq. (95) above.

The total current operator is

$$\frac{e\hbar}{im}\sum_{j=1}^{N} \nabla_j = \mathbf{I}_{\text{op}} \tag{96}$$

and its ground-state eigenvalue $\mathbf{I}$ is given by

$$\mathbf{I}_{\text{op}}\,^0F^0 = \mathbf{I}\,^0F^0 \tag{97}$$

Complex conjugation of both sides of this equation, and the reality of the eigenvalue $\mathbf{I}$ and of the eigenfunction $^0F^0$ establish the result $\mathbf{I} = 0$, regardless of the potential. Thus the current and the spin both vanish in the ground state, and the system is entirely nonmagnetic. This is the quantal generalization of the Bohr-Van Leeuwen theorem.

ELECTRONS IN ONE DIMENSION: A THEOREM [12]

... no one could move to the right or left to make way for passers-by, it followed that no Linelander could ever pass another. Once neighbors, always neighbors. Neighborhood with them was like marriage with us. Neighbors remained neighbors till death did them part.[13]

Because electrons in one dimension can be ordered like beads on a string, the topology of their nodal surfaces turns out relatively simple. One can generalize the result found for two electrons, and prove a powerful theorem concerning N electrons in one dimension, of which the content is roughly this: *In one dimension, not even interacting and overlapping electrons can be ferromagnetic.* A somewhat milder extension of this theorem, in which the type of interactions is restricted, can also be proved for N electrons in three dimensions (as we shall see in a subsequent section).

---

[12] Lieb and Mattis, *op. cit.*
[13] E. A. Abbott, *Flatland.*

Before stating the theorem and proceeding to the proof, it is appropriate to comment on its importance. This theorem occupies a special place as the guardian of our conscience when we speculate concerning the origins of ferromagnetism. Any fundamental explanation or theory, which conceivably would lead to ferromagnetism in one dimension, must *ipso facto* be false! And that is the reason we have discussed angular momentum, atomic theory, and the origins of Hund's rules, for these are intimately connected with the three-dimensionality of space, and, by virtue of the present theorem, are required for understanding the phenomena. Deferring further such considerations, we now go on with the

Theorem: For interacting electrons in one dimension, the ground state in any M subspace is nondegenerate, and belongs to $S_{tot} = |M|$. From this it follows that $E_0(S) < E_0(S + 1)$, that the current vanishes in the ground state of any M subspace, and that electrons in one dimension are entirely nonferromagnetic.

Proof: What we have shown for noninteracting particles in the previous section will be adapted to the present case of interacting electrons, for which the Hamiltonian is

$$\mathscr{H} = -\frac{\hbar^2}{2m} \sum_{j=1}^{N} \frac{\partial^2}{\partial x_j^2} + V(x_1, x_2, \dots, x_N) \tag{98}$$

The potential V includes all external forces, periodic or other, and the interactions among electrons which may be taken to be arbitrary. The only exclusions are as follows: no velocity or spin-dependent forces or nonlocal potentials will be admitted, and V must be integrable for reasons which are or will become clear. We shall adopt a standard boundary condition: If the size of Lineland is D, the boundary condition will be that the wavefunctions vanish whenever any $x_n = \pm\frac{1}{2}D$. Admissible Pauli eigenfunctions are

$$^M\Psi^S(1, 2, \dots, N) \tag{99}$$

where, for compactness, $n = 1, 2, \dots$ stands for the couple of space and spin coordinates (x_n, ξ_n). First, we write the eigenvalue equation,

$$\mathscr{H}\,^M\Psi^S = E(S)\,^M\Psi^S \tag{100}$$

noting that the energy cannot depend on M. (Because $\mathscr{H}$ commutes with the spin operators, we may apply spin raising and lowering operators to both sides of Schrödinger's equation, changing M without affecting the energy eigenvalue.)

As usual, we now eliminate the spins, and consider the space functions $^M f^S$, which themselves obey Schrödinger's equation Eq. (100), with precisely the eigenvalue $E(S)$. All of them can be brought into the $M = 0$ subspace, by application of spin raising or lowering operators if necessary, and therefore we start by examining this particular subspace in which the ground-state eigenfunction is surely to be found. Consider an arbitrary eigenfunction, of unknown S_{tot},

$$^0 f(x_1, \dots, x_{\frac{1}{2}N} | x_{\frac{1}{2}N+1}, \dots, x_N) \tag{101}$$

in the region R defined as follows:

$$R \equiv \begin{cases} -\tfrac{1}{2}D < x_1 < \cdots < \tfrac{1}{2}D \\ -\tfrac{1}{2}D < x_{\frac{1}{2}N+1} < \cdots < x_N < \tfrac{1}{2}D \end{cases} \tag{102}$$

The natural boundaries of R occur where the inequalities are just barely violated, e.g.,

$$x_1 = -\tfrac{1}{2}D \quad \text{or} \quad x_n = x_{n\pm 1} \quad \text{or} \quad x_{\frac{1}{2}N} = \tfrac{1}{2}D \tag{103}$$

etc., and it should be noted that ^0f vanishes identically on these boundaries. Although the total configuration space consists of the variables $x_1, \ldots, x_N$ in any ordering, *when ^0f is known in R it is known everywhere*, because the other regions can be found by trivial permutations $\mathscr{P}$ of the two sets of coordinates. (Recall the definition of *trivial permutations* given on p. 88.) For example, if

$$(x_1, \ldots) \qquad \text{is a point in } R \tag{104}$$

and

$$(x'_1, \ldots) \qquad \text{is a point in } R' \tag{105}$$

and $\mathscr{P}$ is a permutation which connects R to R',

$$\mathscr{P}R = R' \tag{106}$$

then we obtain ^0f in R' by the trivial permutation:

$$^0f(x'_1, \ldots) \equiv (-1)^{\mathscr{P}}\mathscr{P}[^0f(x_1, \ldots)] \tag{107}$$

And in this self-evident manner, we can find the function everywhere. Indeed, with the sign convention used above, it is guaranteed that ^0f will have the proper antisymmetries under its trivial permutations $\mathscr{P}$. The nontrivial permutations, it is seen, are not needed to map R into the entire space; and thus they play only their usual role, which is raising and lowering M.

Now, we state and prove a *lemma* which is at the core of the theorem: The eigenfunction of $\mathscr{H}$ which belongs to the lowest energy eigenvalue and is subject only to the boundary condition that it vanish on the boundaries of R is *nodeless* in R.

The proof proceeds exactly as in the case of two electrons. If the ground-state function had nodes, then its absolute value would be a nodeless function, which would have identically the same variational energy but which would not itself be an eigenfunction. Since the variational energy of any but a ground-state eigenfunction must exceed the ground-state energy, there is a contradiction unless the absolute value of the ground-state eigenfunction is itself a ground-state eigenfunction; which is only possible if the ground state is nodeless. The nodeless state is, moreover, nondegenerate. For two nodeless functions cannot be orthogonal, but all the eigenfunctions of $\mathscr{H}$ can be made mutually orthogonal, and other than nodeless functions have been excluded by the preceding arguments. This nondegeneracy is stronger than we were able to prove for noninteracting particles (in the previous section) because we have restricted the arguments here to one dimension.

The nodeless property is independent of the magnitude of V, and so is the shape of R. We may therefore compare in R the ground state of a Hamiltonian $\mathscr{H}$ with arbitrary V, to that of the noninteracting Hamiltonian $\mathscr{H}_0$ with $V = 0$. In both cases, the ground state is nodeless; the two corresponding functions cannot be orthogonal, therefore they share the same quantum numbers $\mathbf{I}$ and S_{tot}.

What these quantum numbers are for noninteracting electrons ($V = 0$) is something which was already discussed: viz., *zero*. And by the above it follows that both these quantum numbers vanish for arbitrary V as well, in the ground state.

Next, one introduces the fundamental region suitable for $M = 1$, which is

$$R \equiv \begin{cases} -\frac{1}{2}D < x_1 < \cdots < x_{\frac{1}{2}N+1} < \frac{1}{2}D \\ -\frac{1}{2}D < x_{\frac{1}{2}N+2} < \cdots < x_N < \frac{1}{2}D \end{cases} \tag{108}$$

By analogy, one proves that the ground-state function in this region is nodeless and belongs to the same quantum numbers regardless of V. It follows by comparison with the results for $V = 0$ that this function has $S_{tot} = 1$; the proof for higher M proceeding in identically the same manner, until the theorem for the interacting particles is proved.

THE WRONSKIAN [14]

A somewhat different approach may serve to clarify the results obtained so far. Suppose we have a set of real space eigenfunctions of the Schrödinger equation

$$\mathscr{H}f_j(x_1, \ldots) = E_j f_j(x_1, \ldots) \tag{109}$$

with

$$\mathscr{H} = -\frac{\hbar^2}{2m} \sum \frac{\partial^2}{\partial x_n^2} + V(x_1, \ldots) $$

just as in Eq. (98), and it is desired to order the eigenvalues E_j in a sequence of increasing energy.

The lowest energy belongs to the nodeless eigenfunction; since the permutation operators commute with the Hamiltonian, it can also be established that this function is totally symmetric under the interchange of any coordinates and therefore is not of any use for more than two Fermions. But there can only be one nodeless function (compare proof of analogous statements on p. 93), and the others can be examined as to the topology of their nodal surfaces. The nodal surface is defined as the locus of $f = 0$.

We shall not go into any detail beyond proving the simple but interesting *lemma*:

If there are two functions f_i and f_j such that a nodal surface S_i of f_i, encloses a region R_i which neither contains, nor is intersected by any nodal surface of f_j, then $E_i > E_j$. For example, consider any eigenfunction f_i together with the nodeless eigenfunction f_0; the lemma implies $E_i > E_0$, which is obviously true for all i.

To prove the lemma, it is necessary to multiply both sides of Eq. (109) on the left by f_i; to multiply the analogous equation for f_i on the left by f_j, subtract the first from the second, and obtain

$$-\frac{\hbar^2}{2m} \nabla \cdot (f_j \nabla f_i - f_i \nabla f_j) = (E_i - E_j) f_i f_j \tag{110}$$

---

[14] From unpublished work by E. Lieb and D. Mattis.

The potential has been eliminated from this expression, and the left-hand side involves only the kinetic energies or the gradient of the Wronskian, for which we have used the generalized Laplacian notation

$$\nabla \cdot \nabla = \nabla^2 \equiv \sum_{n=1}^{N} \frac{\partial^2}{\partial x_n^2} \tag{111}$$

By assumption, neither function changes sign in R_i so we may, in considering this region, assume both functions are positive, and if not, make them so. Next, integrate over R_i, which by Green's theorem gives an integral of the Wronksian over S_i on the left-hand side, and a positive integral times the energy difference on the right.

$$-\frac{\hbar^2}{2m} \oint_{S_i} d\mathbf{S} \cdot (f_j \nabla f_i - f_i \nabla f_j) = (E_i - E_j) \int_{R_i} d\tau f_i f_j \tag{112}$$

But $f_i = 0$ on the nodal surface S_i; and the normal derivative of f_i is negative on S_i because the function is positive inside the volume bounded by the surface and negative outside (see Fig. 4.1). So the left-hand side is positive, and the equation can only be satisfied if $E_i > E_j$, which proves the lemma.

Evidently, we have used nothing about dimensionality in this demonstration, and it is indeed equally valid for electrons in three dimensions [with $\nabla^2 \equiv \sum_{n=1}^{N} \nabla_n^2$, instead of Eq. (111)]. But the difficulty of finding nodal surfaces has so far frustrated attempts to apply these results to realistic problems for $N > 2$ in three dimensions.

THEOREM IN THREE DIMENSIONS

The great stumbling blocks to proving the theorem in three dimensions are the impossibility of ordering the particles in any sensible manner and the difficulty in locating the nodal surfaces along which the wavefunctions vanish. One may get around both these if he restricts the potential to the form

$$V(x_1, \dots, x_N; y_1, \dots, y_N; z_1, \dots, z_N) \tag{113}$$

which is to say, "separately symmetric" under permutations of the x, y, or z coordinates alone. The periodic potential typical of the solid state may be included, as well as electron–electron interactions. For potentials of this class, we may prove the theorem in the same form as for noninteracting electrons:

$$E_0(S) \leqslant E_0(S + 1) \tag{114}$$

so that *for ferromagnetism to occur*, even in three dimensions, *it does not suffice for electrons to overlap and to interact, no matter how strong the potential*. The *form* of the potential shall play a peculiar role.

In the present section, we shall prove the above inequality for a special case of the potential V, viz.,

$$V = V(x_1, \dots, x_N) + V'(y_1, \dots, y_N) + V''(z_1, \dots, z_N) \tag{115}$$

the separable potential. Extension to the general class of potentials, Eq. (113), is straightforward.

When the kinetic energy operators are included, the Hamiltonian with a separable potential can be written as the sum of three Hamiltonians, one for each dimension. The space eigenfunctions are therefore product functions:

$$\psi = f(x_1, \dots)f'(y_1, \dots)f''(z_1, \dots) \tag{116}$$

and the energy eigenvalues are additive:

$$E = E + E' + E'' \tag{117}$$

We should now introduce the spin functions, minimize the sum of the energies E, E', and E'' subject to the Pauli principle, and finally try to discover the spin of the lowest allowable eigenfunction. The $f(x_1, \dots)$ function obeys a one-dimensional Schrödinger equation which is invariant under permutations of the x coordinates. Similar statements are true for f' and f''. Therefore we may choose f, f', and f'' to be simultaneous eigenfunctions of the permutation operators and write

$$f = f(x_1, \dots , x_p|x_{p+1}, \dots |x_{r+1}, \dots | \dots | \dots , x_N) \tag{118}$$

and similar expressions for f' and f''. The function is antisymmetric under the interchange of coordinates separated by commas; but has no particular symmetry properties under interchange of coordinates separated by one or more vertical bars.

Whereas the Pauli principle restricts the allowable functions in one dimensions to those with either zero or one vertical bar, in the case of electrons obeying the Pauli principle in two or more dimensions we must allow for *any number* of bars, and therein lies part of the difficulty.

Example: Consider a totally antisymmetric space function, F, which belongs to the totally symmetric (totally ferromagnetic) spin function; it can be of the form

$$F = f(x_1, \dots , x_N)f'(y_1|y_2| \dots |y_N)f''(z_1|z_2| \dots |z_N) \tag{119}$$

where f' and f'' are both totally symmetric, and therefore have $N-1$ vertical bars, and f is totally antisymmetric. Or all three functions could be totally antisymmetric; and F would be of the form

$$F = f(x_1, \dots , x_N)f'(y_1, \dots , y_N)f''(z_1, \dots , z_N) \tag{120}$$

with no vertical bars at all. If we require F to have one bar, or if we allow linear combinations of products of f's, then the number of possibilities of bars for the f's becomes virtually endless.

Proof of Theorem in Eq. (114): Given an eigenfunction of $\mathcal{H}$ and S^2_{tot}, which is also a Pauli function, i.e., a totally antisymmetric function of the coordinates $\mathbf{r}_i = (x_i, y_i, z_i, m_i)$ (let $m_i = \uparrow$ or $\downarrow$ denote the spin eigenvalue), express it as a linear combination of product functions of the type:

$$f(\mathbf{u}_1, \dots , \mathbf{u}_p|\mathbf{u}_{p+1}, \dots | \dots | \dots , \mathbf{u}_N)g(\mathbf{v}_1; \dots; \mathbf{v}_p| \dots | \dots; \mathbf{v}_N) \tag{121}$$

where $\mathbf{u}_i = (x_i, m_i)$ and $\mathbf{v}_i = (y_i, z_i)$. In order that a totally antisymmetric Pauli function might be extractable from Eq. (121), it is required that g be symmetric in the variables separated by semicolons if f is antisymmetric in the variables separated by commas. The function above has the same energy as the original Pauli eigenfunction. This is because the latter is a linear combination of Eq. (121) and its permutations, and of course $\mathscr{H}$ is invariant under the permutations, and therefore the energy is unaffected.

A simplified proof of the theorem proceeds as follows: for all practical purposes, f is a Pauli function for p one-dimensional electrons $x_1, \ldots, x_p$, and separately also for $x_{p+1}, \ldots$, etc.; and if we take linear combinations of f-type functions so as to give these groups of variables definite spin, it is clear by virtue of the one-dimensional theorem that the lowest energy is achieved only if the total spin of the first p electrons is zero (or one-half, if the number is odd), and similarly for all the successive groups separated by vertical bars. Such linear combinations are of course once more degenerate with the original function, Eq. (121), as well as with the original Pauli function from which the latter was extracted. Notice that the process by which the sets of electrons are given definite spin does not affect the antisymmetry, so that we may, without loss of generality, assume that in f the various sets of variables have definite spin.

Finally, a Pauli function is constructed from Eq. (121) in two steps: first, an eigenfunction of S_{tot} is constructed with Clebsch-Gordan coefficients; second, the function so obtained is totally antisymmetrized. The sets with zero spin do not contribute to the total spin; thus if all the sets contain an even number of particles, only $S_{\text{tot}} = 0$ is accessible. If N is even, as we usually assume, we may have none, two, four, six, ... sets with odd numbers of variables, for which the lowest energy is achieved with spin one-half. Two spins one-half may be combined to give spin zero, or spin one. Four may be combined to yield $S_{\text{tot}} = 0, 1, 2$, etc. So long as we stick to the functions with the lowest energy in each symmetry class, we see that if a function belonging to total spin S can be constructed, then so can another function which has the same energy but total spin $S - 1$, or less. Because the same cannot be said about $S + 1$, one immediately arrives at a statement of the theorem in the form of the inequality, Eq. (114).[15]

ORDERING THEOREM VERSUS HUND'S RULE

The ordering theorem, as we proved it in three dimensions, differs from its one-dimensional version by not being stated in terms of strict inequalities. And indeed the ground state for the interacting three-dimensional electrons could belong to some nonzero value of the total spin, say S, but then necessarily also to $S - 1, S - 2, \ldots, 1$, and 0. The maximum value of S in the ground state may be estimated, on the basis of noninteracting electrons in three dimensions, not to exceed the *order of magnitude* $S = \frac{1}{2}N^{1/2}$, regardless of how many electrons are present. Since ferromagnetism in the solid state requires that

$$\underset{N \to \infty}{Lim} \frac{S}{N} \neq 0 \tag{122}$$

we see that solids with separately symmetric potentials are never ferromagnetic. Such is not the case for a hypothetical atom with a separately symmetric potential. The atom is typically a collection of less than 100 electrons, and a total spin of the order of

---

[15] For much more detailed and constructive proof including the extension to the general separately symmetric potentials, Eq. (113), see Lieb and Mattis, *Phys. Rev.*, **125**: 164 (1962).

$S = 5$ is not negligible, and indeed is of the order of magnitude which is observed in nature although somewhat longer. But atoms in nature have Coulomb potentials and *not* separately symmetric potentials. The difference between the Coulomb interaction and such a potential may be considered as a perturbation which lifts the degeneracy amongst ground states belonging to S, $S - 1$, ... , etc. So that in nature, the state satisfying Hund's rules does not merely lie among the ground states, but is indeed the lowest state of all.

Isolated atoms can therefore possess a small "permanent" magnetic moment, at least, one which requires some energy to destroy. In the process of constituting molecular or solid matter with these atoms (1) the magnetic moment may become lost in favor of greater binding energy. Then the material has no particular discernible magnetic properties. Or (2) the moments on alternate atoms or alternate layers of atoms may be antiparallel. In this case there is antiferromagnetism, and under certain assumptions one can also prove that the total spin $S = 0$ in the ground state, even though the individual atomic moments do not vanish. Finally (3) the atoms might preserve their magnetic moments to some extent and align them parallel. This is the most interesting case of ferromagnetism, and we shall return subsequently to an explanation of how it may come about.

PART II

STATICS AND

DYNAMICS

OF MAGNETISM

CHAPTER 5

EMICLASSICAL

THEORY OF MAGNETISM

Assume classical spin vectors of fixed length S at every one of the points on a Bravais lattice, interacting with each other and with an external magnetic field. The energy is given by

$$E = -\sum_{i,j} v_{ij}\mathbf{S}_i \cdot \mathbf{S}_j - g\mu_B \mathbf{H} \cdot \sum_i \mathbf{S}_i \qquad \text{where } v_{ij} = v(\mathbf{R}_{ij}) \tag{1}$$

assuming the interaction $(\mathbf{S}_i \cdot \mathbf{S}_j)$ to be caused by the exchange mechanism. (The magnetostatic dipole-dipole interaction has a somewhat different angular dependence discussed on p. 129 *et seq.*) The equations of motion, or torque equations, are

$$\hbar\dot{\mathbf{S}}_i = \mathbf{S}_i \times \left(g\mu_B\mathbf{H} + \sum_i v_{ij}\mathbf{S}_j\right) \tag{2}$$

and by substitution of this into Eq. (1) it is verified that E is a constant of the motion. Another constant of the motion is found by adding all the equations, Eq. (2):

$$\hbar\sum_i \dot{\mathbf{S}}_i = \left(\sum_i \mathbf{S}_i\right) \times g\mu_B\mathbf{H} \tag{3}$$

Since $\sum_i \mathbf{S}_i = $ total spin angular momentum, this last equation has the following significance: In a homogeneous field, the magnitude of the total spin is conserved, although its orientation precesses about the applied field. In the absence of an external field, of course both the direction and the magnitude of the total spin are conserved.

As there are no other constants of the motion in general, it is impossible to give a closed form expression for arbitrary motion. This will be recognized as one of the fundamental difficulties in classical mechanics, and it is probably insuperable. But in the present case we can take advantage of the translational invariance to find certain particular solutions. This we shall do first; later we shall simply linearize the equations of motion, and in that approximation the general solution *can* be found as a super-position of *spin-wave* normal modes.

FERROMAGNETIC SPIN-WAVE—NONLINEAR THEORY

Imagine that the spins, initially all parallel and favorably oriented with respect to the external field, are set into precessional motion, with constant transverse amplitude T (see Fig. 5.1):

$$\mathbf{S}_i = (T \cos f_i, \ T \sin f_i, \ +\sqrt{S^2 - T^2}) \tag{4}$$

where $f_i = f(t, \mathbf{R}_i)$ is to be determined, and the field is $\mathbf{H} = (0, 0, H)$. First, one should verify that the z components are indeed constant, as is affirmed in Eq. (4). By the equation of motion,

$$\hbar \dot{S}_i^z = T^2 \left(\cos f_i \sum_j v_{ij} \sin f_j - \sin f_i \sum_j v_{ij} \cos f_j \right)$$

$$= T^2 \sum_j v_{ij} \sin(f_j - f_i) \tag{5}$$

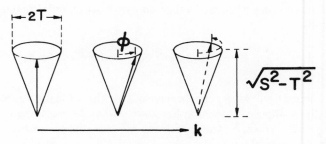

FIG. 5.1. Spin-wave propagating with wavevector $\mathbf{k}$. Each spin precesses about its z axis, sweeping out the surface of a cone in a time $t = 2\pi/\omega(\mathbf{k})$, with $\omega(\mathbf{k})$ given in Eq. (9). Radius of cone = amplitude of spin wave = T. Frequency $\omega(\mathbf{k})$ is function of T. The angle $\phi = ka$ measures the phase difference between nearest neighbors, where a = nearest-neighbor separation.

In order for this to vanish identically, the summand must be translationally invariant [recall that $v_{ij} = v(|\mathbf{R}_i - \mathbf{R}_j|)$], that is,

$$f_j - f_i = F(t, \mathbf{R}_{ij})$$

However, this alone does not suffice to guarantee that $\dot{S}_i^z = 0$. If we look at the equations for the other two components, assuming that $\mathbf{S}_i$ is given by Eq. (4), they give rise to a cyclic problem which is self-evidently solved by the *ansatz*,

$$f_i = \omega t - \mathbf{k} \cdot \mathbf{R}_i \tag{6}$$

and for this form the right-hand side of Eq. (5) does correctly vanish.

Now we should write the equations for the transverse components, not only to verify the *ansatz* above, but also to determine the allowed values of $\mathbf{k}$ and of the frequency $\omega(\mathbf{k})$. It is somewhat easier to combine the two equations and discuss the components of circular motion $S_i^{\pm} = S_i^x \pm i S_i^y$.

If at first we do not make use of the *ansatz* of Eq. (6), we find

$$\hbar \dot{S}_i^{\pm} = \hbar(\dot{S}_i^x \pm i\dot{S}_i^y) = \pm i S_i^{\pm}\left(g\mu_B H + \sum_j v_{ij}\sqrt{S^2 - T^2}\right) \mp \left(i\sqrt{S^2 - T^2}\sum_j v_{ij}S_j^{\pm}\right) \quad (7)$$

But it is well known that the solutions of this are given by Eqs. (4) and (6), subject to the periodic boundary conditions requirement,

$$k_x = \frac{2\pi}{L_x}n \qquad k_y = \frac{2\pi}{L_y}m \qquad k_z = \frac{2\pi}{L_z}l \qquad (8)$$

n, m, l = integers as usual, and the solution we postulated is therefore correct. One immediately finds for the circular frequency

$$\omega(\mathbf{k}) = \frac{1}{\hbar}\left[g\mu_B H + \sqrt{S^2 - T^2}\sum_j v_{ij}(1 - e^{i\mathbf{k}\cdot\mathbf{R}_{ij}})\right] \quad (9)$$

It is interesting to note two points which are clearly brought out in this example, although they are well known from other, approximate, solutions.

1. As the amplitude (T) of the motion is increased, the frequency decreases, i.e., the effective spring constant becomes weaker.
2. In zero magnetic field, the frequency is a quadratic function of $\mathbf{k}$ for small k, provided v_{ij} is a finite-ranged interaction,

$$\omega(\mathbf{k}) \cong \frac{1}{\hbar}\left[g\mu_B H + \sqrt{S^2 - T^2}\frac{k^2}{6}\sum_j v_{ij}\mathbf{R}_{ij}^2 + O(\mathbf{k}^4)\right] \quad (10)$$

TWO SUBLATTICES—NONLINEAR THEORY

Another simply soluble example introduces the concept of the two sublattices in an antiferromagnet. Assume, for concreteness, a simple cubic array, such that every other spin is defined to be a member of the A sublattice. The neighbors of the A spins are *ipso facto* members of the B sublattice; all very much like red and black squares on a chessboard. Let us now solve for the equations of motion of the entire assembly, subject to the constraint that all A spins are initially parallel, and all B spins are initially parallel, although the orientation of A spins relative to the B spins is left arbitrary.

It is obvious that with this initial value the A spins, which are initially all parallel, can exert no torque on one another and so remain perpetually parallel; and similarly for the B spins. So we need only discuss the equation of motion of some typical A spin, $\mathbf{S}_i$, and of some typical B spin, $\mathbf{S}_j$. Introducing the interaction,

$$V \equiv \sum_j v_{ij} \ (i \text{ in } A \text{ and } j \text{ in } B)$$

$$= \sum_i v_{ji} \ (j \text{ in } B \text{ and } i \text{ in } A) \quad (11)$$

we find

$$\hbar \dot{\mathbf{S}}_i = \mathbf{S}_i \times (g\mu_B\mathbf{H} + V\mathbf{S}_j) = \mathbf{S}_i \times (g\mu_B\mathbf{H}) + \frac{V}{2}(\mathbf{S}_i - \mathbf{S}_j) \times (\mathbf{S}_i + \mathbf{S}_j) \qquad (12)$$

and

$$\hbar \dot{\mathbf{S}}_j = \mathbf{S}_j \times (g\mu_B\mathbf{H}) - \frac{V}{2}(\mathbf{S}_i - \mathbf{S}_j) \times (\mathbf{S}_i + \mathbf{S}_j) \qquad (13)$$

Subtracting the second equation from the first, we obtain

$$\hbar \frac{d}{dt}(\mathbf{S}_i - \mathbf{S}_j) = (\mathbf{S}_i - \mathbf{S}_j) \times [g\mu_B\mathbf{H} + V(\mathbf{S}_i + \mathbf{S}_j)] \qquad (14)$$

Adding the two [cf. Eq. (3)], we have

$$\hbar \frac{d}{dt}(\mathbf{S}_i + \mathbf{S}_j) = (\mathbf{S}_i + \mathbf{S}_j) \times (g\mu_B\mathbf{H}) \qquad (15)$$

The last equation is solved by inspection:

$$\mathbf{S}_i + \mathbf{S}_j = (a \cos \omega t, \; -a \sin \omega t, \quad b) \qquad (16)$$

with

$$\hbar\omega = |g\mu_B\mathbf{H}| \qquad (17)$$

and the solution is then inserted into the equation for $\mathbf{S}_i - \mathbf{S}_j$. However the latter is unexpectedly difficult to solve except in the special cases,

$$a = 0 \qquad \text{or} \qquad \omega = 0 \qquad (18)$$

and we shall not attempt to solve it in general, but only under one of these restrictions. For in that case, we can again solve the equation by inspection, obtaining

$$\mathbf{S}_i - \mathbf{S}_j = (a' \cos \Omega t, \; -a' \sin \Omega t, \quad b') \qquad (19)$$

with

$$\hbar\Omega = |g\mu_B\mathbf{H} + V(\mathbf{S}_i + \mathbf{S}_j)| \qquad (20)$$

and the coordinates in Eq. (19) expressed in a *new* coordinate system, chosen such that the z direction is along the vector $g\mu_B\mathbf{H} + V(\mathbf{S}_i + \mathbf{S}_j)$. Even with the simplification of a or $\omega = 0$, a whole range of frequencies is available from $\Omega = 0$ to a maximum when $\mathbf{S}_i$ and $\mathbf{S}_j$ are parallel to $\mathbf{H}$. This is again behavior typical of nonlinear systems.

LINEARIZED EQUATIONS OF MOTION

Because it is quasi-impossible to solve the nonlinear equations of motion for three or more spins interacting, it is usual practice to assume an equilibrium configuration in which the spins are all at rest, and to obtain the equations of motion for small amplitude motion about the assumed equilibrium.

If we imagine the z direction taken along the magnetic field, or along an arbitrary (but fixed) direction in the absence of such a field, then it is clear that excepting perhaps some unusual arrangements, the only stable equilibrium configurations have every spin either parallel or antiparallel to this direction. In this way, the torque on each spin is identically zero, and the equilibrium situation is self-perpetuating.

$$* \quad * \quad * \quad * \quad * \quad *$$

One particularly important example of this is the *ferromagnetic* state, when all spins are parallel. If we assume that

$$\mathbf{S}_i = (\delta S_i^x(t), \delta S_i^y(t), S') \tag{21}$$

and that $\delta S_i^{x, y}$ are in the nature of infinitesimals, then $S' = S + O(\delta^2 S)$. Second-order infinitesimals can also be ignored in the equations of motion with the result that dynamically also $S_i^z \approx S' \approx S =$ constant within this approximation. It is only necessary to examine the equations for the transverse components. As we already saw, the convenient linear combination is $S^\pm = \delta S^x \pm i\delta S^y$, and we find directly

$$\hbar \dot{S}_i^\pm = \pm iS_i^\pm \left(g\mu_B H + \sum_j v_{ij}S \right) \mp iS \sum_j v_{ij}S_j^\pm \tag{22}$$

This has the solutions,

$$S_i^\pm = \sum_{\mathbf{k}} S_{\mathbf{k}}^\pm e^{\pm i(\omega_{\mathbf{k}} t - \mathbf{k} \cdot \mathbf{R}_i)} \tag{23}$$

with small, but otherwise arbitrary Fourier amplitudes $S_{\mathbf{k}}^\pm$, and

$$\hbar \omega_{\mathbf{k}} = g\mu_B H + S \sum_j v_{ij}(1 - e^{i\mathbf{k} \cdot \mathbf{R}_{ij}}) \tag{24}$$

The above is quite similar to the exact solution for one spin wave, except for the possibility of superposing solutions, which the linearizing approximation allows. This may, for example, permit arbitrary initial-value conditions to be fitted.

$$* \quad * \quad * \quad * \quad * \quad *$$

A second important application of the linearization procedure is to *antiferromagnetism*. For simplicity, assume a simple cubic lattice in which the Néel state is stable. We recall that in the Néel state every other spin is "up" and surrounded by nearest neighbors which are "down", i.e.,

$$\mathbf{S}_i = (\delta S_i^x(t), \delta S_i^y(t), S'), \qquad \mathbf{S}_j = (\delta S_j^x(t), \delta S_j^y(t), -S') \tag{25}$$

with i in the A and j in the B sublattice. The Néel ordering is best described by the phase factor

$$e^{i\mathbf{Q} \cdot \mathbf{R}_n}, \qquad \text{where} \qquad \mathbf{Q} \equiv \frac{\pi}{a}(1, 1, 1) \tag{26}$$

In defining this phase factor which has the values ± 1 in the simple cubic lattice, we are taking advantage of the simplicity of this particular structure. Thus the two spin vectors may be described by a single formula, replacing Eq. (25),

$$\mathbf{S}_i = (\delta S_i^x, \delta S_i^y, S' e^{i\mathbf{Q} \cdot \mathbf{R}_i}) \tag{27}$$

assuming that the up spins are on even-numbered sites and the down spins on odd-numbered sites.

As in the ferromagnetic case discussed just previously, the normalization requirement, $S_i^2 = S^2$, does not affect the magnitude of S_i^z to within second-order infinitesimals. As the same results from the equations of motion, we again set $S' \cong S$ and consider only the two equations for S^x and S^y. First, introduce the vectors

$$\delta \mathbf{S}_i = (\delta S_i^x, \delta S_i^y, 0) \qquad \text{and} \qquad \mathbf{T}_i = (0, 0, S e^{i\mathbf{Q} \cdot \mathbf{R}_i}) \tag{28}$$

so that the linearized equations of motion are

$$\hbar \delta \dot{\mathbf{S}}_i = \delta \mathbf{S}_i \times \left(g\mu_B \mathbf{H} + \sum_j v_{ij} \mathbf{T}_j \right) - \mathbf{T}_i \times \sum_j v_{ij} \delta \mathbf{S}_j \tag{29}$$

which, when combined as usual, give [cf. Eq. (22)]

$$\hbar \omega S_i^{\pm} = \pm S_i^{\pm} \left(g\mu_B H + \sum_j v_{ij} S e^{i\mathbf{Q} \cdot \mathbf{R}_j} \right)$$
$$\mp S e^{i\mathbf{Q} \cdot \mathbf{R}_i} \sum_j v_{ij} S_j^{\pm} \tag{30}$$

Because of the phase factor, these equations are no longer strictly cyclic and therefore a single plane wave does not solve them. If we try

$$S_i^{\pm} \cong e^{i\mathbf{k} \cdot \mathbf{R}_i}$$

we immediately find additional terms arising of the form

$$e^{i(\mathbf{k}+\mathbf{Q}) \cdot \mathbf{R}_i}, \; e^{i(\mathbf{k}+2\mathbf{Q}) \cdot \mathbf{R}_i}, \; \dots \; e^{i(\mathbf{k}+n\mathbf{Q}) \cdot \mathbf{R}_i}$$

etc. But these terms are actually repetitive; for by Eq. (26),

$$e^{i(2n)\mathbf{Q} \cdot \mathbf{R}_i} = 1 \qquad e^{i(2n+1)\mathbf{Q} \cdot \mathbf{R}_i} = e^{i\mathbf{Q} \cdot \mathbf{R}_i} \tag{31}$$

and therefore we may assume a solution of the form

$$S_i^{\pm} = A e^{i\mathbf{k} \cdot \mathbf{R}_i} + B e^{i(\mathbf{k}+\mathbf{Q}) \cdot \mathbf{R}_i} \tag{32}$$

It is useful to introduce the Fourier transform of the interaction

$$v(\mathbf{k}) \equiv \sum_j v_{ij} e^{i\mathbf{k} \cdot \mathbf{R}_{ij}} \tag{33}$$

Substitution of $S_i^{\pm}$ in the form of Eq. (32) above into the equation of motion, Eq. (30), and use of the definition of $v(\mathbf{k})$ just given, results in the following simple solution:

$$\hbar \omega_{\mathbf{k}} = g\mu_B H \pm S \sqrt{[v(\mathbf{k}) - v(\mathbf{Q})][v(\mathbf{k}+\mathbf{Q}) - v(\mathbf{Q})]} \tag{34}$$

We may suppose, as usual, that for long wavelengths (small k),

$$v(\mathbf{k}) = v(0) + c\mathbf{k}^2 + O(\mathbf{k}^4) \tag{35}$$

and similarly near $\mathbf{k} = \mathbf{Q}$,

$$v(\mathbf{k}) = v(\mathbf{Q}) - c'(\mathbf{k} - \mathbf{Q})^2 + O[(\mathbf{k} - \mathbf{Q})^4] \tag{36}$$

Thus, at long wavelengths, the frequency,

$$\hbar\omega_{\mathbf{k}} \cong g\mu_B H \pm |\mathbf{k}| S\sqrt{[v(\mathbf{Q}) - v(0)]c'} \tag{37}$$

changes linearly with wavevector, whereas in the ferromagnetic case it was seen to depend quadratically on the wavevector. This is a very important difference, as we see elsewhere in studying the statistical mechanics of magnetic materials.

It is possible for the argument of the square root to be negative, in which case the Néel state is certainly not stable. For, within the range of validity of the linear approximation, this corresponds to exponentially increasing (or decreasing) solutions, as opposed to the sinusoidally varying ones we assumed. The frequencies are *always* real if either $v(\mathbf{Q})$ is the absolute maximum of the function $v(\mathbf{k})$ or $v(\mathbf{Q})$ is the absolute minimum. In other cases the frequencies *may* become imaginary, but are not necessarily so.

Problem 1: Anisotropy can be simulated by an effective magnetic field which is "up" for the A spins and "down" for the B spins. This is achieved by adding to the applied field H a term $H_{\text{Anis.}} \times \exp i\mathbf{Q} \cdot \mathbf{R}_i$. Show that the solution to the linearized equations of motion is

$$\hbar\omega_{\mathbf{k}} = g\mu_B H \pm \sqrt{[Sv(\mathbf{k}) - Sv(\mathbf{Q}) - g\mu_B H_A][Sv(\mathbf{k} + \mathbf{Q}) - Sv(\mathbf{Q}) - g\mu_B H_A]}$$

Problem 2: *Ferrimagnetism*, in a certain crude approximation, may be conceived as a special case of antiferromagnetism in which the B spins have a magnitude S_B, different from the A spins, S_A. What are their equations of motion? Show that in the long wavelength limit the frequency does not depend linearly on $\mathbf{k}$ as in antiferromagnetics, Eq. (37), but *quadratically as in ferromagnets*, Eq. (10).[1]

MAGNETOSTATIC MODES

Walker[2] first derived an eigenvalue equation for the magnetostatic modes of an ellipsoidal ferromagnet. The point of view to be taken here is diametrically opposite from the preceding sections and, in fact, from the rest of the book. For in this section the exchange will be totally neglected. This is justified if very little incremental exchange energy comes into play at the long wavelengths of interest.

Let

$$\mathbf{M} = (M_x, M_y, M_s) \tag{38}$$

and

$$\mathbf{H} = (H_x, H_y, H_z - N_z M_s) \tag{39}$$

where N_z is the demagnetizing factor in the z direction, chosen along one of the principal axes. This factor takes into account the magnetostatic dipole-dipole interactions. In samples of arbitrary shape and composition, the demagnetizing factor is a

---

[1] H. Kaplan, *Phys. Rev.*, **86**: 121 (1952).

[2] L. R. Walker, *Phys. Rev.*, **105**: 390 (1957); also P. Fletcher and C. Kittel, *Phys. Rev.*, **120**: 2004 (1960). The saturation magnetization M_s is often denoted M_0.

tensor, $N_{ij}(\mathbf{r})$. Schlömann[3] has proved the interesting theorem $\sum_i N_{ii}(\mathbf{r}) = 4\pi$, when $\mathbf{r}$ is within the material, and zero otherwise. From this, the special cases of sphere, disk, long cylinder, etc., are obvious by symmetry; e.g., in a sphere $N_{11} = N_{22} = N_{33} = 4\pi/3$. The torque equation

$$\frac{d\mathbf{M}}{dt} = \gamma \mathbf{M} \times \mathbf{H} \qquad (40)$$

(where $\gamma =$ magnetomechanical ratio $= g\mu_B/\hbar = ge/2mc$) and the continuity equation

$$\mathbf{V} \cdot (\mathbf{H} + 4\pi\mathbf{M}) = 0 \qquad (41)$$

are soluble assuming $(\ddot{M}_x, \ddot{M}_y) = -\omega^2 (M_x, M_y)$. One introduces a magnetostatic potential ψ,

$$(H_x, H_y, 0) = \mathbf{V}\psi \qquad (42)$$

and two frequencies

$$\omega_i = \gamma(H_z - N_z M_s) \qquad \omega_s = 4\pi\gamma M_s \qquad (43)$$

Differentiating the equations (40) for M_x and M_y, with respect to x and y, we find

$$4\pi\mathbf{V} \cdot \mathbf{M} = \kappa \left(\frac{\partial^2 \psi}{\partial x^2} + \frac{\partial^2 \psi}{\partial y^2} \right) \qquad (44)$$

where

$$\kappa = \frac{\omega_i \omega_s}{\omega_i^2 - \omega^2} \qquad (45)$$

The equation of continuity is finally used to obtain the Walker equation,

$$(1 + \kappa)\left(\frac{\partial^2 \psi}{\partial x^2} + \frac{\partial^2 \psi}{\partial y^2} \right) + \frac{\partial^2 \psi}{\partial z^2} = 0 \qquad (46)$$

inside, and

$$\mathbf{V}^2 \psi = 0$$

outside the material. The boundary conditions are that

$$B_\perp \text{ and } \psi \qquad (47)$$

be continuous at the surface, which will determine the spectrum of eigenvalues $\kappa(\omega)$.

A fairly general solution of these equations is detailed in a recent review by Walker.[4]

---

[3] E. Schlömann, *J. Appl. Phys.*, **33**: 2825 (1962).
[4] L. R. Walker, in G. Rado and H. Suhl (eds.), *Magnetism*, Academic, New York, 1963, vol. I, chap. 8.

BROWN'S EQUATIONS

One drawback to the application of spin-wave theory to technical materials is that the assumptions about spatial homogeneity are not always obeyed. The competition between exchange energy, magnetostatic energy, magnetocrystalline energy, and the interaction with the applied field and magnetic impurities is what determines the equilibrium configuration. Spin waves are just the normal modes of vibration about an equilibrium situation which may be quite complex. For example, the existence in equilibrium of *domains* is the reason why ferromagnetic material does not always display a net magnetic moment to the outside world. Stroking a piece of iron with a magnet produces a permanent moment merely by lining up the magnetic domains which already existed in the iron. The fundamental size of domains, the shape and thickness of domain walls, the effect of chemical and physical inhomogeneities and impurities are but some of the interesting branches of study quite beyond the scope of the present introduction.

Here we shall examine some very basic nonlinear equations, that have been found to have extremely complicated and varied solutions. It is entirely possible that eventually they will explain the quasistatic properties of ferromagnetic materials, with quantum theory providing the values of some of the parameters.

We follow the discussion in a recent article by Shtrikman and Treves,[5] to which the reader is referred for further details and references. The exchange energy in the long wavelength approximation is E_x:

$$E_x = D \int [(\nabla v_x)^2 + (\nabla v_y)^2 + (\nabla v_z)^2] \, d\tau \qquad (48)$$

where
$$\mathbf{M} = \mathbf{v} M_s \qquad |\mathbf{M}| = M_s \qquad (49)$$

defines $\mathbf{v}$, the unit vector in the direction of the local magnetization. Because $E_x = 0$ when $\mathbf{v} = $ constant, we may deduce by comparison with Eqs. (10) and (1) that

$$D \simeq \frac{S}{6} \sum_j v_{ij} \mathbf{R}_{ij}^2 \qquad (50)$$

although for present purposes there is no need for such an estimate.

The self-magnetostatic energy E_m is

$$E_m = -\frac{1}{2} \int \mathbf{M} \cdot \mathbf{H}' \, d\tau = \frac{1}{8\pi} \int \mathbf{H}'^2 \, d\tau \qquad (51)$$

with
$$\nabla \cdot (\mathbf{H}' + 4\pi \mathbf{M}) = \nabla \cdot \mathbf{H}' + 4\pi M_s \nabla \cdot \mathbf{v} = 0 \qquad (52)$$

the equation of continuity, as in the previous section. The magnetocrystalline anisotropy energy E_k is

$$E_k = \int \omega(\mathbf{v}) \, d\tau \qquad (53)$$

---

[5] S. Shtrikman and D. Treves, in *ibid.*, vol. III, chap. 8, W. F. Brown, *Micromagnetics*, Interscience, New York, 1963.

the combined result of spin-orbit coupling and of the crystal field symmetry on the electronic orbits. It might involve a function such as

$$\omega(\mathbf{v}) = K(1 - v_z^2) \tag{54}$$

which would align the magnetization preferentially along the z axis, depending on the magnitude of K. In materials of cubic symmetry it might take the form

$$\omega(\mathbf{v}) = K(v_x^4 + v_y^4 + v_z^4) \tag{55}$$

But the precise form can only be obtained using quantum mechanics.[6]

The final term is the interaction energy with externally applied fields,

$$E_H = -M_s \int \mathbf{v} \cdot \mathbf{H} \, d\tau \tag{56}$$

The total energy $E = E_x + E_m + E_k + E_H$ is then minimized with respect to variations in $v_{x,y,z}$ subject to the constraint $\mathbf{v}^2 = 1$. Although this minimization will then ensure that spin waves have positive frequency (energy), it will sometimes also lead to solutions which are merely metastable as well as to the true minimum energy. The variational equations require that the torque on $\mathbf{v}$ vanish, i.e.,

$$\mathbf{v} \times \left[2D\nabla^2\mathbf{v} - \frac{\partial\omega}{\partial\mathbf{v}} + M_s(\mathbf{H} + \mathbf{H}') \right] = 0 \tag{57}$$

where

$$\frac{\partial\omega}{\partial\mathbf{v}} \equiv \left(\frac{\partial\omega}{\partial v_x}, \frac{\partial\omega}{\partial v_y}, \frac{\partial\omega}{\partial v_z} \right)$$

The boundary conditions at the surface of the material are

$$\mathbf{v} \times \frac{\partial\mathbf{v}}{\partial\hat{\mathbf{n}}} = 0 \tag{58}$$

and together with the differential equation above, comprise Brown's equations, the basis of "micromagnetics."

These coupled nonlinear equations must be solved numerically in general, although special solutions for ellipsoids, infinite cylinders, etc., are available as a guide. We shall present a demonstration that a multitude of solutions of these equations does exist.

Let us solve Eq. (57) by the *ansatz*

$$-2D\nabla^2\mathbf{v} - \frac{\partial\omega}{\partial\mathbf{v}} - M_s(\mathbf{H} + \mathbf{H}') = \lambda\mathbf{v} \tag{59}$$

Consider the special case: $\omega = 0$, $\mathbf{H} = $ constant, and $\lambda = $ constant. Taking the gradient of both sides of this equation, we obtain for $\psi \equiv \nabla \cdot \mathbf{v}$ the relation

$$-2D\nabla^2\psi + 4\pi M_s^2\psi = \lambda\psi \tag{60}$$

---

[6] Cf. F. Keffer and T. Oguchi, *Phys. Rev.*, 117: 718 (1960).

The reader will recognize this as mathematically identical to the Schrödinger equation of a particle of mass $m = (\hbar^2/4D)$, with $\lambda = 4\pi M_s^2$ corresponding to the nodeless solution. But unlike that in the case of the Schrödinger equation, the energy is not equal to the eigenvalue λ and generally, the lowest-energy solution corresponds to a function with the one or more nodes. It is by this sort of analysis that the existence of two or more magnetic domains in the ground state can be proved "from first principles."

Unfortunately Eq. (60) hides the dependence on external magnetic field. In the limit of large fields (note that near T_c *any* field is "large") there can only be one domain, and the magnetization must be everywhere parallel to the applied field. The growth and motion of domains and domain walls and of spin waves[7] can be studied by the time-dependent generalization of Brown's equations, which consists of replacing 0 on the right-hand-side of Eq. (57) by

$$\frac{M_s}{\gamma} \frac{d\mathbf{v}}{dt} \tag{61}$$

which would embrace Walker's equation as a special case.

Another generalization to increase the validity of this approach would be to include the entropy at finite temperatures and minimize the total *free energy*. (The meaning of this is discussed elsewhere in the book.) In any event, the detailed understanding of the macroscopic behavior of magnetic materials, based on a semimicroscopic approach of the type discussed above, is hopefully considered likely in the not-too-distant future.

---

[7] For a review on the subject of domains see J. F. Dillon, in G. Rado and H. Suhl (eds.), *Magnetism, op. cit.*, vol. III, chap. 9; also R. M. Bozorth's monumental *Ferromagnetism*, Van Nostrand, Princeton, N.J., 1951, chap. 11. However, the best introduction is a film available without charge from the Bell Telephone Company, entitled "The Formation of Ferromagnetic Domains." See also R. F. Soohoo's "General Spin-Wave Dispersion Relations," *Phys. Rev.*, **120**: 1978 (1960). Also valuable is the approach based on Green functions by J. F. Janak, "Quantum theory of domain wall motion," *Techn. Rept.* 187 (Lab. for Ins. Res., M.I.T., 1964), unpublished.

CHAPTER 6

MAGNONS: QUANTUM THEORY OF SPIN WAVES IN INSULATORS

There are some similarities between the elementary excitations in a ferromagnet and those of an elastic solid. In the latter, we know that if an atom is displaced from its equilibrium position, it will oscillate with the motion and frequencies associated with the harmonic oscillators, or *normal modes*, of the crystal. The effect of quantum mechanics on this motion is to quantize the amplitudes of the normal modes, with the resulting quanta known as *phonons*. The analogous normal modes, in materials with an ordered magnetic structure, are the spin waves of motion. When the quantum-mechanical nature of spins is taken into account, these are also quantized, with the quanta known as *magnons*. The thermodynamics of magnons is discussed on p. 242, and in the present chapter only properties of magnons at $T = 0\,°K$ will be discussed.

Just as the validity of the notion of lattice vibrations, and phonons, is restricted to small amplitude motion, so is that of spin waves and magnons. (The motion of an atom over distances greater than an interatomic separation leads to the creation of a pair of defects: a vacancy and an interstitial, which are of course completely outside the scope of the harmonic approximation.) We recall that the equations of motion of the spin waves were nonlinear and were practically impossible to solve when more than two modes were involved. But for small amplitude motion, these equations could be, and were, legitimately linearized and solved (indeed, in great generality because of the superposition principle). Quantum mechanically, the problem becomes even more difficult. For it is not possible to understand the magnons, which are the supposed elementary excitations of the magnetic system, without knowing something about the ground state of this system. But with certain notable exceptions, we do not know the ground state of any N-body system and so are not in any position to obtain the excited states except in some more or less crude approximation.

We shall discuss some of the well-known approximate theories, and develop these to the point where contact will be possible with the statistical mechanics developed elsewhere in this book. For definiteness, we shall be guided by semiclassical theory which is valid in the limit of large spins ($s \to \infty$). We shall also consider $s = \frac{1}{2}$ as a special case.

To retain the discussion within bounds, the present chapter with slight exceptions shall be limited to considerations of the Heisenberg Hamiltonian with nearest-neighbor interactions. This restricts the validity of the various results to insulators.

When the range of the interactions becomes large and the magnitudes of the spins are no longer constant but fluctuate because of electronic excitations—which is the case in metals—a somewhat different approach is required. And so the problem is reexamined in the following chapter.

SPIN WAVES AS HARMONIC OSCILLATORS

The approximation of spin waves by harmonic-oscillator functions, as opposed to a description "based on creation and annihilation operators, is to a considerable extent only a semantic one, but nevertheless is probably of use to those readers to whom harmonic oscillators are more intuitive than the techniques of quantum-mechanical field theory."[1]

For concreteness, let us assume (for the present) a ferromagnetic Heisenberg Hamiltonian with nearest-neighbor interactions, in an external homogeneous magnetic field H:

$$\mathscr{H} = -J \sum_{\substack{i>j=\text{nearest}\\\text{neighb}}} \mathbf{S}_i \cdot \mathbf{S}_j - Hg\mu_B \sum_i S_i^z \qquad J > 0 \tag{1}$$

where $\qquad \mathbf{S}_i \cdot \mathbf{S}_j \equiv S_i^x S_j^x + S_i^y S_j^y + S_i^z S_j^z = \frac{1}{2}(S_i^+ S_j^- + S_j^+ S_i^-) + S_i^z S_j^z$

Beside the isotropic interactions which are included therein, we may also consider anisotropic interactions of various origins. Those of lowest order are of "dipolar" structure,

$$\frac{1}{2} \sum_i \sum_j D_{ij} \frac{\mathbf{S}_i \cdot \mathbf{S}_j - 3\mathbf{S}_i \cdot \mathbf{r}_{ij} \mathbf{S}_j \cdot \mathbf{r}_{ij}}{\mathbf{r}_{ij}^2} \tag{2}$$

which represents the magnetic dipole-dipole interaction (the magnetostatic potential of each spin in the magnetic field of the others) with

$$D_{ij} = g^2 \mu_B^2 r_{ij}^{-3} \tag{3}$$

But there may be additional contributions to D_{ij}, principally those arising from the spin-orbit coupling mechanism.[2] These, like the exchange force itself, tend to be very short-ranged and are not so important in cubic materials as the magnetostatic long-ranged interaction, weak though the latter be. For concreteness, let us limit the present

---

[1] J. Van Kranendonk and J. H. Van Vleck, review article on the subject of spin waves, *Rev. Mod. Phys.*, **30**: 1 (1958). The present section has been modeled on this article.

[2] F. Keffer and T. Oguchi, *Phys. Rev.*, **117**: 718 (1960).

discussion to cubic materials and the anisotropic interactions to Eq. (3) in lowest order.

In Chapter 3 on angular momentum, we have shown how rigorous representations of spins may be constructed with the aid of harmonic-oscillator operators; and in particular, the Holstein-Primakoff representation, and approximations to it, were introduced. Let us review the latter from a new point of view. First, the spins are defined by the three nonvanishing matrix elements:

$$\langle n_i|S_i^x|n_i + 1\rangle = \langle n_i + 1|S_i^x|n_i\rangle^* = \tfrac{1}{2}\sqrt{(n_i + 1)(2s - n_i)}$$

$$\langle n_i|S_i^y|n_i + 1\rangle = \langle n_i + 1|S_i^y|n_i\rangle^* = -\tfrac{1}{2}i\sqrt{(n_i + 1)(2s - n_i)} \qquad (4)$$

$$\langle n_i|S_i^z|n_i\rangle = s - n_i, \qquad 0 \leqslant n_i \leqslant 2s$$

The quantum numbers of other spins (n_j) have been suppressed, because the components of $\mathbf{S}_i$ cannot change these; but all occupation numbers $n_1, n_2, \ldots , n_N$ must be specified in a definite state of the N spins, and therefore there are exactly $(2s + 1)^N$ such states if all spins have the same magnitude s. Note that to within the constant s, the quantum number n_i is merely the eigenvalue of S_i^z, and Eq. (4) is just the usual representation of angular momentum, p. 65.

Matrix elements of harmonic-oscillator operators have a structure very similar to the above. For example, if we symbolize the integrals

$$\int \psi_n^*(x_i)(\text{op})\psi_m(x_i)\,dx_i$$

where $\psi_n(x)$ is the nth harmonic-oscillator function, by means of the Dirac bracket notation, $\langle n|(\text{op})|m\rangle$, then for the very important operators x_i coordinate and p_i momentum, we have the well-known formulas

$$\langle n_i|x_i|n_i + 1\rangle = \langle n_i + 1|x_i|n_i\rangle^* = \sqrt{\frac{\hbar}{2m\omega}(n_i + 1)}$$

$$\hspace{10cm} (5)$$

$$\langle n_i|p_i|n_i + 1\rangle = \langle n_i + 1|p_i|n_i\rangle^* = -i\sqrt{\frac{\hbar m\omega}{2}(n_i + 1)}$$

and the quantum number n_i may also be defined as the eigenvalue of an operator, now the energy operator:

$$\left\langle n_i \left| \frac{p_i^2}{2m} + \tfrac{1}{2}m\omega^2 x_i^2 - \tfrac{1}{2}\hbar\omega \right| n_i \right\rangle = n_i\hbar\omega \qquad (6)$$

The connection between harmonic oscillator and spin is now established, by use of the dimensionless canonical variables P, Q, defined by

$$Q_i = x_i\sqrt{\frac{m\omega}{\hbar}} \qquad P_i = p_i\sqrt{\frac{1}{\hbar m\omega}} \qquad [P_i, Q_j] = \delta_{ij}\frac{1}{i} \qquad (7)$$

In terms of these,

$$\langle n_i|Q_i\sqrt{s}|n_i+1\rangle = \langle n_i+1|Q_i\sqrt{s}|n_i\rangle^* = \tfrac{1}{2}\sqrt{(n_i+1)2s}$$

$$\langle n_i|P_i\sqrt{s}|n_i+1\rangle = \langle n_i+1|P_i\sqrt{s}|n_i\rangle^* = -\tfrac{1}{2}i\sqrt{(n_i+1)2s} \qquad (8)$$

$$\langle n_i|s-\tfrac{1}{2}(P_i^2+Q_i^2-1)|n_i\rangle = s-n_i$$

which is quite similar to Eq. (4) for small values of the n_i.

Note that for values of $n_i \approx s$, the harmonic-oscillator approximation becomes quantitatively incorrect, although the matrix structure is still qualitatively similar to the correct one. The error however becomes catastrophic only when some n_i equals or exceeds the value $2s$, for although Eq. (8) continues to define matrix elements for the harmonic oscillators, there is no corresponding structure in angular-momentum space. So it must be understood that the whole theory which will be developed on the base of similarity between spins and harmonic oscillators will only be valid for low occupation numbers of every harmonic oscillator, and that it will be quite consistent to make whatever further linearization approximations are compatible with this.

In the Hamiltonian of Eq. (1) we now make the substitutions,

$$S_i^x = Q_i\sqrt{s},\ S_i^y = P_i\sqrt{s}, \qquad S_i^z = s - \tfrac{1}{2}(P_i^2+Q_i^2-1) \qquad (9)$$

and in accord with the above instructions, systematically discard cubic and quartic terms. One obtains the "linearized" Hamiltonian (i.e., the equations of motion are linearized, the Hamiltonian itself is of course quadratic):

$$\mathscr{H}_{\text{lin}} = E_0 + g\mu_B(H+H_0)\sum_i \tfrac{1}{2}(P_i^2+Q_i^2-1) - Js\sum_{\substack{\text{nearest}\\\text{neighb}}}(P_iP_j+Q_iQ_j) \qquad (10)$$

where

$$H_0 = \frac{Jsz}{g\mu_B} \qquad (11)$$

(z = number of nearest neighbors of any given spin) is precisely the molecular field constant which is introduced in the molecular field approximation, p. 228. The constant energy term

$$E_0 = -NHg\mu_Bs - \tfrac{1}{2}NzJs^2 \qquad (12)$$

is the energy of the completely saturated state in which all spins are parallel to the applied field.

The linearized Hamiltonian bears an obvious resemblance to the Hamiltonian of lattice vibrations, which also involves interactions among neighboring harmonic oscillators. An important difference arises from the presence of "velocity-dependent forces" P_iP_j, to which may be attributed the difference between the spectra of spin waves and that of sound.

We now make the plane-wave transformation:

$$Q_i = \frac{1}{\sqrt{N}} \sum_{\mathbf{k}} e^{i\mathbf{k}\cdot\mathbf{R}_i} Q_{\mathbf{k}} \qquad P_i = \frac{1}{\sqrt{N}} \sum_{\mathbf{k}} e^{i\mathbf{k}\cdot\mathbf{R}_i} P_{\mathbf{k}}$$

note $\qquad\qquad Q_{\mathbf{k}}^* = Q_{-\mathbf{k}}$ etc., $\qquad\qquad\qquad\qquad\qquad$ (13)

and $\qquad\qquad [P_k^*, Q_{\mathbf{k}'}] = \frac{\delta_{\mathbf{k}\mathbf{k}'}}{i}$

where $k_{x,\,y,\,z}$ = integer multiples of $2\pi/L$ in cube of volume $L^3 = Na^3$. A further discussion of this is given following Eq. (104). This diagonalizes the linear Hamiltonian, and we find

$$\mathscr{H}_{\text{lin}} = \sum_{\mathbf{k}} \tfrac{1}{2}(P_{\mathbf{k}}^* P_{\mathbf{k}} + Q_{\mathbf{k}}^* Q_{\mathbf{k}} - 1)\hbar\omega(\mathbf{k}) + E_0 = \sum_{\mathbf{k}} \mathfrak{n}_{\mathbf{k}} \hbar\omega(\mathbf{k}) + E_0 \qquad (14)$$

It may be verified that all harmonic operators, $P_{\mathbf{k}}$, $Q_{\mathbf{k}'}^*$, etc., which refer to different momenta commute, and so we have N new oscillators, which are uncoupled in the above approximation, and for each of which

$$\mathfrak{n}_{\mathbf{k}} \equiv \tfrac{1}{2}(P_{\mathbf{k}}^* P_{\mathbf{k}} + Q_{\mathbf{k}}^* Q_{\mathbf{k}} - 1) \qquad\qquad\qquad (15)$$

has eigenvalues $= 0, 1, 2, \ldots$. Fortunately, it is not at all necessary that each of these eigenvalues be restricted to the range $\ll s$, and it is sufficient for the validity of the linearization procedure merely that $\sum n_{\mathbf{k}} \ll Ns$.

As for the energies of the plane-wave "magnons,"

$$\boxed{\hbar\omega(\mathbf{k}) = Hg\mu_B + Js\sum_{\boldsymbol{\delta}}(1 - \cos\mathbf{k}\cdot\boldsymbol{\delta})} \qquad\qquad (16)$$

the sum runs over the vectors $\boldsymbol{\delta}$ which connect a typical spin to the z nearest neighbors with which it interacts. It is not surprising to find that this agrees precisely with the frequency which was previously derived by the semiclassical equations of motion, for indeed all that has been achieved so far is the quantization of this simple wave motion.

Let us now include the dipolar interactions, to see what is their effect on the magnon energy spectrum. Defining the direction cosines, α, β, and γ of the unit vector joining the spins,

$$\frac{\mathbf{r}_{ij}}{r_{ij}} = (\alpha_{ij}, \beta_{ij}, \gamma_{ij}) \qquad\qquad\qquad (17)$$

we find three contributions to the dipolar Hamiltonian of Eq. (2), after omitting cubic and higher terms outside the scope of the linearized theory:

$$\mathscr{H}_{d,\,0} = \tfrac{1}{2}s^2 \sum_i \sum_j D_{ij}(1 - 3\gamma_{ij}^2) \qquad\qquad\qquad (18)$$

$$\mathscr{H}_{d,1} = -3s^{3/2}\sum_i\sum_j D_{ij}(\alpha_{ij}\gamma_{ij}Q_j + \beta_{ij}\gamma_{ij}P_j) \tag{19}$$

$$\mathscr{H}_{d,2} = \tfrac{1}{2}s\sum_i\sum_j D_{ij}[1 - 3\alpha_{ij}^2)Q_iQ_j - 3\alpha_{ij}\beta_{ij}(Q_iP_j + P_iQ_j)$$

$$+ (1 - 3\beta_{ij}^2)P_iP_j - (1 - 3\gamma_{ij}^2)(P_i^2 + Q_i^2 - 1)] \tag{20}$$

For the purposes of the present discussion, it is convenient to imagine that our (cubic) ferromagnet has the shape of an ellipsoid with one of the principal axes in the z direction. The zeroth order term above is then readily interpreted in terms of the classical demagnetizing factor N_z,

$$N_z = a^3\sum_j \frac{1}{r_{ij}^3}(1 - 3\gamma_i^2) + \frac{4\pi}{3} \tag{21}$$

with α and β replacing γ above in the similar definitions of N_x and N_y. The sum in Eq. (21) being independent of $\mathbf{r}_i$, provided this point is within the crystal, we may express the zeroth order dipolar contribution in terms of the demagnetizing factor, introducing

$$M_0 = \frac{g\mu_B s}{a^3} = \text{saturation magnetization per unit volume} \tag{22}$$

where a^3 = volume per spin, and we find

$$\mathscr{H}_{d,0} = -\tfrac{1}{2}VM_0\left[\frac{4\pi}{3}M_0 - N_zM_0\right] \tag{23}$$

The factor in brackets is the sum of the Lorentz field $(4\pi/3)M_0$ and the demagnetizing field (which is uniform in an ellipsoidally shaped material) $-N_zM_0$, and is therefore the "effective field" acting at a given lattice site; $V = Na^3$ is the total volume.

Aside from this constant energy term and the constant E_0 in the exchange Hamiltonian, Eq. (10), the dynamic terms are the nontrivial terms in Eq. (10) plus $\mathscr{H}_{d,1}$ and $\mathscr{H}_{d,2}$, which all together are of the form

$$\mathscr{H} = \sum_{i,j}(V_{ij}P_iP_j + W_{ij}Q_iQ_j + U_{ij}P_iQ_j)$$

$$- 3s^{3/2}\sum_j\left[\left(\sum_i D_{ij}\alpha_{ij}\gamma_{ij}\right)Q_j + \left(\sum_i D_{ij}\beta_{ij}\gamma_{ij}\right)P_j\right] \tag{24}$$

allowing V_{ij}, W_{ij}, and U_{ij} to indicate schematically the coefficients in Eqs. (10) and (20). The linear term may be eliminated altogether by means of the canonical transformation,

$$P_i \to P_i + f_i \quad\text{and}\quad Q_i \to Q_i + g_i \tag{25}$$

where f_i, g_i are appropriately determined constants. As it happens, perturbation theory also converges for these linear terms, and the shift in ground-state energy which can be calculated by treating $\mathscr{H}_{d,1}$ by second-order perturbation theory agrees identically with the result of the exact canonical transformation above. Clearly the result is small, for it is second order in such quantities as

$$\sum_j D_{ij}\alpha_{ij}\gamma_{ij} \tag{26}$$

which vanish at any point $\mathbf{r}_i$ which is a point of symmetry. This would be at *every* point not on the surface of the cubic material if D_{ij} were not of such long range. Calculation of this term is left as an exercise for the reader, and it is likely to be a tedious one.

The complete elimination of $\mathscr{H}_{d,1}$ still leaves the first line in Eq. (24), that is $\mathscr{H}_{\text{lin}} + \mathscr{H}_{d,2}$ unaffected; and this is now to be diagonalized by a transformation, first to running waves, Eq. (13),

$$\mathscr{H} \to \tfrac{1}{2}\sum_{\mathbf{k}}[A(\mathbf{k})Q_{\mathbf{k}}^*Q_{\mathbf{k}} + B(\mathbf{k})P_{\mathbf{k}}^*P_{\mathbf{k}} + 2C(\mathbf{k})Q_{\mathbf{k}}^*P_{\mathbf{k}}] + \text{const} \tag{27}$$

where, with $\hbar\omega(\mathbf{k})$ given in Eq. (16),

$$A(\mathbf{k}) = \hbar\omega(\mathbf{k}) + A_{xx}(\mathbf{k}) - A_{zz}(0)$$

$$B(\mathbf{k}) = \hbar\omega(\mathbf{k}) + A_{yy}(\mathbf{k}) - A_{zz}(0) \tag{28}$$

$$C(\mathbf{k}) = A_{xy}(\mathbf{k})$$

The various A's are seen by comparison with the original equations, Eqs. (10) and (20), to be dipolar lattice sums,

$$A_{xx}(\mathbf{k}) = \frac{s}{N}\sum_{i,j} D_{ij}(1 - 3\alpha_{ij}^2)e^{i\mathbf{k}\cdot\mathbf{R}_{ij}} \tag{29}$$

and A_{yy}, A_{zz} are given similarly by replacing α_{ij} by β_{ij} or γ_{ij}.

Also
$$A_{xy}(\mathbf{k}) = \frac{-3s}{N}\sum_{i,j} D_{ij}\alpha_{ij}\beta_{ij}e^{i\mathbf{k}\cdot\mathbf{R}_{ij}} \tag{30}$$

and A_{xz} etc., can also be obtained by obvious permutations. These dipolar sums occur in several other problems of interest in solid-state physics, and have been investigated numerically quite thoroughly by Cohen and Keffer.[3] As an example of the size effect, these authors give $A_{xx}(\mathbf{k})$ calculated for a spherical sample of radius R, and $\mathbf{r}_i$ near the center of the crystal:

$$A_{xx}(\mathbf{k}) \sim \left(1 - 3\frac{k_x^2}{k^2}\right)\left(1 - \frac{3j_1(kR)}{kR}\right) \tag{31}$$

(omitting constant multiplicative factors). We see a not entirely unexpected phenomenon: as k is decreased to a value $\approx 10/R$, the dipolar sums in a finite crystal begin to differ significantly from their value in an infinite material, and the shape of the surface, and the position of the origin become of importance. However, precisely at

---

[3] M. H. Cohen and F. Keffer, "Dipolar Sums in Primitive Cubic Lattices," *Phys. Rev.*, **99**: 1128 (1955); "Dipolar Ferromagnetism at 0°K," *ibid.*, 1135.

$\mathbf{k} = 0$, this lattice sum approaches a well-defined limit related to the demagnetizing factor defined in Eq. (21), and we shall make use of this fact.

Assuming, then, that the coefficients $A(\mathbf{k})$, $B(\mathbf{k})$, and $C(\mathbf{k})$ are known, it is a straightforward matter to perform a canonical transformation to a new set of normal modes:

$$P'_{\mathbf{k}} = a_{\mathbf{k}}P_{\mathbf{k}} + b_{\mathbf{k}}Q_{\mathbf{k}} \qquad Q'_{\mathbf{k}} = c_{\mathbf{k}}Q_{\mathbf{k}} + d_{\mathbf{k}}P_{\mathbf{k}} \tag{32}$$

choosing the numerical coefficients $a_{\mathbf{k}}, \dots, d_{\mathbf{k}}$ so as to diagonalize the Hamiltonian yet preserve the canonical commutation relations,

$$[P'^*_{\mathbf{k}_1}, Q'_{\mathbf{k}_2}] = \frac{\delta_{\mathbf{k}_1, \mathbf{k}_2}}{i} \tag{33}$$

all other commutators $= 0$. The final result is,

$$\mathcal{H} = \sum \tfrac{1}{2}(P'^*_{\mathbf{k}}P'_{\mathbf{k}} + Q'^*_{\mathbf{k}}Q'_{\mathbf{k}} - 1)\hbar\omega'(\mathbf{k}) + \text{const} \tag{34}$$

with
$$\hbar\omega'(\mathbf{k}) = \sqrt{A(\mathbf{k})B(\mathbf{k}) - C^2(\mathbf{k})} \tag{35}$$

an anisotropic function of the direction of $\mathbf{k}$, as is seen from the definition of $A(\mathbf{k})$, $B(\mathbf{k})$, and $C(\mathbf{k})$ given in Eq. (28), and as plotted in Fig. 6.1.

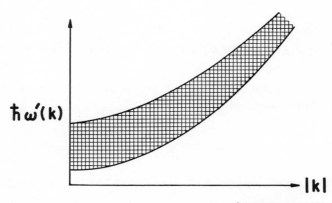

FIG. 6.1. Spectrum of energies $\hbar\omega'(\mathbf{k}) = \sqrt{A(\mathbf{k})B(\mathbf{k}) - C^2(\mathbf{k})}$. Spread, and gap at $k = 0$, are caused by anisotropy.

In *ferromagnetic resonance* an oscillating electromagnetic field is applied to the sample. Usually, the electromagnetic wavelengths are sufficiently long that only the $\mathbf{k} = 0$ mode need be considered, and we therefore obtain a resonance phenomenon at applied frequencies in the neighborhood of $\omega'(\mathbf{0})$. To calculate the magnitude of this frequency, it is reasonable to set $A_{xy}(0) = 0$ [note the resemblance of this quantity, defined in Eq. (30), to the small term discussed in Eq. (26)]; whereas the other coefficients may be expressed in terms of the various demagnetizing factors to obtain

$$\hbar\omega'(\mathbf{0}) = g\mu_B\sqrt{[H + (N_x - N_z)M_0][H + (N_y - N_z)M_0]} \tag{36}$$

This differs from a correct, empirically verified relation:

$$\hbar\omega(\mathbf{0}) = g\mu_B\sqrt{[H + (N_x - N_z)M][H + (N_y - N_z)M]} \tag{37}$$

apparently only because of the limited range of validity of the spin-wave theory, which breaks down when the true magnetization M becomes far less than the saturation magnetization M_0.

It should be noted that the effects of dipolar forces (and of pseudodipolar anisotropy which may be treated similarly) are limited to the long wavelengths. Thus the predictions of the theory based on the exchange Hamiltonian alone are sufficient for obtaining many of the gross properties of the ferromagnet, and also for calculating the spin-wave energy over most of the Brillouin zone excluding the neighborhood of $\mathbf{k} \cong \mathbf{0}$. See, for example, Fig. 6.1 for a plot of $\omega'(\mathbf{k})$, where a typical frequency spectrum is given. The actual, complicated anisotropic curves quickly become asymptotic to the idealized parabolic dispersion law of a pure exchange ferromagnet. This is a justification for the systematic neglect of dipolar and other anisotropic effects in many fundamental investigations of ferromagnetism and in the remainder of this chapter.

It should also be noted that for spherically shaped samples, $N_x = N_y = N_z = 4\pi/3$ (by Schlömann's theorem, p. 124) and therefore only the *applied* field H (if any) appears in the expression for the frequency of the long wavelength magnons. In the remainder of this book, the geometry will always be assumed to be spherical because of this convenient simplification of the formulas, which more than compensates for the loss of generality.

ONE-MAGNON EIGENSTATES IN FERROMAGNETS

So far, we have not taken advantage of the unique fact that the ferromagnetic ground state of $\mathscr{H}$ is known, where

$$\mathscr{H} = -J\sum_{\substack{i>j=\text{nearest}\\ \text{neighb}}} \mathbf{S}_i\cdot\mathbf{S}_j + Hg\mu_B\sum S_i^z \tag{38}$$

and the state in question consists of all spins "down" and will be hereinafter denoted

$$\Psi_0 = |0\rangle \qquad \text{energy } E_0 = -NHg\mu_B s - \tfrac{1}{2}NzJs^2 \tag{39}$$

the "vacuum" state. There are N different orthogonal and normalized states containing one spin deviate each:

$$\psi_i = (2s)^{-\frac{1}{2}}S_i^+|0\rangle \tag{40}$$

corresponding to all the choices of $\mathbf{R}_i$. Now, amazingly enough, one finds that when $\mathscr{H}$ is applied to the state ψ_i, it generates other states of the same type but no states with two or more spin deviations are introduced. This would not be the case if we had included the anisotropic interactions in the Hamiltonian, and it is a lucky property of the exchange Hamiltonian. Thus $\mathscr{H}$ may be diagonalized within the N-dimensional subspace of the functions of Eq. (40).

If, as we shall assume, there is translation invariance (and periodic boundary conditions), the energy is immediately diagonalized by the introduction of plane waves:

$$\psi_{\mathbf{k}} \equiv \frac{1}{\sqrt{N}} \sum_i e^{i\mathbf{k}\cdot\mathbf{R}_i} \psi_i \tag{41}$$

and the energy eigenvalues are

$$\langle \mathbf{k}|\mathscr{H}|\mathbf{k}\rangle = E(\mathbf{k}) = E_0 + \hbar\omega(\mathbf{k}) \tag{42}$$

with E_0 and $\hbar\omega(\mathbf{k})$ exactly as defined in the preceding section, Eqs. (12) and (16). This is precisely the result we would have obtained in the harmonic-oscillator approximation to the isotropic Hamiltonian discussed on p. 132 by setting $n_{\mathbf{k}} = 1$ and all other $n_{\mathbf{k}'} = 0$ [cf. Eq. (14)].

TWO-MAGNON STATES AND EIGENSTATES IN FERROMAGNETS

We have found that the ferromagnetic ground state, and the one-magnon eigenstates have precisely the energies predicted in the linearized harmonic-oscillator approximation. This is very encouraging, but not entirely unexpected in view of the agreement with the earlier semiclassical analysis. One might even be tempted to predict that states of two or more plane wave magnons are approximate eigenstates with an error of no more than $O(1/N)$. But this prediction is only partly correct, as we shall see in the present study of two-magnon states. For although most of the two-plane-wave magnon states undergo negligible scattering and energy shifts (which may be ascribed to the nonlinear corrections to the harmonic-oscillator approximation), a number of *bound states* appear. These are totally unexpected on the basis of our previous considerations, although they are of considerable importance in the demise of the spin-wave picture at or below the Curie temperature. Fortunately, the two-magnon problem can be solved exactly in any number of dimensions, and for any magnitude of the spins s, and so the relative importance of these bound states can be estimated under the various regimes.[4] Although the first modern approach to this problem in three dimensions is in the recent work of Hanus,[5] the one-dimensional problem had been solved a generation earlier, by the work of Bethe and Hulthén which we shall describe in some detail subsequently.

Let us introduce a notation, so that we may develop qualitative arguments for why nonlinearities should be insignificant at long wavelengths. This will be followed by an exact analysis, with particular bearing on the bound states. Let the normalized, two spin-deviate states be

$$\psi_{ij} = C_{ij} S_i^+ S_j^+ |0) = \psi_{ji} \tag{43}$$

---

[4] Cf. the discussions by M. Wortis, *Phys. Rev.*, **132**: 85 (1963) and N. Fukuda and M. Wortis, *J. Phys. Chem. Solids*, **24**: 1675 (1963).

[5] J. G. Hanus, M.I.T. report, 1962, unpublished.

For $s > \frac{1}{2}$, there are $\frac{1}{2}N(N + 1)$ states in this orthonormal set. For $s = \frac{1}{2}$, the non-existence of states of type ψ_{ii} reduces the number to $\frac{1}{2}N(N - 1)$. In any case, the energy and wavefunctions of N of these may be found without further calculation, using only previously derived results. To see this, consider the two-plane-wave states

$$\psi_{\mathbf{kk'}} = C \sum_{i, j} e^{i(\mathbf{k} \cdot \mathbf{R}_i + \mathbf{k'} \cdot \mathbf{R}_j)} \psi_{ij} = \psi_{\mathbf{k'k}} \tag{44}$$

where C is an appropriate normalization constant. When $\mathbf{k} = \mathbf{0}$, this is identical to a one-magnon eigenstate, to which the total spin raising operator $S^+ = \sum S_i^+$ has been applied:

$$\psi_{\mathbf{0k'}} = C'S^+\psi_{\mathbf{k'}} \tag{45}$$

Now while S^+ (as well as S^- and S^z) commutes with the exchange part of the Hamiltonian, it is a raising operator for S^z. (The total spin is, of course, a good angular momentum. Note that here, as elsewhere whenever convenient, $\hbar = 1$.)

$$[S^z, S^+] = S^+$$
$$\tag{46}$$
that is, $\qquad\qquad S^z(S^+\psi) = S^+(S^z + 1)\psi$

Thus, for the Hamiltonian $\mathscr{H}$ of Eq. (38),

$$\mathscr{H}\psi_{\mathbf{0k'}} = C'S^+(\mathscr{H} + g\mu_B H)\psi_{\mathbf{k'}} = (E(\mathbf{k'}) + g\mu_B H)\psi_{\mathbf{0k'}} \tag{47}$$

and therefore,

$$E(\mathbf{0k'}) = E_0 + \hbar\omega(\mathbf{k'}) + g\mu_B H = E_0 + \hbar\omega(\mathbf{k'}) + \hbar\omega(\mathbf{0}) \tag{48}$$

In the absence of an external field H, $\omega(\mathbf{0}) = 0$, and this particular two-magnon state is degenerate with the one-magnon state to which it is related. Since it is in any case an eigenstate, there is no "scattering," and there is no energy shift in a magnetic field beyond the simple change in Zeeman energy. By continuity, we may expect that if $\mathbf{k}$ and $\mathbf{k'}$ are reasonably small,

$$E(\mathbf{kk'}) = E_0 + \hbar\omega(\mathbf{k}) + \hbar\omega(\mathbf{k'}) + \text{corrections} \tag{49}$$

with corrections $O(1/N)$, as is usual in scattering processes; and this is indeed the computed result, if the states, Eq. (44), are taken as a set of variational states, and the energy is computed by the variational formula:

$$E(\mathbf{kk'}) = (\psi_{\mathbf{kk'}}^* |\mathscr{H}| \psi_{\mathbf{kk'}})/(\psi_{\mathbf{kk'}}^* |\psi_{\mathbf{k'k'}}) \tag{50}$$

But regardless of the qualitative merits of this argument, it is *not* mathematically correct for two important reasons, as follows:

1. The functions $\psi_{\mathbf{kk'}}$ are not orthogonal. Their failure to be orthogonal, although it is only to $O(1/N)$, leads to what Dyson has denoted the "kinematical interactions" which must be taken into account in solving for the energy eigenvalues. Note that for

$s = \frac{1}{2}$, the set of two-magnon states is *overcomplete*: there are $\frac{1}{2}N(N+1)$ functions to describe $\frac{1}{2}N(N-1)$ physical states, which shows that the functions in that case cannot all be orthogonalized, *even in principle*.

2. These functions do not diagonalize the Hamiltonian, except when **k** or **k'** vanish; to the extent that both wavevectors are finite, there is scattering, i.e., "dynamical interactions" in Dyson's language, which may even lead to bound states. To see this, it is necessary to go beyond the approximate treatment and diagonalize $\mathscr{H}$ exactly within the proper subspace of states ψ_{ij}. Fortunately, the Hamiltonian has no matrix elements connecting any of these states with a state outside the subspace, so that the problem is quite well defined, as it was in the case of the one-magnon eigenstates.

Let one of the eigenstates be defined by

$$\psi = \sum_{i > j} f_{ij} S_i^+ S_j^+ |0) \qquad f_{ji} \equiv f_{ij} \tag{51}$$

and let us solve the eigenvalue equation,

$$\mathscr{H}\psi = E\psi \tag{52}$$

for the amplitudes f_{ij}. There is no need to use the normalized configurations, Eq. (43), and the normalization constants may be considered absorbed in the f_{ij}. For the properties of the Hamiltonian are always such, that eigenstates belonging to different energies are automatically orthogonal. One takes the inner product of both sides of the Schrödinger equation, Eq. (52), with every state

$$(0|S_i^- S_j^- \tag{53}$$

to obtain the equations obeyed by the amplitudes f_{ij}, which are, respectively,

$$(E - E_0 - 2g\mu_B H - 2sJz)f_{ij} + s\sum_n (J_{nj}f_{in} + J_{in}f_{nj}) = \tfrac{1}{2}J_{ij}(f_{ii} + f_{jj} - f_{ij} - f_{ji}) \tag{54}$$

where each of the bonds $J_{ij}, J_{nj}, J_{in} = J$, when their respective scripts (ij) (nj) and (in) are nearest neighbor pairs, and vanish otherwise. This equation is correct for all values of s. Even when $s = \frac{1}{2}$, the unphysical amplitudes f_{ii}, etc., cancel between both sides of Eq. (54). In that case, nevertheless, it is convenient to define fictitious f_{ii} in order to simplify the calculation. There are at least two manners of doing this: The way chosen by Bethe in his solution of the linear chain problem (see section on his one-dimensional solution, p. 163) was to set $f_{ii} + f_{jj} = f_{ij} + f_{ji}$ when j, i are nearest neighbors, a sort of "boundary condition" ensuring that the homogeneous equation is obeyed at every pair of sites. But in general, it is more satisfactory to treat the special case $s = \frac{1}{2}$ on the same footing as $s > \frac{1}{2}$, and allow Eq. (54) with $i = j$ to *define* the unphysical amplitude f_{ii}. Note that in any event, J_{ij} vanishes unless i, j are nearest neighbors, so that with this exception, the right-hand side of Eq. (54) vanishes.

Periodic boundary conditions require

$$f_{ij} = f_{i\bar{j}} \qquad \text{where } \mathbf{R}_j - \mathbf{R}_{\bar{j}} \equiv (L, 0, 0) \qquad \text{or } (0, L, 0) \tag{55}$$

etc., for a volume L^3 in three dimensions, a square of area L^2 in two dimensions, or a length L in one dimension. And if the right-hand side of Eq. (54) did in fact vanish everywhere (instead of *nearly* everywhere), then the above boundary conditions could be met by the plane-wave solutions of Eq. (54),

$$f_{ij} = e^{i(\mathbf{k}\cdot\mathbf{R}_i + \mathbf{k}'\cdot\mathbf{R}_j)} + e^{i(\mathbf{k}'\cdot\mathbf{R}_i + \mathbf{k}\cdot\mathbf{R}_j)}$$

with the Cartesian components of the wavevectors

$$k_x, \dots \text{ and } k_x', \dots = \frac{2\pi}{L}\cdot\text{integer} \tag{56}$$

These *are* the eigenstates when either $\mathbf{k}$ or $\mathbf{k}' = \mathbf{0}$. For nonzero $\mathbf{k}, \mathbf{k}'$, it is necessary, because of the interaction, to take linear combinations of such plane waves to obtain the eigenstates. It is convenient to separate out the center of mass motion by introducing the center of mass wavevector, and coordinate,

$$\mathbf{K} = \mathbf{k} + \mathbf{k}' \qquad \mathbf{R} = \frac{\mathbf{R}_i + \mathbf{R}_j}{2} \tag{57}$$

and a relative wavevector, and coordinate,

$$\mathbf{q} = \frac{\mathbf{k} - \mathbf{k}'}{2} \qquad \mathbf{r} = \mathbf{R}_i - \mathbf{R}_j \tag{58}$$

and in terms of these, we may express f_{ij} in the form

$$f_{ij} = e^{i\mathbf{K}\cdot\mathbf{R}}\left\{\frac{1}{N}\sum_{\mathbf{q}} e^{i\mathbf{q}\cdot\mathbf{r}}f(\mathbf{q})\right\} \equiv e^{i\mathbf{K}\cdot\mathbf{R}}\{F(\mathbf{r})\} \tag{59}$$

and because this must also equal f_{ji}, we require

$$F(\mathbf{r}) = F(-\mathbf{r}) \qquad \text{or} \qquad f(-\mathbf{q}) = f(\mathbf{q}) \tag{60}$$

In postulating this form for the amplitudes f_{ij}, one has taken advantage of the fact that the interaction J_{ij} depends on the coordinates $\mathbf{R}_i$ and $\mathbf{R}_j$ only through the relative coordinate $\mathbf{r}$, and therefore the total momentum must be a constant of the motion. For each $\mathbf{K}$, the spectrum of eigenfunctions $f(\mathbf{q})$ must be separately determined, but it is easily verified that two solutions belonging to distinct values of $\mathbf{K}$ are orthogonal.

Assuming this form for f_{ij}, let us now determine the equations which are to be solved for the amplitudes $f(\mathbf{q})$, given $\mathbf{K}$. This is done by inserting the function of Eq. (59) into Eq. (54), and one finds

$$(E - E_0 - 2g\mu_B H - 2sJz)F(\mathbf{r}) + sJ\sum_{\boldsymbol{\delta}}\left(\cos\frac{\mathbf{K}}{2}\cdot\boldsymbol{\delta}\right)F(\mathbf{r}+\boldsymbol{\delta})$$

$$= J(\mathbf{r})\left[\left(\cos\frac{\mathbf{K}}{2}\cdot\mathbf{r}\right)F(0) - \frac{F(\mathbf{r}) - F(-\mathbf{r})}{2}\right] \tag{61}$$

Thus, $\mathbf{K}$ is a parameter in the equations; but for a *given* $\mathbf{K}$, such equations generate orthogonal solutions; and so, recalling the previous remark about different $\mathbf{K}$'s, we see that this procedure will yield the complete, orthonormal set of states for the problem. The vectors δ are the vectors connecting the central spin to its z nearest neighbors for which the interaction $J(\delta) = J \neq 0$. At all other distances $J(r)$ vanishes. Next, multiply the equation for $F(r)$ by $e^{-iq \cdot r}$, and sum on all r to obtain the equation for $f(q)$:

$$\left[E - E_0 - 2g\mu_B H - 2sJ \sum_\delta \left(1 - \cos \frac{K}{2} \cdot \delta \cos q \cdot \delta \right) \right] f(q)$$

$$= \frac{J}{N} \sum_\delta \cos q \cdot \delta \sum_k \left(\cos \frac{K}{2} \cdot \delta - \cos k \cdot \delta \right) f(k) \qquad (62)$$

We have made use of the usual identity,

$$\frac{1}{N} \sum_r e^{i(k-k') \cdot r} = \delta_{k, k'}$$

For brevity, define a symbol which will be used repeatedly:

$$\gamma_K(q) = E_0 + 2g\mu_B H + 2sJ \sum_\delta \left(1 - \cos \frac{K}{2} \cdot \delta \cos q \cdot \delta \right) \qquad (63)$$

This "unperturbed energy" is bounded between a minimum at $q = 0$, and a maximum at $q_x = \pi/a$ where x stands for all $z/2$ Cartesian axes, assuming $\cos K \cdot \delta/2 \geqslant 0$. The bound states, if they exist, must be outside the continuum of states lying between this maximum and minimum value of $\gamma_K(q)$ and so must lie either lower than

$$E_0 + 2g\mu_B H + 2sJ \sum \left(1 - \cos \frac{K}{2} \cdot \delta \right)$$

or higher than

$$E_0 + 2g\mu_B H + 2sJ \sum \left(1 + \cos \frac{K}{2} \cdot \delta \right)$$

The equations are further reduced by two steps. The first, is to define a $z/2$ dimensional vector $V = (V_x, \dots)$ by the equation,

$$V_x = \frac{1}{N} \sum_k \left(\cos \frac{K_x}{2} \delta_x - \cos k_x \cdot \delta_x \right) f(k) \qquad (64)$$

and similarly for the other components. Next, we divide both sides of Eq. (62) by $E - \gamma_K(q)$, multiply both sides by

$$\frac{1}{N} \left(\cos \frac{K_y}{2} \delta_y - \cos q_y \delta_y \right)$$

where y is also a Cartesian coordinate axis of the crystal, not necessarily the same one as x (except in one dimension!), and sum on q. The result is

$$V_y = \sum_{x=1}^{z/2} M_{y, x} V_x \qquad \text{or} \qquad V = M \cdot V \qquad (65)$$

where we now define the $(z/2) \times (z/2)$ dimensional matrix $M_{y, x}$

$$M_{y, x} = 2 \frac{J}{N} \sum_{\mathbf{q}} \frac{\cos q_x a \, [\cos(K_y/2)a - \cos q_y a]}{E - \gamma_{\mathbf{K}}(\mathbf{q})} \tag{66}$$

Equation (65) is a standard matrix eigenvalue equation, of dimensionality $z/2$, and the condition for the existence of solutions is the determinantal equation,

$$\mathrm{Det} \left\| \delta_{i, j} - M_{i, j} \right\| = 0 \qquad \left(i, j = 1, \ldots, \frac{z}{2} \right) \tag{67}$$

First, note that the unperturbed solutions are recovered if slightly displaced $O(1/N)$. This is seen by letting $E = \gamma_{\mathbf{K}}(\mathbf{q}') + N^{-1} e(\mathbf{q}')$, where $\mathbf{q}'$ is some allowed wavevector. The summand is infinite at $\mathbf{q}'$ if $e = 0$, unless the numerator accidentally vanishes. For small finite magnitude of e, the matrix $M_{i, j}$ can be made to assume any values between $-\infty$ and $+\infty$, and so, in particular, a small value $e(\mathbf{q}')$ can be found to satisfy the determinantal equation. The new solutions *interlace* the old and are known as scattering solutions, and their density (number of states per unit energy range) is proportional to N.

However, a solution can drop significantly below the continuum or rise above it. This is a bound state if in the limit $N \to \infty$ the energy of the state is independent of N. It will then follow that $F(\mathbf{r})$ extends over only a finite distance (e.g., will decay like e^{-r/r_0} at large distances) and the wavefunction can be normalized without regard to N, in this limit (by analogy with localized electronic wavefunctions or localized modes of vibration around impurities in an elastic solid.)

This localization distinguishes the bound states from scattering solutions, for the latter extend over the entire crystal, and like the plane waves, which are their unperturbed counterparts, possess normalization constants $\propto N^{-\frac{1}{2}}$. Thermodynamically, the quantity of interest is the energy. The fact that the scattering solutions interlace the unperturbed ones means that the density of states has remained constant to $O(1/N)$. Only the bound states make a significant change in this picture, due to the appearance of new energy levels outside the framework of linearized, noninteracting spin-wave theory. Let us study these bound states then, and by taking advantage of the fact that they do not depend on the size of the crystal, replace

$$\frac{1}{N} \sum_{\mathbf{q}} \qquad \text{by} \qquad \left(\frac{a}{2\pi} \right)^{z/2} \int_{\mathrm{B.z.}} d\mathbf{q}$$

where the Brillouin zone (B.z.) of the simple-(hyper-) cubic structure extends from $-\pi/a \leqslant q_x \leqslant +\pi/a$, for x any of the $z/2$ Cartesian components.

BOUND STATES IN ONE DIMENSION

The easiest application of this theory is to the one-dimensional linear chain. The determinantal equation reduces to

$$1 = M_{x, x} = \frac{Ja}{\pi} \int_{-a\pi}^{a\pi} dq \frac{\cos qa(\cos \frac{1}{2}Ka - \cos qa)}{(E - E_0 - 2g\mu_B H - 4sJ) + 4sJ \cos \frac{1}{2}Ka \cos qa} \tag{68}$$

With the sum replaced by an integral, this is an algebraic equation for the bound-state energy of E, which the following standard integral formulas help to evaluate:

$$\frac{1}{\pi}\int_0^\pi \frac{dx}{A + B\cos x} = \frac{1}{\sqrt{A^2 - B^2}} \quad \text{and} \quad \frac{1}{\pi}\int_0^\pi \frac{dx\,\cos^2 x}{A + B\cos x} = \frac{A}{B^2}\left[\frac{A}{\sqrt{A^2 - B^2}} - 1\right]$$

For greater clarity, one introduces dimensionless parameters. Let,

$$A = (E - E_0 - 2g\mu_B H - 4sJ)\,/4sJ\cos\tfrac{1}{2}Ka$$

$$x = qa$$

(69)

and therefore, Eq. (68) becomes

$$1 = \frac{1}{2s\pi}\int_0^\pi dx\,\frac{1}{A + \cos x}\left(\cos x - \frac{\cos^2 x}{\cos\tfrac{1}{2}Ka}\right)$$

$$= \frac{1}{2s}\left(1 - \frac{A}{\sqrt{A^2 - 1}}\right)\left(1 + \frac{A}{\cos\tfrac{1}{2}Ka}\right)$$

(70)

There are solutions only for $A < -1$, proving that the bound state exists only below the continuum, and that there is no bound state above the continuum (which would correspond to positive values of A). This is not surprising in view of the fact that the effective interaction is attractive: two spin deviations have lower energy when they are nearest neighbors than when they are farther apart.

On the other hand, one might have thought of the effective interaction when two spin deviations occur on the same site, as a repulsive (or "hard core") potential which could lead to bound states above the continuum. The actual calculation shows this latter point of view to be false.

The equation is easiest to solve analytically when $s = \tfrac{1}{2}$, in which case we find

$$A\cos\tfrac{1}{2}Ka = -\tfrac{1}{2}(1 + \cos^2\tfrac{1}{2}Ka) = -1 + \tfrac{1}{2}\sin^2\tfrac{1}{2}Ka$$

(71)

and therefore,

$$E = E_0 + 2g\mu_B H + J\sin^2\tfrac{1}{2}Ka \qquad \text{bound state}$$

(72)

This may be compared to the lowest energy of a scattering state, i.e., the bottom of the continuum, which occurs at $\mathbf{q} = 0$ [cf. Eq. (63)]:

$$E_{\min}(\mathbf{q} = 0) = E_0 + 2g\mu_B H + 4J\sin^2\tfrac{1}{4}Ka$$

(73)

The bound state lies lower than this by a "binding energy" δE in the amount of

$$\delta E = 4J\sin^2\tfrac{1}{4}Ka - J\sin^2\tfrac{1}{2}Ka$$

which ranges from

$$\frac{J}{4}\left(\frac{Ka}{2}\right)^4 \quad \text{for } Ka \ll 1 \quad \text{to } J \quad \text{for } Ka = \pi$$

A schematic plot is given in Fig. 6.2 for arbitrary value of the spin s [see also Eqs. (75) and ff. for further discussion on the bound states].

It is significant that bound states appear for arbitrarily small K, hence at arbitrarily small excitation energy in zero external field. As a consequence, linear spin-wave theory is not even approximately applicable to a model one-dimensional Heisenberg ferromagnet, because there is no range of momentum space, hence no range of temperature,

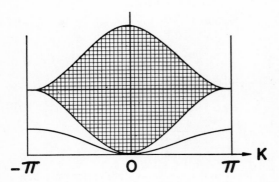

FIG. 6.2. Energy of 2-magnon states in linear chain. Shading indicates continuum, single line represents bound state.

over which the nonlinearities may be neglected. This is, of course, in perfect accord with results mentioned elsewhere indicating the lack of long-range order in the linear chain (and therefore the breakdown of any simple approximations). We return to the one-dimensional chain shortly, but first consider bound states in the square and cubic lattices.

BOUND STATES IN TWO AND THREE DIMENSIONS

The results obtained by Wortis[6] in two dimensions show that there is at least one bound state below the continuum for all $\mathbf{K}$, and that for some $\mathbf{K}$ there may be *two* bound states. In three dimensions, he found that there are no bound states whatever for small $\mathbf{K}$, and it is only for sufficiently large values of $\mathbf{K}$ that one, two, or up to a maximum of *three* bound states make their appearance. This is a most important result, for the absence of any bound-state solution over a significant range of $\mathbf{K}$ is what gives some validity to the linear spin-wave theory in three dimensions, even though the linearization is not valid in one or two dimensions.

Before considering the region of small $\mathbf{K}$, which because of the low spin-wave and bound-state energies will be of the greatest importance in thermodynamics, let us first examine the special case when all components of K are equal to π/a, the maximum possible value, in which case

$$\cos\frac{K_x}{2}a = \cos\frac{K_y}{2}a = \cos\frac{K_z}{2}a = \cos\frac{\pi}{2} = 0$$

---

[6] *Op. cit.*

and all the integrals in the eigenvalue equation become trivial. Because the denominators are now all constant, the nondiagonal matrix elements $M_{x,y}$ defined in Eq. (66) all vanish, while the diagonal ones are all equal. The bound state will therefore be $z/2$ fold degenerate. Note that the continuum has collapsed to a single point at

$$\gamma_\pi \equiv \gamma_\pi(\mathbf{q}) \equiv E_0 + 2g\mu_B H + 2sJz \tag{74}$$

and therefore the integral equation reduces to an algebraic one. The bound-state solutions of Eq. (67) are easily found to have energy

$$E = \gamma_\pi - J \tag{75}$$

by solving this algebraic equation. The bound state is identified as the complex formed by keeping the two spin deviates nearest neighbors; and the degeneracy can be understood as the $z/2$ distinct directions along which two spins can be nearest neighbors.

The existence of at least one bound state for every value of $\mathbf{K}$ in *two dimensions* is guaranteed by the behavior of the various integrals near $\mathbf{q} = 0$. Let us denote the energy of the lowest state in the continuum by E_{min}, then the integrands in the vicinity of $\mathbf{q} = 0$ all contribute on the order of

$$\approx \int \frac{\text{numerator}}{E - E_{min} - Dq^2} q\,dq$$

for suitable positive constant D, and appropriate nonvanishing numerator. This contribution, as a function of E, ranges from zero to $-\infty$ as E varies from $-\infty$ to E_{min}, and in the limit, $E_{min} - E \equiv \delta E \to 0$, varies as $\approx \log \delta E$. Thus one expects, even without the benefit of explicit calculation, that the "binding energy" δE will depend exponentially on the various parameters. Indeed, for $K_x = K_y \approx 0$, Wortis finds

$$\delta E \sim e^{-2\pi sC/1 - C}$$

where $C = \cos(K_x/2)a$, and for more general $\mathbf{K}$ he obtains the binding energy in terms of various elliptic integrals.

Turning finally to the more realistic case of a three-dimensional structure, for which the integrals cannot be evaluated analytically, one may find it advantageous to represent them by Laplace transform methods. That is, the substitution

$$\frac{1}{D} = \int_0^\infty dt\, e^{-Dt}$$

combined with the definition of the Bessel functions of imaginary argument (cf. p. 246),

$$I_n(z) = \frac{1}{\pi} \int_0^\pi e^{z \cos x} \cos nx\, dx$$

permits the replacement of three-dimensional integrals by a rapidly converging one-dimensional integral. But these substitutions are not required to determine the threshold for the existence of a bound-state solution.

For this, we may presume $K_x = K_y = K_z$, which yields the lowest edge of the continuum and is more likely to produce the bound state than some less isotropic direction. In this case the three diagonal matrix elements $M_{i,\,i}$ are all equal, and the off-diagonal elements are also equal to each other. Expansion of the determinant gives an eigenvalue equation:

$$(1 - M_{x,\,x} - 2M_{x,\,y})(1 - M_{x,\,x} + M_{x,\,y})^2 = 0 \tag{76}$$

The lowest solutions occur for the single root, i.e., for

$$1 = M_{x,\,x} + 2M_{x,\,y}$$

$$= \frac{2J}{N} \sum_{\mathbf{q}} \frac{\cos q_x a [3 \cos(K_x/2)a - \cos q_x a - 2 \cos q_y a]}{E - E_0 - 2g\mu_B H - 12sJ + 4sJ[\cos q_x a + \cos q_y a + \cos q_z a]\cos(K_x/2)a}$$

$$= \frac{E - E_0 - 2g\mu_B H - 12sJ \, \sin^2(K_x/2)a}{24s^2 J \cos^2(K_x/2)a} \left[1 - \frac{E - E_0 - 2g\mu_B H - 12sJ}{N} \sum_{\mathbf{q}} \frac{1}{E - \gamma_{\mathbf{K}}(\mathbf{q})} \right] \tag{77}$$

Use has been made only of the cubic symmetry, and of the equality of the three components of $\mathbf{K}$ to arrive at the last, simplified expression. The bound-state threshold occurs for that $\mathbf{K}$ at which E just drops below the bottom of the continuum at $\gamma_{\mathbf{K}}(0)$. This occurs for

$$E = E_0 + 2g\mu_B H + 24sJ \sin^2 \frac{K_x}{4} a$$

$$= E_0 + 2g\mu_B H + 24s^2 J(2s + .516386)^{-1} \tag{78}$$

in which we have anticipated Eq. (80) to arrive at the second line.

Replacing the sum in Eq. (77) by an integral in the standard manner, we use the first line to determine the threshold value of K_x:

$$1 = \frac{-1 + \cos(K_x/2)a}{2s \cos(K_x/2)a} (1 - W) \tag{79}$$

where W is Watson's integral (see *Note* at end of section):

$$W = \frac{1}{(2\pi)^3} \iiint_{-\pi}^{\pi} \frac{dq_x \, dq_y \, dq_z}{1 - \frac{1}{3}(\cos q_x + \cos q_y + \cos q_z)} = 1.516386$$

Thus, combining this result with that of Eq. (75), we see that the bound state exists in the range

$$0 \leqslant \cos \frac{K_x}{2} a \leqslant \frac{.516386}{2s + .516386} \tag{80}$$

provided $K_x = K_y = K_z$. This results in $140° \leqslant K_x a \leqslant 180°$ for $s = \frac{1}{2}$, $157° \leqslant K_x a \leqslant 180°$ for $s = 1$, $167° \leqslant K_x a \leqslant 180°$ for $s = 2$, etc. As K is increased beyond the minimum, the other solutions make their appearance. For example, we have already found that there are three solutions at $K_x a = K_y a = K_z a = 180°$, which is the largest total momentum wavevector in the positive direction. This small range of momentum space over which bound-state solutions are available, even in the most favorable case of spins one-half, is in sharp contrast with the results of the one- and two-dimensional calculations; and in the correspondence limit $s \to \infty$, the bound states simply disappear.

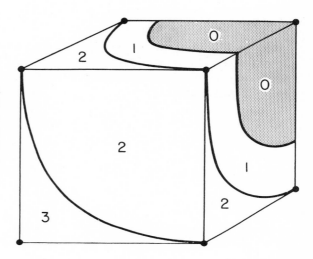

FIG. 6.3. Section of Brillouin zone showing regions of 0, 1, 2, and 3 bound-state solutions for two spin waves, $s = \frac{1}{2}$. For $s > \frac{1}{2}$, the region of 0 solutions grows, and for $s \to \infty$ occupies the entire Brillouin zone. (Sketch after Wortis.)

In Fig. 6.3, a sketch is given of the regions in which one, two, and three distinct bound states exist. Even without detailed numerical calculations, one may suspect that although the binding energy increases with $\mathbf{K}$, so does the total energy of the bound states, and Eq. (78) therefore gives the minimum energy for a bound state in three dimensions.

Note: Concerning Watson's integral:

... it is strange that any one of his own free will would have investigated such integrals. Actually van Peijpe encountered the integral in constructing a theory of ferromagnetic anisotropy based on spin wave theory. Unable to evaluate it in closed form, he resorted to graphical integration. H. A. Kramers, van Peijpe's thesis supervisor, then put the problem ... to R. H. Fowler who communicated it to G. H. Hardy, whereupon, to quote Watson, "the problem then became common knowledge in Cambridge and subsequently in Oxford whence it made the journey to Birmingham without difficulty."[7]

ONE-MAGNON EIGENSTATES IN HEITLER-LONDON SOLID

It is not to be supposed that the Heisenberg Hamiltonian has exactly the same spectrum of solutions as the Heitler-London Hamiltonian, and the reason lies in the nonorthogonality of the electronic wavefunctions used in this theory. As this point was discussed in the chapter on exchange, we refer to that chapter for further elaboration, and proceed forthwith to calculate the one-magnon eigenstates in the H-L theory. This is simple to do *in principle,* for by translational symmetry the eigenfunctions are plane

---

[7] E. W. Montroll, "Lattice Statistics," in E. F. Beckenback (ed.), *Applied Combinatorial Mathematics.*

waves. We then obtain the energies as functions of the interaction and normalization parameters.

Suppose, then, there is a single unpaired electron at each of N sites labeled $\mathbf{R}_i$, and that we use as the basic product functions

$$\psi(m_1, \ldots, m_N) = \prod_{j=1}^{N} \varphi(\mathbf{r}_j - \mathbf{R}_j)\chi_{m_j}(\xi_j) \tag{81}$$

where r_j and ξ_j are the space and spin coordinates of the electron, respectively, and the 2^N sets of m_j's $(\pm\frac{1}{2})$ provide the same number of degrees of freedom as in a similar Heisenberg model. In evaluating energy, normalization, etc., the totally antisymmetrized wavefunctions

$$\Psi = \frac{1}{\sqrt{N!}} \sum_{\mathscr{P}} (-1)^{\mathscr{P}}\mathscr{P}\psi(m_1, \ldots, m_N) \tag{82}$$

must be used. Let us denote the totally ferromagnetic product function by ψ_0,

$$\psi_0 \equiv \psi(-\tfrac{1}{2}, \ldots, -\tfrac{1}{2}) \tag{83}$$

and one spin-deviate states by ψ_i,

$$\psi_i = S_i^+ \psi_0 \qquad i = 1, \ldots, N \tag{84}$$

and use the same indices on the corresponding totally antisymmetrized (determinantal) wavefunctions, Ψ_0 and Ψ_i, constructed from the above by means of the prescription (82). Because of the overlap of the one-electron wavefunctions, the Ψ_i do not form an orthonormal set. Therefore, instead of the usual Schrödinger equation, the energy variation principle yields an equation involving an overlap matrix $\mathbf{\Omega}$

$$\mathscr{H}_{ii}f_i + \sum_{j \neq i} \mathscr{H}_{ij}f_j = E\Big(\mathbf{\Omega}_{ii}f_i + \sum_{j \neq i} \mathbf{\Omega}_{ij}f_j\Big) \tag{85}$$

for an eigenfunction assumed of the form

$$\Phi = \sum_i f_i\Psi_i \tag{86}$$

The Hamiltonian matrix elements are

$$\mathscr{H}_{ij} = \int d\tau\Psi_i^*\mathscr{H}\Psi_j \tag{87}$$

and the overlap matrix elements are simply

$$\mathbf{\Omega}_{ij} = \int d\tau\Psi_i^*\Psi_j \tag{88}$$

including the spin variables in both integrations.

$\mathscr{H}$ presumably depends on the spatial coordinates only, and is translationally invariant. Therefore both sets of matrix elements depend on i and j only through the relative distance $\mathbf{R}_{ij}$, and the equations can be solved by setting

$$f_i = e^{i\mathbf{k}\cdot\mathbf{R}_i} \tag{89}$$

Consequently, the one-magnon eigenvalues $E(k)$ are simply ratios,

$$E(\mathbf{k}) = \frac{\sum \mathscr{H}_{ij}e^{i\mathbf{k}\cdot\mathbf{R}_{ij}}}{\sum \Omega_{ij}e^{i\mathbf{k}\cdot\mathbf{R}_{ij}}} = \frac{\mathscr{H}(\mathbf{k})}{\Omega(\mathbf{k})} \tag{90}$$

By measuring these energies relative to the ferromagnetic energy ($\mathbf{k}=0$), we find

$$E(\mathbf{k}) - E(0) = \frac{\Omega(0)[\mathscr{H}(\mathbf{k}) - \mathscr{H}(0)] - \mathscr{H}(0)[\Omega(\mathbf{k}) - \Omega(0)]}{\Omega(0)[\Omega(0) + (\Omega(\mathbf{k}) - \Omega(0))]} \approx \frac{D\mathbf{k}^2 + O(\mathbf{k}^4)}{1 + O(\mathbf{k}^2)} \tag{91}$$

The various parameters $\mathscr{H}_{ij}$ and Ω_{ij} may be evaluated by the theory of determinants (cf. section on "the method of Löwdin and Carr" in the nonorthogonality problem; however the present integrals are somewhat more difficult to evaluate than the ones solved in that section). They have reasonable magnitudes (i.e., they are not off by factors of N); and in fact Eq. (91) would be in exactly the form of the Heisenberg theory result given in Eqs. (42) and (16) of the present chapter, were it not for the $\mathbf{k}$-dependence of the denominator. At long wavelengths this affects k^4 (and higher-order) terms in the expansion of $E(\mathbf{k}) - E(0)$, and may eventually lead to some experimental determination of the importance of effects of nonorthogonality.

It may be presumed that a linearized version of H-L theory can be constructed which for many magnons in three dimensions would reproduce some of the results of "harmonic-oscillator spin-wave" theory in the Heisenberg ferromagnet. But this has not yet been attempted. Nor have the two-magnon problem and the existence of two-magnon bound states been studied in the H-L theory, although this would involve but slight generalizations of the analysis of the preceding section. In Chapter 7 the Heisenberg Hamiltonian is derived by means of perturbation theory, an approach which makes it possible to identify the discrepancies with the H-L theory as the result of third- and higher-order perturbation corrections. The "nonorthogonality" can be seen to arise from a one-electron transfer operator, in lowest approximation. Thus the H-L scheme is an approximation which goes slightly beyond the Heisenberg Hamiltonian without being in any way more fundamental, and suffers in comparison, because of its greater mathematical difficulty.

NONLINEAR SPIN-WAVE THEORY

A recent pioneering analysis of the low-lying states of the Heisenberg Hamiltonian by Dyson[8] set forth much of what is definitively known on the subject today. The program of nonlinear spin-wave theory may be stated as follows: It is desired to

---

[8] F. J. Dyson, *Phys. Rev.*, **102**: 1217 and 1230 (1956).

go beyond the harmonic-oscillator approximation, and to calculate the nonlinear corrections for the three-dimensional Heisenberg ferromagnet in a simple and fruitful manner. This is not necessarily done in order to develop a theory describing ferromagnets at arbitrary temperatures, for desirable as this goal might seem, it might not be attainable by any simple yet accurate technique. Rather the corrections are calculated to provide a purely internal and theoretical estimate of the limits of validity of harmonic-oscillator theory. In this way it may be known whether any experimentally observed deviations are in accord with the Heisenberg model or if the nonlinearities arise from other sources.

In classical theory, we have already observed that as the amplitude of a spin wave is increased its frequency decreases. This leads up to expect the following features in a nonlinear spin-wave theory: a change (renormalization) of the frequencies with increasing excitations of the system, and a concomitant lifetime (or finite free path) of the plane-wave quasinormal modes. Here we shall give a somewhat oversimplified calculation of these effects, but there exist review articles in which this problem is discussed[9] and the quantitative merits of various schemes analyzed.

Spin waves are harmonic oscillators in a first approximation, therefore it is desirable to introduce Bosons into the Heisenberg Hamiltonian. Let us examine first how this might be done for spins one-half taking spin "down" as the reference state, or vacuum. The two eigenstates of S_i^z are thus

$$|0) \text{ and } S_i^+|0) \equiv |1) \qquad \text{we also have} \qquad |0) = S_i^-|1) \qquad (92)$$

and in addition,

$$S_i^z = S_i^+ S_i^- - \tfrac{1}{2} \qquad \text{and} \qquad S_i^-|0) = 0 \qquad (93)$$

all of which are similar to properties of harmonic-oscillator operators. What prevents a simple substitution of Boson operators into the Heisenberg Hamiltonian is a final equation:

$$S_i^+|1) = 0 \qquad \text{that is, } (S_i^+)^2 = (S_i^-)^2 = 0 \qquad (94)$$

This is the "kinematical" restriction which conserves the spin magnitude $S^2 = S(S+1) = \tfrac{3}{4} = \text{constant}$, and of course it is not obeyed by Boson operators. But we have seen how the Schwinger, Holstein-Primakoff, and other techniques may be used to express spin operators as nontrivial functions of some idealized Boson operators, and so we know that the desired procedure can be carried through. Let us first introduce the raising (stepping-up) operator a_i^* and the lowering operator a_i, and a complete set of harmonic-oscillator occupation-number states $|n)$ such that

$$a_i^*|n) = \sqrt{n+1}\,|n+1) \qquad a_i|n) = \sqrt{n}\,|n-1)$$

$$a_i|0) = 0 \quad \therefore \quad a_i^* a_i|n) = n|n) \qquad (95)$$

$$|n) \equiv \frac{1}{\sqrt{n!}}\,(a_i^*)^n|0)$$

---

[9] L. R. Walker, in G. Rado and H. Suhl (eds.), *Magnetism*, Academic, New York, 1963, vol. I, chap. 8; F. Keffer, "Spin Waves," in *Handbuch der Physik*, to be published.

It is convenient to define the Boson number operator,

$$\mathfrak{n}_i = a_i^* a_i \tag{96}$$

having the eigenvalue n_i indicated in the state $|n_i\rangle$. To introduce the cutoff on the spectrum corresponding to Eq. (94), we must now find some projection operators.

An operator which has zero eigenvalue on every state of the ith harmonic oscillators except on the ground state will be denoted the vacuum projection operator $X_i(0)$:

$$X_i(0) \equiv 1 - a_i^* a_i + \frac{1}{2!} a_i^* a_i^* a_i a_i - \cdots$$

$$= \sum_{r=0}^{\infty} (-1)^r \frac{1}{r!} (a_i^*)^r (a_i)^r \tag{97}$$

such that $\qquad X_i(0)a_i^* \equiv 0 \qquad$ and $\qquad X_i(0)|0\rangle = |0\rangle$

We use it to construct the operator which has zero eigenvalue on every state but $|1\rangle$, denoted

$$X_i(1) = a_i^* X_i(0) a_i$$

More generally the projection operator for any state $|n\rangle$ is

$$X_i(n) = \frac{1}{n!} (a_i^*)^n X_i(0) a_i^n \tag{98}$$

By comparing the equations for $s = \frac{1}{2}$, Eqs. (92) to (94), with those for Bosons, Eqs. (95) and (96), we can now see that all that is required to make them identical is the introduction of these projection operators, viz.,

$$S_i^+ \equiv a_i^* X_i(0) \qquad S_i^- \equiv a_i[X_i(0) + X_i(1)] \equiv a_i X_i(0, 1) \qquad S_i^z \equiv a_i^* a_i - \tfrac{1}{2} \tag{99}$$

It is convenient to indicate the *joint* projection operator for states $|0\rangle$ and $|1\rangle$, $[X_i(0) + X_i(1)]$, by $X_i(0, 1)$, an obvious notation.

Problem 1: Show that $(S_i^-)^* = S^+$, where these are given in Eq. (99) and the asterisk (*) indicates Hermitean conjugation.

Before proceeding with the Boson operators, recall the commutation relations from which Eq. (95) may be derived:

$$a_i a_j^* - a_j^* a_i \equiv [a_i, a_j^*] = \delta_{i,j} \qquad [a_i, a_j] = [a_i^*, a_j^*] = 0 \tag{100}$$

Any transformation which preserves these properties will be an allowed *canonical* transformation, such as the unitary or, more generally, the similarity transformations.

The representation, Eq. (99), is now introduced into the Heisenberg Hamiltonian. In addition, a small positive quantity ε is introduced in such a manner that any unphysical states will have energy $\sim 1/\varepsilon$, which can be made indefinitely great. Thus, for spins one-half and ferromagnetic bonds $J_{ij} > 0$,

$$\mathscr{H} = -\frac{1}{2} \sum_i \sum_j J_{ij} \left[a_i^* a_j X_i(0) X_j(0, 1) + \lim_{\varepsilon \to 0^+} \frac{(\mathfrak{n}_i)(\mathfrak{n}_j)}{X_j(0, 1) - \varepsilon} \right]$$
$$+ E_0 + \sum_i \mathfrak{n}_i \left(g\mu_B H + \frac{1}{2} \sum_j J_{ij} \right) \qquad (101)$$

The energy of unphysical states (any $n_i > 1$) is $\approx \lim_{\varepsilon \to 0^+} (J_{ij}/\varepsilon) \to +\infty$, assuming all $J_{ij} > 0$ (if some $J_{ij} < 0$, another expression must be concocted). One recovers the results of linear harmonic-oscillator theory by discarding all terms quartic or higher-order in the a's or a^*'s, for example, discarding $\mathfrak{n}_i \mathfrak{n}_j$ and dropping all but the leading term in the projection operators. The linearized Hamiltonian.

$$\mathscr{H}_{\text{lin}} = -\frac{1}{2} \sum_{i,j} J_{ij}(a_i^* a_j - \mathfrak{n}_i + \tfrac{1}{4}) + g\mu_B H \sum_i (\mathfrak{n}_i - \tfrac{1}{2}) \qquad (102)$$

is of course rigorous for the zero and one spin-wave states, as the terms we have discarded have zero eigenvalue in these states. $\mathscr{H}_{\text{lin}}$ is diagonalized by transformation to plane waves, and we now give a discussion of this and a definition of the Brillouin zone which will be useful in the next two chapters as well. Let

$$a_i = \frac{1}{\sqrt{N}} \sum_{\mathbf{k}} e^{i\mathbf{k}\cdot\mathbf{R}_i} a_{\mathbf{k}} \qquad a_i^* = \frac{1}{\sqrt{N}} \sum_{\mathbf{k}} e^{-i\mathbf{k}\cdot\mathbf{R}_i} a_{\mathbf{k}}^*$$

$$\mathbf{k} = \frac{2\pi}{L}(n, m, l) \qquad (103)$$

where n, m, l = integers. It may be verified that this transformation is canonical, by showing that the $a_{\mathbf{k}}$'s obey a set of commutation relations identical to Eq. (100). For if one inverts the transformation, he obtains

$$a_{\mathbf{k}} = \frac{1}{\sqrt{N}} \sum_i e^{-i\mathbf{k}\cdot\mathbf{R}_i} a_i \qquad a_{\mathbf{k}}^* = \frac{1}{\sqrt{N}} \sum_i e^{i\mathbf{k}\cdot\mathbf{R}_i} a_i^* \qquad (104)$$

and then verifies the commutation relations, using Eq. (100) for the right-hand sides of the equations. Note also that because the sums in the last equation are over discrete lattice sites $\mathbf{R}_i$, there exists a set of *reciprocal lattice vectors* $\mathbf{K}_n$ for which

$$a_{\mathbf{k}+\mathbf{K}_n} \equiv a_{\mathbf{k}}$$

For the simple cubic structure, the smallest such vectors are (K_1, K_2, K_3), with $K_i = \pm 2\pi/a$ and a = lattice spacing. It is therefore necessary to define operators only in the so-called *first Brillouin zone*, which (again for the simple cubic lattice) consists of the cube with its corners at $\frac{1}{2}(K_1, K_2, K_3)$. According to (103), every point in momentum space "occupies" a volume $(2\pi/L)^3$, so that the total number of points within this Brillouin zone is precisely $(L/a)^3 = N$. This is also the correct number of $a_{\mathbf{k}}$ operators.

Substitution of Eq. (103) into Eq. (102) yields

$$\mathscr{H}_{\text{lin}} = \sum_{\mathbf{k}CB\cdot Z\cdot} \mathfrak{n}_{\mathbf{k}}\hbar\omega(\mathbf{k}) + E_0, \qquad (\mathfrak{n}_{\mathbf{k}} \equiv a_{\mathbf{k}}^* a_{\mathbf{k}}) \tag{105}$$

in precise agreement for $s = \frac{1}{2}$, with the derivation in terms of P's and Q's which resulted in Eqs. (14)–(16).

The next approximation consists in discarding all terms in $\mathscr{H}$ of sixth or higher order in the a's or a^*'s. To this accuracy, $X_i(0, 1) \cong 1$, and $X_i(0) \cong 1 - \mathfrak{n}_i$. The corresponding form of the Hamiltonian is

$$\mathscr{H}_{\text{nonlin}} = -\frac{1}{2}\sum_{i,j} J_{ij}[(a_i^* - a_j^*)(1 - \mathfrak{n}_i)a_j + \tfrac{1}{4}] + g\mu_B H \sum (\mathfrak{n}_i - \tfrac{1}{2}) \tag{106}$$

and it is exact for states involving two or fewer spin deviations. For example, the entire discussion of two interacting spin waves could have been based on this truncated Hamiltonian equally as well as on the full Heisenberg Hamiltonian. But notice a surprising feature which seems to make this last form more accurate than we had any right to expect for arbitrary number of spin deviations. By starting with any allowed configuration, say

$$|ijn\rangle \equiv a_i^* a_j^* a_n^* |0\rangle \qquad (i \neq j \neq n \neq i)$$

and applying $\mathscr{H}_{\text{nonlin}}$ to it, one obtains a linear combination of other states:

$$\mathscr{H}_{\text{nonlin}}|ijn\rangle = \sum_{rst} F_{rst}|rst\rangle$$

all of which are *also* allowed, in the sense that $r \neq s \neq t \neq r$. (For example for spin $\frac{1}{2}$, $(a_i^*)^2|0\rangle$ is not allowed, whereas $a_i^* a_j^*|0\rangle$ is, provided $i \neq j$.) Therefore, unlike the linear Hamiltonian, the nonlinear one of Eq. (106) reproduces correctly *all* the eigenstates of the Heisenberg Hamiltonian. But in addition to these, it also possesses an infinity of eigenstates which are *unphysical*, in the sense that two or more spin deviations occur on one or more sites. That is the other side of the coin. The unphysical states may lie far below the physical ones in energy—something which could not happen with the linear Hamiltonian, whatever were its other defects, nor in Eq. (101) for spins one-half, where projection operators and a limiting procedure were used to ensure $+\infty$ energy for the unphysical states.

It should be a straightforward matter to see if an eigenstate of the nonlinear truncated Hamiltonian is a physical state of the Heisenberg Hamiltonian, or if it is an unphysical, spurious, solution owing to the substitution of Boson operators for the spins. We have merely to calculate $\mathfrak{n}_i(\mathfrak{n}_i - 1) = (a_i^*)^2 a_i^2$ in this state, and if this operator has eigenvalue 0 in this state, for all i, it is a physical state. Bearing this in mind, one operates as though Eq. (106) were the exact Hamiltonian for the problem. Let us perform a similarity transformation which will render it explicitly Hermitean. Let

$$a_i \to \sqrt{1 - \mathfrak{n}_i}\; a_i \qquad \text{and} \qquad a_i^* \to a_i^*\frac{1}{\sqrt{1 - \mathfrak{n}_i}} \tag{107}$$

but note that this leaves the $\mathfrak{n}_i = a_i^* a_i$ invariant, and conserves the fundamental set of commutation relations given in Eq. (100). The Hermitized Hamiltonian is now

$$\mathcal{H} = -\frac{1}{2}\sum_{i,j} J_{ij}[\tfrac{1}{2}a_i^*\sqrt{(1 - \mathfrak{n}_i)(1 - \mathfrak{n}_j)}a_j + H\cdot c\cdot + (\mathfrak{n}_i - \tfrac{1}{2})(\mathfrak{n}_j - \tfrac{1}{2})]$$

$$+ g\mu_B H \sum (\mathfrak{n}_i - \tfrac{1}{2}) \qquad (108)$$

and one is not too surprised to see that it is precisely the original Heisenberg Hamiltonian, written in terms of the *Holstein-Primakoff representation* of spins one-half:

$$S_i^+ = a_i^*\sqrt{1 - \mathfrak{n}_i} \qquad S_i^- = \sqrt{1 - \mathfrak{n}_i}\ a_i \qquad S_i^z = \mathfrak{n}_i - \tfrac{1}{2} \qquad (109)$$

This clarifies the situation. *The Hamiltonian in Eq.* (106) *or in its physically equivalent Hermitized version, Eq.* (108), *is in fact the identical original Hamiltonian within the physically meaningful subspace of the H-P (Holstein-Primakoff) operators and has nonphysical solutions* only *when the H-P operators themselves become meaningless.*

Because we wish to study all values of s, it is rewarding to generalize the foregoing. This is done in a few steps, starting with the Heisenberg Hamiltonian of Eq. (1). First, express the spin operators in the H-P language, viz.,

$$S_i^+ = a_i^*\sqrt{2s}\sqrt{\left(1 - \frac{\mathfrak{n}_i}{2s}\right)} \qquad S_i^- = \sqrt{2s}\sqrt{\left(1 - \frac{\mathfrak{n}_i}{2s}\right)}a_i \qquad S_i^z = \mathfrak{n}_i - s \qquad (110)$$

Next, rationalize the square roots by a similarity transformation inverse to the one performed in Eq. (107) so that, finally,

$$\boxed{\mathcal{H} = E_0 - s\sum_{i,j} J_{ij}(a_i^* - a_j^*)\left(1 - \frac{\mathfrak{n}_i}{2s}\right)a_j + g\mu_B H \sum \mathfrak{n}_i} \qquad (111)$$

the constant E_0 being the usual ground-state energy first defined in Eq. (12). This non-Hermitean operator has all the eigenvalues of the Heisenberg Hamiltonian, plus an infinite number of unphysical ones. Whether an eigenstate is physically admissible or not can be tested by seeing whether it is an eigenfunction of the positive semidefinite operator

$$\left[\frac{1}{N}\sum_{i=1}^{N} (a_i^*)^{2s+1}(a_i)^{2s+1}\right] \qquad (112)$$

with eigenvalue 0, or not.

For the purposes of spin-wave theory, one now transforms the above $\mathcal{H}$ to running waves, by use of Eq. (103). The Hamiltonian in terms of a_k's is

$$\mathcal{H} = E_0 - s\sum_{i,j} J_{ij} \sum_{k_1 k_2} \frac{a_{k_1}^*}{\sqrt{N}}(e^{ik_1\cdot R_i} - e^{ik_1\cdot R_j})$$

$$\times \left(1 - \frac{1}{2s}\sum_{k_3 k_4} \frac{a_{k_3}^*}{\sqrt{N}} e^{ik_3\cdot R_i} \frac{a_{k_4}}{\sqrt{N}} e^{-ik_4\cdot R_i}\right)\frac{a_{k_2}}{\sqrt{N}} e^{-ik_2\cdot R_j}$$

$$+ g\mu_B H \sum_i \sum_{k, k'} \frac{a_k^*}{\sqrt{N}} e^{ik\cdot R_i} \frac{a_{k'}}{\sqrt{N}} e^{-ik'\cdot R_i} \qquad (113)$$

Let us isolate, in this large sum of terms, the contribution of operators diagonal in the occupation number representation (that is, of operators such as constants and functions of $\mathfrak{n}_k = a_k^* a_k$) from the nondiagonal terms. Terms bilinear in the a's, such as the last term in the magnetic field, are automatically diagonal by virtue of momentum conservation. Quartic terms are not, although a subset of them, for which

$$(\mathbf{k}_1, \mathbf{k}_3) = (\mathbf{k}_2, \mathbf{k}_4) \qquad \text{or} \qquad (\mathbf{k}_4, \mathbf{k}_2) \qquad\qquad (114)$$

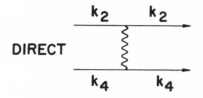

DIRECT

FIG. 6.4. Direct and exchange contributions to nonlinear magnon Hamiltonian.

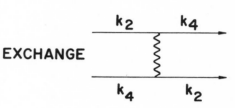

EXCHANGE

(see Fig. 6.4) only involve $\mathfrak{n}_k$'s and so will be included in the important diagonal part, which we shall call $\mathscr{H}_D$. As the Fourier transform of J_{ij} consistently occurs, it is convenient to denote it $J(\mathbf{k})$, defined as

$$J(\mathbf{k}) = \frac{1}{2N} \sum_{i,j} e^{i\mathbf{k}\cdot(\mathbf{R}_i - \mathbf{R}_j)} J_{ij} \qquad\qquad (115)$$

In the cubic structure, $J^*(\mathbf{k}) = J(-\mathbf{k}) = J(\mathbf{k})$. For example, in the *simple cubic structure nearest-neighbor interaction* (which we study in Chapter 8)

$$J(\mathbf{k}) = 2J(\cos k_x a + \cos k_y a + \cos k_z a) \qquad\qquad (116)$$

And in this manner one obtains the compact expression

$$\mathscr{H}_D = E_0 + \sum_k [2sJ(0) - 2sJ(\mathbf{k}) + g\mu_B H]\mathfrak{n}_k$$

$$- \frac{1}{N} \sum_{\mathbf{k},\mathbf{k}'} [J(0) + J(\mathbf{k} - \mathbf{k}') - J(\mathbf{k}) - J(\mathbf{k}')]\mathfrak{n}_k \mathfrak{n}_{k'} \qquad (117)$$

There is a slight error made in terms for which $\mathbf{k} = \mathbf{k}'$; the correct biquadratic term is $(a_k^*)^2(a_k)^2$ rather than $(\mathfrak{n}_k)^2$. This can be taken into account by modifying $\mathscr{H}$ in an amount of $O(1/N)$; however, such a correction is completely negligible and we shall have nothing more to say about it.

The study of $\mathscr{H}_D$ involves only minor generalizations of the theory of the linear Hamiltonian. The only important question is the following. Given a state occupied by

n_1 magnons of wavevector $\mathbf{k}_1$, n_2 of wavevector $\mathbf{k}_2$, etc., how much energy is required to add one magnon of wavevector $\mathbf{k}$ to this state? Let $W(n_k)$ and $W(n_k + 1)$ indicate the eigenvalue of $\mathscr{H}_D$ in the two states $|n_k)$ and $a_k^*|n_k)$; then

$$\mathscr{H}_D a_k^*|n_k) = a_k^* \mathscr{H}_D|n_k) + [\mathscr{H}_D, a_k^*]|n_k)$$

$$= W(n_k)a_k^*|n_k) + \left\{2sJ(\mathbf{0}) - 2sJ(\mathbf{k}) + g\mu_B H \right.$$

$$\left. - \frac{2}{N}\sum_{\mathbf{k}'}[J(\mathbf{0}) + J(\mathbf{k} - \mathbf{k}') - J(\mathbf{k}) - J(\mathbf{k}')]\cdot\mathfrak{n}_{\mathbf{k}'}\right\}a_k^*|n_k)$$

$$\equiv W(n_k + 1)a_k^*|n_k) \tag{118}$$

and therefore

$$W(n_k + 1) = W(n_k) + [2sJ(\mathbf{0}) - 2sJ(\mathbf{k}) + g\mu_B H]$$

$$- \frac{2}{N}\sum_{\mathbf{k}'}[J(\mathbf{0}) + J(\mathbf{k} - \mathbf{k}') - J(\mathbf{k}) - J(\mathbf{k}')]\mathfrak{n}_{\mathbf{k}'} \tag{119}$$

In terms of the magnon energy $\hbar\omega(\mathbf{k})$ as previously defined, for example, Eq. (14),

$$W(n_k + 1) - W(n_k) = \hbar\omega(\mathbf{k}) - \frac{1}{Ns}\sum_{\mathbf{k}'}[\hbar\omega(\mathbf{k}) + \hbar\omega(\mathbf{k}') - \hbar\omega(\mathbf{k} - \mathbf{k}') - \hbar\omega(\mathbf{0})]\mathfrak{n}_{\mathbf{k}'}$$

$$\equiv \varepsilon(\mathbf{k}) \tag{120}$$

with the sum representing the corrections to linear spin-wave theory. It is important to note that $\mathbf{k}' = \mathbf{0}$ spin waves do not contribute to this correction, for this confirms the rotationally invariant nature of the theory. The nonlinear magnon energies are denoted $\varepsilon(\mathbf{k})$.

Note that for nearest-neighbor interactions,

$$\overline{\varepsilon(\mathbf{k})} \leqslant \overline{\hbar\omega(\mathbf{k})}$$

(indicating average over the directions of $\mathbf{k}$ by a bar). So, by increasing the occupation numbers n_k, all magnon energies can be reduced, as we shall see elsewhere in a discussion of thermal effects. However the above inequality does not hold for arbitrary long-range interactions, and is *reversed* in nearest-neighbor *ferrimagnets*, so that it appears to be a special property associated with the postulates of the present theory only.

There is also an approximate superposition principle: the energy required to add *two* magnons of wavevectors $\mathbf{k}$ and $\mathbf{k}'$ to a given state equals the sum of the energies required for each, $\varepsilon(\mathbf{k}) + \varepsilon(\mathbf{k}')$, to within a correction term $O(1/N)$ arising from the interaction. The proof is given as Problem 2.

Problem 2: $W(n_k + 1, n_{k'} + 1) \equiv W(n_k + 1, n_{k'}) + W(n_k, n_{k'} + 1) - W(n_k, n_{k'}) + w.$ Find the correction term w; verify that it is $O(1/N)$.

PERTURBATION-THEORETIC CORRECTION

So far we have not focused any attention on the nondiagonal terms $\mathscr{H}' = \mathscr{H} - \mathscr{H}_D$. At this juncture we shall try to estimate the effect of such terms by perturbation theory. In principle, if carried out to all orders, this is a systematic means of diagonalizing the Hamiltonian. Once this is done, the proper and improper eigenstates can be separated out by the test that has been established in Eq. (112). In practice, the perturbation expansion might not converge, and we shall only carry it out to second order by the following means.

Consider the similarity transformation generated by T,

$$\mathrm{op} \to e^{-T}\,\mathrm{op}\,e^{+T}$$

This is a unitary transformation if and only if $T^* = -T$, that is, if $T = i \times$ Hermitean operator. Such a unitary transformation could not diagonalize the Hamiltonian, which in its present form is non-Hermitean and which when diagonalized will be explicitly real, diagonal, and therefore Hermitean. The connection between the two is possible only through an unrestricted T. To lowest order in the interaction, it is determined by expanding,

$$e^T = 1 + T + \frac{T^2}{2} + \cdots$$

and choosing T so as to eliminate $\mathscr{H}'$ from the Hamiltonian. Of what remains, we shall keep only the lowest-order diagonal terms. That is,

$$
\begin{aligned}
\mathscr{H} &\to \left(1 - T + \frac{T^2}{2}\right)\mathscr{H}_D\left(1 + T + \frac{T^2}{2}\right) + (1 - T)\mathscr{H}'(1 + T) \\
&\approx \mathscr{H}_D + ([\mathscr{H}_D, T] + \mathscr{H}') - T\mathscr{H}_D T + \tfrac{1}{2}(T^2\mathscr{H}_D + \mathscr{H}_D T^2) \\
&\quad - T\mathscr{H}' + \mathscr{H}'T + \mathrm{O}(\mathscr{H}'^3)
\end{aligned}
\tag{121}
$$

together with the relation

$$[\mathscr{H}_D, T] + \mathscr{H}' = 0 \tag{122}$$

specify the transformed Hamiltonian to the desired approximation. [Compare Eq. (122) with Eq. (126), where this equation is solved for the matrix elements of T.] The quantum numbers of the eigenstates of $\mathscr{H}_D$ are the sets of occupation numbers, and let $a, b, \ldots$ stand for such sets. One finds for the new eigenvalues of Eq. (121) after solving Eq. (122):

$$\mathscr{H}_{a,a} = (\mathscr{H}_D)_{a,a} - \sum_b \frac{\mathscr{H}'_{a,b}\mathscr{H}'_{b,a}}{(\mathscr{H}_D)_{b,b} - (\mathscr{H}_D)_{a,a}} \tag{123}$$

a familiar expression of the second-order perturbation correction to the energy. We have rederived it so as to remove (legitimate) doubts concerning its use for a non-Hermitean perturbation. (Discrepancies with the usual formulas are not apparent before third- or higher-order corrections are evaluated.)

Substituting $\mathcal{H}'$ into this expression, one obtains the leading correction to $\mathcal{H}_D$:

$$\mathcal{H} = \mathcal{H}_D - \frac{1}{4N^2} \sum_{k_1 k_2 k_3 k_4}$$

$$\times \frac{\Delta(k_1 + k_3 - k_2 - k_4)[J(k_2) - J(k_2 - k_1)][J(k_3) - J(k_3 - k_4)]}{W(n_{k_1} + 1, n_{k_2} - 1, n_{k_3} + 1, n_{k_4} - 1) - W(n_{k_1}, n_{k_2}, n_{k_3}, n_{k_4})}$$

$$\times [(1 + n_{k_1})(1 + n_{k_3})n_{k_2}n_{k_4} - (1 + n_{k_2})(1 + n_{k_4})n_{k_1}n_{k_3})] \tag{124}$$

This expression may be verified by use of the following properties of the interaction: $J(k) = J(-k)$, and $J(k + K_n) = J(k)$, where K_n is one of the reciprocal lattice vectors, e.g., as defined following Eq. (104). The symbol $\Delta(k)$, which is often used to generalize the Kronecker delta to crystal physics, is defined to vanish except when its argument $k = 0$ or K_n, in which case it equals unity. The contribution of terms for K_n is called *umklapp*, after the German meaning *to be brought back into* (the Brillouin zone). The denominator equals

$$\varepsilon(k_1) + \varepsilon(k_3) - \varepsilon(k_2) - \varepsilon(k_4) + O\left(\frac{1}{N}\right)$$

Whereas the linear spin-wave theory gave magnon energies proportional to s; and whereas the nonlinear corrections in $\mathcal{H}_D$, Eq. (119), were independent of s; we now find that the perturbation-theoretic correction just obtained vanishes as $\sim s^{-1}$ and therefore will be negligible compared to $\mathcal{H}_D$ in the correspondence limit $s \to \infty$. This is due to the s-dependence of the denominator. Higher-order corrections vanish even more strongly as the number of energy denominators is increased.

Thus there appears to be a well-defined semiclassical limit [just as in the bound-state problem, Eq. (80)] $s \to \infty$, which in practice means $s \gg \frac{1}{2}$, where $\mathcal{H}_D$ is a sufficiently accurate approximation to the correct Hamiltonian that it may be used with confidence, provided

$$\sum n_k \ll Ns$$

$\mathcal{H}_D$ can therefore be considered as the effective Hamiltonian of nonlinear, semiclassical spin-wave theory, with perturbation theory and projection operators required to obtain further corrections.

Even though the elimination of $\mathcal{H}'$ is not very important to the low-lying energies when s is large, it does contribute substantially toward the satisfaction of the sum rule,

$$\left[\frac{1}{N} \sum_i (a_i^*)^{2s+1}(a_i)^{2s+1}\right] = 0 \tag{112}$$

for physical states. That the sum rule is not obeyed in the original spin-wave representation, can be seen by expanding the operators in plane waves. Retaining only the diagonal operators $\mathfrak{n}_k$, we find there are $(2s + 1)!$ ways of pairing the creation and annihilation operators and thus obtain for the above,

$$(2s + 1)!\left(\frac{1}{N} \sum n_k\right)^{2s+1} \tag{125}$$

which may not be large when $\sum n_k \ll Ns$, but is nevertheless nonzero.

After the similarity transformation, with

$$T = -\frac{1}{2N} \sum_{\substack{\mathbf{k}_1 \mathbf{k}_2 \mathbf{k}_3 \mathbf{k}_4 \\ \mathbf{k}_4 \neq \mathbf{k}_1, \mathbf{k}_3}} \frac{\Delta(\mathbf{k}_1 + \mathbf{k}_3 - \mathbf{k}_2 - \mathbf{k}_4)[J(\mathbf{k}_2) - J(\mathbf{k}_2 - \mathbf{k}_1)]a^*_{\mathbf{k}_1}a^*_{\mathbf{k}_3}a_{\mathbf{k}_4}a_{\mathbf{k}_2}}{W(n_{\mathbf{k}_1} + 1, n_{\mathbf{k}_2} - 1, n_{\mathbf{k}_3} + 1, n_{\mathbf{k}_4} - 1) - W(n_{\mathbf{k}_1}, n_{\mathbf{k}_2}, n_{\mathbf{k}_3}, n_{\mathbf{k}_4})} \quad (126)$$

where the denominator equals $\varepsilon(\mathbf{k}_1) + \varepsilon(\mathbf{k}_3) - \varepsilon(\mathbf{k}_2) - \varepsilon(\mathbf{k}_4) + O(1/N)$, we obtain for the diagonal part of the sum-rule operator, Eq. (112),

$$(1 - T + \cdots)\left(\frac{1}{N^{2s+1}} \sum_{\mathbf{k}_1 \dots \mathbf{k}_{4s+2}} \Delta(\mathbf{k}_1 + \cdots + \mathbf{k}_{2s+1} - \mathbf{k}_{2s+2} - \cdots - \mathbf{k}_{4s+2})\right.$$

$$\left. \times \, a^*_{\mathbf{k}_1} \cdots a^*_{\mathbf{k}_{2s+1}} a_{\mathbf{k}_{2s+2}} \cdots a_{\mathbf{k}_{4s+2}}\right)(1 + T + \cdots)$$

$$= (2s + 1)!\left(\frac{1}{N}\sum n_{\mathbf{k}}\right)^{2s+1}\left\{1 - \frac{(2s + 1)(2s)}{2N^3[(1/N)\sum n_{\mathbf{k}}]^2}\right.$$

$$\left. \times \sum \frac{\Delta(\mathbf{k}_1 + \mathbf{k}_3 - \mathbf{k}_2 - \mathbf{k}_4)[J(\mathbf{k}_2) - J(\mathbf{k}_2 - \mathbf{k}_1)]}{\varepsilon_1 + \varepsilon_3 - \varepsilon_2 - \varepsilon_4}F + \cdots\right\} \quad (127)$$

with $F = (1 + n_{\mathbf{k}_2})(1 + n_{\mathbf{k}_4})n_{\mathbf{k}_1}n_{\mathbf{k}_3} - (1 + n_{\mathbf{k}_1})(1 + n_{\mathbf{k}_3})(n_{\mathbf{k}_2}n_{\mathbf{k}_4})$, the ellipsis indicating nondiagonal and higher-order corrections. The improvement is schematically indicated in Fig. 6.5.

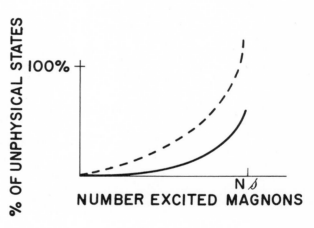

FIG. 6.5. Schematic effect of transformation T on elimination of unphysical states in nonlinear spin-wave theory. Upper curve is before, and lower curve after the transformation.

ANTIFERROMAGNETIC MAGNONS

The following theorems can be proved about the Heisenberg *antiferromagnet*

$$\mathscr{H} = +\sum_{i,\,j=1}^{N} J_{ij}\mathbf{S}_i\cdot\mathbf{S}_j \qquad J_{ij} > 0 \qquad \text{for nearest neighbors} \qquad (128)$$

1. With some minor restrictions on the J_{ij}, the ground state is a nondegenerate singlet ($S_{\text{tot}} = 0$). What is more, the lowest energy of any state with total spin angular momentum S is lower than the lowest energy of any state belonging to $S + 1$.

2.   For spins one-half there is no energy gap against excited states, in the limit $N \to \infty$.

It is probably safe to conjecture that (2) holds for spins $s > \frac{1}{2}$. The proofs of these theorems are given elsewhere,[10] but it does not require inordinate stretching of the imagination to believe in the existence of spin waves in antiferromagnets, nor to believe theorem (2) that they form a continuum of energy levels down to the ground state energy. For when a spin deviation propagates at very long wavelengths, the relative orientation of nearest-neighbor spins is maintained to a very good approximation, and consequently the cost in energy must be low.

In 1931 Hans Bethe, followed by Hulthén and others, succeeded in solving for the eigenstates of the Heisenberg linear chain model with nearest-neighbor interactions. We shall discuss this in the following section. Unfortunately, because of its difficulty, the Bethe solution has not given any insight into the question of long-range correlations, excited states, etc., and so it must be considered physically incomplete. But by truncating the full Hamiltonian somewhat, in fact by eliminating the z components of the interactions entirely, one arrives at a model which is completely soluble in one dimension for spins one-half and nearest-neighbor interactions. It has many of the features of the Bethe solution, but it is quasilinear and fully transparent. We call it the XY model.[11]

$$\mathscr{H}_{XY} = \frac{1}{2} \sum_{i=1}^{N} (S_i^+ S_{i+1}^- + \text{H.c.}) \qquad s = \frac{1}{2} \qquad \text{and} \qquad \mathbf{S}_{N+1} \equiv \mathbf{S}_1 \qquad (129)$$

The vacuum (all spins down) is an eigenstate, with energy 0. By translational invariance, one may guess that the one-particle states ($N-1$ spins down, one spin up) are

$$\psi_k = \frac{1}{\sqrt{N}} \sum_i e^{ik \cdot R_i} S_i^+ |0) \qquad (130)$$

with easily computed energy eigenvalues,

$$E_k = \cos ka \qquad \text{with } |ka| < \pi \qquad (131)$$

Periodic boundary condition $N + 1 = 1$ results in the discrete set,

$$k = \frac{2\pi}{Na} \times \text{integer} = \frac{\pi(2p)}{Na} \qquad p = 0, \pm 1, \ldots \qquad (132)$$

A product of two plane waves does not vanish in the configurations $S_i^+ S_i^+$ as it should, but a determinant does. However, a determinant is antisymmetric under the interchange of the coordinates, whereas spins on different sites commute and therefore

[10] See E. Lieb and D. Mattis, *J. Math. Phys.*, **3**: 749 (1962); E. Lieb, T. Schultz, and D. Mattis, *Ann. Phys.* (*N.Y.*), **16**: 407 (1961), Appendix B; and D. Mattis, *Phys. Rev.*, **130**: 76 (1963). The reader interested in a general introduction to the various aspects of the theory of antiferromagnetism should read the extensive review article by T. Nagamiya et al., in *Advances in Phys.* (*Phil. Mag. Suppl.*), vol. 4, no. 13, p. 1 (1955).

[11] E. Lieb, T. Schultz, and D. Mattis, *Ann. Phys.*, *loc. cit.*; S. Katsura, *Phys. Rev.*, **127**: 1508 (1962), has calculated the magnetic susceptibility in the XY model.

have a wavefunction symmetric under interchange. The following choice thus imposes itself:

$$
\psi_{k,\,k'} =
\begin{cases}
\dfrac{1}{\sqrt{N(N-1)}} \displaystyle\sum_{i,\,j>i} [e^{i(k\cdot R_i + k'\cdot R_j)} - e^{i(k\cdot R_j + k'\cdot R_i)}] S_i^+ S_j^+ |0\rangle \\[1.5em]
\dfrac{-1}{\sqrt{N(N-1)}} \displaystyle\sum_{i,\,j<i} [e^{i(k\cdot R_i + k'\cdot R_j)} - e^{i(k\cdot R_j + k'\cdot R_i)}] S_i^+ S_j^+ |0\rangle
\end{cases}
\tag{133}
$$

When j is increased to $N-1$, then to N, and finally to $N+1$, the second spin becomes the first and the wavefunction changes discontinuously from the upper form to the lower unless the proper boundary condition is imposed. Because the position of the origin of the numbering system is completely arbitrary for the cyclic problem we are solving, such discontinuities at a particular site are inadmissible. The resolution of this difficulty is to take, instead of Eq. (132),

$$
k = \frac{\pi(2p+1)}{Na}
\tag{134}
$$

(and similarly for k') which is known as an *antiperiodic* boundary condition. The generalization to any number of spins up is straightforward. Let

$$
\psi_{k_1,\,k_2,\,\dots} = C \sum_{i_1,\,i_2,\,\dots} F_{k_1,\,k_2,\,\dots}^{i_1,\,i_2,\,\dots} S_{i_1}^+ S_{i_2}^+ \dots |0\rangle
\tag{135}
$$

where C is the normalization constant, and F is the determinant

$$
F_{k_1,\,\dots}^{i_1,\,\dots} = \varepsilon_P
\begin{vmatrix}
e^{ik_1 R_{i_1}} & e^{ik_2 R_{i_1}} \dots \\
e^{ik_1 R_{i_2}} & e^{ik_2 R_{i_2}} \dots \\
\vdots & \vdots
\end{vmatrix}
\tag{135A}
$$

$\varepsilon_P = +1$ when the spins are in a natural order, $i_1 < i_2 < i_3 < \dots$, or an even permutation of this order, and $\varepsilon_P = -1$ when the spins are arranged in an odd permutation of the natural order. If i_n is the farthest spin, then the translation of i_n from N to $N+1$ involves a reordering equivalent to an odd permutation for $n+1$ odd, and an even permutation for $n+1$ even. Thus

$$
n+1 = \text{odd} \rightarrow k = \frac{\pi}{Na}(2p+1)
\tag{136}
$$

and

$$
n+1 = \text{even} \rightarrow k = \frac{\pi}{Na}(2p)
$$

This is a very interesting situation. For although the many-spin wavefunctions at first appear to be essentially independent particle wavefunctions, yet when one particle is added (that is, when one more spin is turned up) *all* the other plane-wave states are modified. This is in the nature of a cooperative effect, due to the effective hard core repulsion (from $(S_i^+)^2 = 0$) of two nearby spin deviations. Whether the k's are members of the even or of the odd set, the energy corresponding to the wave-function above is

$$E_{k_1, k_2, \ldots} = \sum_{i=1}^{n} \cos k_i a = \sum_i \cos \frac{\pi}{N} \binom{2p_i}{2p_i + 1} \tag{137}$$

Note that all k's must be distinct, or else $F \equiv 0$. The ground state energy is achieved by allowing all the states of negative energy to be occupied, that is, all k's in the range

$$\frac{\pi}{2} \leqslant ka \leqslant \frac{3\pi}{2} \qquad \frac{N}{4} \leqslant p \leqslant \frac{3N}{4} \tag{138}$$

However, we must consider *two* ground states: the ground state for the even k's and the ground state for the odd ones. Denote these by E' and E respectively, with values

$$E' = \sum_p \cos \frac{\pi}{N} (2p + 1)$$

$$\tag{139}$$

and
$$E'' = \sum_p \cos \frac{\pi}{N} (2p)$$

with the sums in either set restricted to the range, Eq. (138). The separation of energies E' and E'' depend on whether N is divisible by 4, or merely by 2, or whether it is odd. In any event, it is of $O(1/N)$, which is the order of magnitude of the smallest elementary excitations.

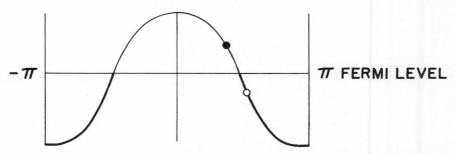

$-\pi$ π **FERMI LEVEL**

FIG. 6.6. *XY* model, showing occupied and unoccupied states. Bubble and dot indicate "quasihole" and "quasiparticle" created in elementary excitation.

Either ground state may be represented by an energy-level diagram shown in Fig. 6.6. The Fermi level intersects the cosine curve at $ka = \pi/2$ and $3\pi/2$, and all allowed states below this are filled and all those above it are empty in either ground state. Excited states correspond to occupying states above the Fermi level, or emptying states below it. If k is a wavevector of either category in Eq. (136), as measured from $\pm \pi/2a$, the energy of an elementary excitation, $\varepsilon(q)$ is described by a doubly degenerate spectrum

$$\varepsilon(q) = |\sin q| \qquad \text{setting } q \equiv ka \tag{140}$$

in addition to any correction due to changes in parity of the state. Each elementary excitation represents an antiferromagnetic magnon, and it should be noted that unlike the ferromagnetic magnons, these depend *linearly* on wavevector q, for small q. This appears to be a model-independent property of all antiferromagnetics.

BETHE'S ONE-DIMENSIONAL SOLUTION

Progress in solving the Heisenberg antiferromagnet even in one dimension has been slow. Although Bethe gave the wavefunctions in 1931, the ground-state energy was not obtained before 1938, by Hulthén. It was subsequently generalized by Orbach, who discussed an anisotropic Hamiltonian, also by Walker who showed the analytic properties of the Orbach solutions. Finally, fully 32 years after the initial progress, Des Cloizeaux and Pearson have calculated the one-magnon spectrum and Griffiths the magnetic susceptibility.[12]

It is desired to calculate the eigenstates of

$$\mathscr{H} = \sum_{i=1}^{N} \left[\tfrac{1}{2}(S_i^+ S_{i+1}^- + \text{H.c.}) + g S_i^z S_{i+1}^z \right] \tag{141}$$

for $s = \tfrac{1}{2}$, $g = 1$, and $N + 1 = 1$. $g = 0$ results in the XY model, Eq. (129), whereas $g \to \infty$ results in the Ising model. The present choice $g = 1$ corresponds to the *Heisenberg isotropic chain*. By virtue of a theorem on antiferromagnets,[13] the ground state is a singlet, and is therefore to be found only in the $M = 0$ subspace. This corresponds to $N/2$ "particles" or spin reversals. Let us approach this ground-state problem gradually, by studying the states with a small number of spin reversals first. The vacuum, or all spins down, has energy $E_f \equiv + N/4$. The states with one spin reversal are the spin-wave states, studied in some generality under the section on one-magnon eigenstates in ferromagnets. The two-magnon eigenstates were examined in the following section, and it is with a modification of the analysis there, beginning with Eq. (54), that we begin.

For present purposes, it is most convenient to use a procedure valid only for spins one-half and assign to the unphysical amplitudes f_{ii} the value determined by

$$f_{i,i} + f_{i+1,i+1} = 2f_{i,i+1} \tag{142}$$

where the physical amplitudes $f_{ij} = f_{ji}$ for $j \neq i$, obey the equations

$$(E - E_f + 2)f_{ij} - \tfrac{1}{2}(f_{ij+1} + f_{ij-1} + f_{i+1j} + f_{i-1j}) = 0 \tag{143}$$

This is the left-hand side of Eq. (54), with $s = \tfrac{1}{2}$, $J = -1$, and $H = 0$, whereas the boundary condition above ensures that the right-hand side of that equation always vanishes. The homogeneous equation is solved by plane waves, e.g.,

$$f_{ij} = e^{i(ki + k'j + \frac{1}{2}\psi)} + e^{i(kj + k'i - \frac{1}{2}\psi)} \tag{144}$$

[12] H. Bethe, *Z. Physik*, **71**: 205 (1931); L. Hulthén, *Arkiv Met. Astron. Fysik*, **26A**: Na. 11 (1938); R. Orbach, *Phys. Rev.*, **112**: 309 (1958); L. R. Walker, *Phys. Rev.*, **116**: 1289 (1959); J. Des Cloizeaux and J. J. Pearson, *Phys. Rev.*, **128**: 2131 (1962); R. B. Griffiths, *Phys. Rev.*, **133**: A768 (1964).

[13] E. Lieb and D. Mattis, *J. Math. Phys.*, **3**: 749 (1962).

for $j > i$. The phase factor may range anywhere over the interval $-\pi$ to $+\pi$, and it should be noted that the corresponding solution in the XY model has $\psi = \pm \pi$, cf. Eq. (133), and otherwise differs from the above only by a trivial multiplicative constant. But we make no attempt here to normalize the solutions, for this is not required in the calculation of energy eigenvalues.

If we insert this form of f_{ij} into the boundary condition, combine coefficients of $\cos \psi/2$ and of $\sin \psi/2$, factor out $\exp i(k + k')/2$ and simplify the remainder, there results the following equation determining ψ:

$$2 \cot \tfrac{1}{2}\psi = \cot \tfrac{1}{2}k' - \cot \tfrac{1}{2}k \qquad (145)$$

The other boundary condition,

$$f_{iN} = f_{0i} \qquad (146)$$

results in

$$k' = \frac{\pi(2p') - \psi}{N} \quad \text{and} \quad k = \frac{\pi(2p) + \psi}{N} \qquad (147)$$

with p, $p' = $ integers.

The energy, measured from the ferromagnetic level $E_f = (N/4)$, is

$$E - E_f = -(1 - \cos k) - (1 - \cos k') \qquad (148)$$

just the energy of two scattered magnons including the phase shift ψ. Note that $k + k' = [2\pi(p + p')]/N$ independent of ψ, and corresponds to the center of mass wavevector $\mathbf{K}$ in the section on ferromagnetic two-magnon bound states (p. 140). $k - k'$ corresponds to the relative wavevector q. We recall that a bound state appeared *below* $q = 0$, outside the continuum of scattering states. This same state is, however, now *above* the continuum of scattering states because of the change of sign in the interaction. It corresponds to complex ψ, k and k'. Because in antiferromagnets the bound state fortuitously lies above the continuum, it can have nothing to do with the ground-state problem and we shall forthwith ignore it and concentrate on the spectrum of *real k, k' and ψ*.

The two-spin calculation is readily generalized. Let the unnormalized n-particle function be

$$f_{ij...mn} = e^{i(k_1 i + k_2 j + \cdots + k_n n + \frac{1}{2} \overset{n}{\underset{r<t}{\sum}}\overset{n}{\sum} \psi_{k_r k_t})} + \text{all permutations} \qquad (149)$$

That is, the state consists of products of plane waves, summed over all permutations of the n k's. The phase shifts $\psi_{kk'}$ are antisymmetric in the indices k, k', and are easily shown to obey the coupled equations:

$$2 \cot \tfrac{1}{2}\psi_{kk'} = \cot \tfrac{1}{2}k - \cot \tfrac{1}{2}k' \qquad (150)$$

and

$$k = \frac{\pi(2p) + \overset{n}{\underset{1}{\sum}} \psi_{kk'}}{N} \qquad p = 0, \pm 1, \ldots \qquad (151)$$

The sum in this equation, as well as in the next, is over the wavevectors k' in Eq. (149). The energy, measured relative to $N/4 = $ the ferromagnetic reference energy, is

$$E - E_f = - \sum_1^n (1 - \cos k') \tag{152}$$

Note that if we translate the entire chain by one site, that is, let $i, j, \ldots \to i + 1$, $j + 1, \ldots$, the wavefunction, Eq. (149), is multiplied by a phase factor

$$e^{i \sum_1^n k} = e^{\pi i \sum_1^n 2p/N} \tag{153}$$

The exponent is identified as the total momentum of the state, which is again independent of the phase shifts $\psi_{kk'}$. This is important, because the phase shifts themselves are now rather large. Each $\psi_{kk'}$ is O(1); there are a number of them contributing to each k, and the total shift in k is O(n/N) or a substantial fraction of k.

In the two-particle problem, there is no traveling wave solution of Eqs. (150) and (151) for $k - k' \approx 0$. This is the case corresponding to the bound-state complex values. Similarly, in the many-particle state, one must choose the interval between k's such that no $p = 0$, and such that for all p and p',

$$|p - p'| > 1 \tag{154}$$

to ensure that a real solution exists. For $N/2$ particles, $N = $ even, the set $\{p\}$ subject to the above restriction is

$$\{p\} = 1, 3, \ldots, N - 1 \tag{155}$$

Notice an interesting effect of the $S_i^z S_{i+1}^z$ "interaction," which is to spread the integers p (restricted over the range $N/4 < p < 3N/4$ in the ground state of the XY model) to cover the entire range of phase space at present.

The regular spacing permits us to replace sums by integrals in the limit $N \to \infty$, and thus,

$$E - E_f = - \frac{N}{2} \int_0^1 [1 - \cos k(x)] \, dx = - N \int_0^1 \sin^2 \frac{k(x)}{2} \, dx \tag{156}$$

where

$$2 \cot \frac{\psi(x, y)}{2} = \cot \frac{k(x)}{2} - \cot \frac{k(y)}{2} \tag{157}$$

and

$$k(x) = 2\pi x + \frac{1}{2} \int_0^1 \psi(x, y) \, dy \tag{158}$$

Eliminate the phase shift from the last equation:

$$k(x) = 2\pi x + \int_0^1 \text{arccot}\left\{ \frac{\cot[k(x)/2] - \cot[k(y)/2]}{2} \right\} dy \tag{159}$$

Differentiate with respect to x:

$$\frac{dk(x)}{dx} = 2\pi + \int_{-\infty}^{\infty} \frac{f(\eta)/f(\xi)}{1 + \frac{1}{4}(\xi - \eta)^2} \, d\eta \tag{160}$$

with the following short-hand:

$$\cot \frac{k(x)}{2} = \xi \quad \text{and} \quad \cot \frac{k(y)}{2} = \eta$$

$$\left(\frac{d\eta}{dy}\right)^{-1} = -f(\eta) \quad \text{and} \quad \frac{d\xi}{dx} = \frac{-1}{f(\xi)} \tag{161}$$

Multiply both sides of the equation by $f(\xi)$, and use the identity

$$f(\xi) \frac{dk(x)}{dx} = \frac{+2}{1 + \xi^2}$$

to obtain

$$\frac{2}{1 + \xi^2} = 2\pi f(\xi) + 4 \int_{-\infty}^{\infty} \frac{f(\eta) \, d\eta}{4 + \{\xi - \eta\}^2} \tag{162}$$

This type of equation is soluble precisely because the kernel is a function of only the difference $(\xi - \eta)$. One may take Fourier transforms, and solve for F_k, defined by

$$F_k = \int_{-\infty}^{\infty} d\theta f(\theta) e^{ik\theta} \quad \text{and} \quad f(\theta) = \int_{-\infty}^{\infty} \frac{dk}{2\pi} F_k e^{-ik\theta} \tag{163}$$

to obtain a simple formula,

$$F_k = (2 \cosh k)^{-1} \tag{164}$$

The ground state energy has the form

$$E - E_f = -2N \int_{-\infty}^{\infty} d\xi \frac{f(\xi)}{1 + \xi^2} = -2N \int_{-\infty}^{\infty} \frac{dk F_k}{2\pi} \int_{-\infty}^{\infty} d\xi \frac{e^{-ik\xi}}{1 + \xi^2}$$

$$= -2N \int_0^{\infty} dk F_k e^{-|k|} = -2N \int_0^{\infty} \frac{dk e^{-2|k|}}{1 + e^{-2|k|}} = -N \ln 2 \tag{165}$$

This is a very famous result for it is one of the very few exact solutions known of a nontrivial many-body problem.

Des Cloizeaux and Pearson[14] have extended the analysis to obtain the energy of lowest excited states, which are found to be triplet states. $N/2 - 1$ values of k are chosen by them, to obtain the eigenstates of lowest energy belonging to a finite total momentum $\sum k$. This procedure is very delicate, however, and somewhat too complicated to reproduce here or to justify. There is an unanswered question of whether bound states participate among the low-lying excitations. If this is the case, then the Bethe-Hulthén formalism is incapable of describing them since the validity of the various equations

---

[14] *Op. cit.*

above seems predicated on having real k's. Nevertheless, it is entirely possible that further mathematical study of Eqs. (149) and those following may allow the extension of the known results to complex k plane and that a complete classification scheme will result. For example, following Orbach one might consider the $S_i^z S_{i+1}^z$ coupling terms with variable parameter g, and study the energy levels as g is adiabatically increased. At $g = 0$, we recover the XY model (of which the solutions are completely determined) and then increase it to $g = 1$ which is the present Heisenberg model. As g is further

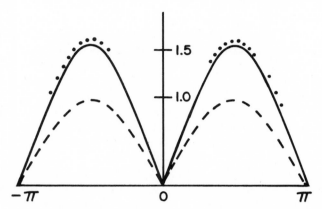

FIG. 6.7. Quasiparticle spectrum $\varepsilon(ka)$ obtained by Des Cloizeaux and Pearson for the infinite Heisenberg antiferromagnetic chain, $\pi/2 \sin ka$ (upper curve), compared with their numerical results for chain of 48 spins (dots); analogous spectrum for infinite XY antiferromagnetic chain (lower, dashed curve). Anderson's linearized antiferromagnons coincide precisely with the XY model.

increased, the Ising model is approached. In every case the ground-state energy can be computed as the solution of slight modifications of the present equations. The properties of the ground-state energy as a function of g have been discussed by Orbach and by Walker.[15]

Pending the discovery of the suggested classification scheme for excited states, we may accept the Cloizeaux-Pearson results for the one-magnon states, particularly because of the close agreement they obtain with numerical calculations for finite chains. In Fig. 6.7, the one-magnon excitation spectrum of a chain of 48 spins is compared with the theoretical curve for an infinite chain, and also with the corresponding excitation spectrum of the XY model ($g = 0$). This comparison will have further significance when we study the approximate theories of antiferromagnetism in the following pages. In any event, these calculations established the one-magnon excitation energy spectrum in the Heisenberg antiferromagnetic, viz.,

$$\varepsilon(q) = \frac{\pi}{2} |\sin q| \tag{166}$$

This may be compared to Eq. (140) for the XY model, also plotted in Fig. 6.7.

For the linear chains—both Heisenberg and XY models—the magnetic susceptibility can be calculated; but this would take us too far afield.[11,12]

---

[15] *Op. cit*

LINEARIZED ANTIFERROMAGNETIC MAGNONS

The quantization of magnons in the linear approximation is performed with great similarity to the procedure in the theory of ferromagnetism. Such an approximate quantum theory, in which only terms quadratic in the P's and Q's are retained in the Hamiltonian, was originally proposed by Anderson,[16] and was very successful in the early interpretation of the dynamics of antiferromagnets. As can be expected, the frequencies are identically the same as found in the classical linearized equations of motion of the antiferromagnet (discussed earlier); only the amplitudes are quantized as Bosons. Below, we shall indicate in what vital manner procedures which are satisfactory in ferromagnetism must be adapted for the present problem.

The paramount difficulty is that the ground state of the Heisenberg antiferromagnet is not known, with the exception of the linear chain. Alas, it is quite apparent that the procedure which worked in one dimension is not generalizable to three because of the heavy reliance on ordering the spin deviates along a line. The somewhat simpler XY model is similar to the quantum-mechanical hard-sphere Boson problem, for which also no adequate intermediate- or high-density theory exists in two or three dimensions.

Fortunately, there exists a perturbation theory of sorts, which gives us a "handle" on an approximate, variational ground state. It is a series in powers of $1/s$. The off-diagonal parts of the Hamiltonian are linearized, and diagonalized as best can be, in the standard way. The starting, or zeroth, point of this perturbation procedure is the classical ground state; or the configuration of lowest energy of the Hamiltonian with spins replaced by classical vectors of fixed length and position but variable orientations. The choice of this classical ground state is a soluble problem (discussed on p. 198). Here, assume a two-sublattice antiferromagnet with the following properties:

Antiferromagnetic coupling between nearest neighbors, and a lattice geometry such that two spins which are nearest neighbors of a third are not nearest neighbors of each other. These requirements are met, e.g., in the linear chain, simple square, simple cubic, and body-centered cubic lattices (but not in the face-centered cubic lattice). The classical ground state is then the Néel state: every spin *up* is surrounded by nearest neighbors which are *down*, and vice versa.

To give them a name, denote the spins down the *A sublattice*, and the spins up the *B sublattice*. Perform a canonical transformation on the *B* (but not on the *A*) spins: rotate them by 180° about the S^x axis,

$$S_j^{\pm} \rightarrow + S_j^{\mp}, \qquad S_j^z \rightarrow - S_j^z \qquad (j \text{ in } B) \tag{167}$$

At first, assume that i is in A and j is a nearest neighbor of i in B to write the Hamiltonian in the form:

$$\mathscr{H} = \sum_{i \subseteq A} \sum_{j \subseteq B} [(\tfrac{1}{2} S_i^+ S_j^+ + \text{H.c.}) - S_i^z S_j^z] \tag{168}$$

It is convenient to take the exchange constant J to be the unit of energy, so that it need

---

[16] P. W. Anderson, *Phys. Rev.*, **86**: 694 (1952); also Nagamiya et al., *op. cit.* An accurate perturbation theory by H. L. Davis, *Phys. Rev.*, **120**: 789 (1960), yields agreement with Table 6.1 to within a few percent.

not be written explicitly. Now, because the last result is explicitly symmetric in the two sublattices, one allows i to range over the entire crystal and j over all nearest neighbors of i, denoted by $j(i)$, and divides by 2 so as not to double-count bonds.

$$\mathscr{H} = \frac{1}{2} \sum_{\text{all } i} \sum_{j(i)} [\tfrac{1}{2}(S_i^+ S_j^+ + \text{H.c.}) - [S_i^z S_j^z]] \qquad (169)$$

In the linear approximation, the Hamiltonian becomes

$$\mathscr{H}_{\text{lin}} = \frac{1}{2} \sum_i \sum_{j(i)} [s(a_i^* a_j^* + \text{H.c.}) - s^2 + s(a_i^* a_i + a_j^* a_j)]$$

$$\rightarrow -\tfrac{1}{2} N z s^2 + z s \sum_{\mathbf{k}} a_{\mathbf{k}}^* a_{\mathbf{k}} + \frac{s}{2} \sum_{\mathbf{k}} \left(a_{\mathbf{k}}^* a_{-\mathbf{k}}^* \sum_{\delta} e^{i\mathbf{k}\cdot\delta} + \text{H.c.} \right) \qquad (170)$$

After the transformation to running-wave Boson operators, it is not yet diagonal. We eliminate the pair-creation terms by a method first due to Holstein and Primakoff.[17] Subsequently rediscovered by Bogolubov in his theory of Bose condensation, and now generally known as the *Bogolubov transformation*, it is described by the following law:

$$a_{\mathbf{k}} \rightarrow (\cosh u_{\mathbf{k}}) a_{\mathbf{k}} + (\sinh u_{\mathbf{k}}) a_{-\mathbf{k}}^*$$

$$a_{\mathbf{k}}^* \rightarrow (\cosh u_{\mathbf{k}}) a_{\mathbf{k}}^* + (\sinh u_{\mathbf{k}}) a_{-\mathbf{k}} \qquad \text{with } u_{\mathbf{k}} = u_{-\mathbf{k}} = u_{\mathbf{k}}^* \qquad (171)$$

One must choose the function $u_{\mathbf{k}}$ so that the terms $a_{\mathbf{k}}^* a_{-\mathbf{k}}^*$ are eliminated. It is a matter of some simple algebra to determine that what is required is

$$\tanh 2u_{\mathbf{k}} = \frac{-1}{z} \sum_{\delta} \cos \mathbf{k} \cdot \delta \qquad (172)$$

with δ, a vector connecting any spin with any of its z nearest neighbors. This reduces the Hamiltonian to the diagonal form,

$$\mathscr{H}_{\text{lin}} = -\tfrac{1}{2} N z s(s + 1) + \sum_{\mathbf{k}} (\mathfrak{n}_{\mathbf{k}} + \tfrac{1}{2})(zs)\sqrt{1 - \tanh^2 2u_{\mathbf{k}}} \qquad (173)$$

Before discussing the magnon spectrum it is not unwise to digress somewhat and examine the ground-state energy. In this representation, it is the energy eigenvalue when all $n_{\mathbf{k}} = 0$, that is, the vacuum energy. Conventionally, one writes it in the following form:

$$E_0 = -\tfrac{1}{2} N s^2 z \left(1 + \frac{\gamma}{zs} \right) \qquad (174)$$

The parameter γ may be shown to be bounded between 0 and 1. Indeed, Hulthén's exact result for the linear chain of Eq. (165) ($z = 2$, $s = \tfrac{1}{2}$) yields $\gamma = 0.7726$, which is perhaps the largest attainable value. The results in Table 6.1 were computed by the

[17] *Op. cit.*

linear theory,[16] Eq. (173). The restriction to nearest-neighbor interactions robs these numerical results of any very general validity. But it is interesting to see the good agreement (within ≈ 6 percent) with the exact result for the linear chain, where the spin-wave theory might have been expected to fail badly. Although for the one-dimensional magnon spectrum, the agreement will not appear so favorable, it is not farfetched to conceive that the ground state and excited states of the simple theory may be in good agreement with the (yet unknown) exact result for three dimensional lattices.

TABLE 6.1
γ for Various Lattices

Lattice	z	γ
Linear chain	2	0.726
Square	4	0.632
Simple cubic	6	0.58
Body-centered cubic	8	0.58

Again for one dimension, using Eqs. (172) and (173), we find for the magnon energy,

$$\varepsilon(k) = (2s)|\sin ka| \tag{175}$$

with a = lattice spacing. For spins $\frac{1}{2}$ the result is similar to the exact result for the XY model, but is too low by a factor $2/\pi$ for spins $\frac{1}{2}$ in the Heisenberg model, which the spin-wave theory is supposed to approximate. The discrepancy is seen in Fig. 6.7.

In any number of dimensions, the magnon spectrum

$$\varepsilon_{\mathbf{k}} = s\sqrt{z^2 - \left(\sum_{\delta} \cos \mathbf{k}\cdot\mathbf{\delta}\right)^2} \tag{176}$$

is doubly degenerate, and is linear in $\mathbf{k}$ for small $\mathbf{k}$.

Problem 3: Show that the magnon spectrum, Eq. (176), is the special case for nearest-neighbor interactions of the frequency spectrum given in Eq. (34) of Chapter 5 on semi-classical spin waves (p. 122).

The existence of two distinct modes of zero energy, one at $\mathbf{k} = \mathbf{0}$ and the other at the edge of the Brillouin zone, means that magnons belonging to these wavevectors can be emitted at no cost of energy, and indicates a high degeneracy of the approximate ground state. This is sufficient to ensure that the theory express correctly the rotational invariance of the spin Hamiltonian. By the emission of zero energy magnons, a state can also be reached in which the A and B sublattices have been interchanged. However, the *true* ground state is *non*degenerate.

The diagonalization of $\mathscr{H}_{\text{lin}}$ leads to a reduction of the S^z spin components from their saturation magnitude in the Néel state. Calculating this reduction we find

$$\langle \delta S_i^z \rangle \equiv \left\langle \frac{1}{N}\sum_i (s - |S_i^z|) \right\rangle = \frac{1}{2N}\sum_{\mathbf{k}}\left(\frac{1}{\sqrt{1 - \tanh^2 2u_{\mathbf{k}}}} - 1\right) \approx .078 \quad \text{sc} \tag{177}$$

The numerical value represents an estimate by Anderson of the integral, for the simple cubic (sc) structure. Note that for the linear chain this formula yields

$$\langle \delta S_i^z \rangle = \infty \qquad \text{lin chain} \tag{178}$$

due to the divergence of the integral at long wavelengths. This implies an absence of long-range order in one dimension even in the spin-wave approximation, a result in accord with other calculations.

NONLINEARITIES IN ANTI- AND FERRIMAGNETISM

Ferrimagnets are generally insulators containing localized spins which are anti-ferromagnetically coupled. One example pointed out by Néel, who coined the term *ferrimagnetism* (because of its existence in the *ferrites*, of which the lodestone is an example) occurs if the spins on the A and B sublattices of the previous section are of unequal magnitude $s_A \neq s_B$. Other, vastly more complicated examples of ferrimagnetism exist in theory and in nature,[18] but their study is a complex and specialized field. In the present section, we want to accomplish two goals: to display the spin-wave Hamiltonian for the simple two-sublattice model of ferrimagnetism, including leading nonlinear terms, and to show the leading nonlinear terms in antiferromagnetism, obtained from the former by setting $s_A = s_B$. We also kill two birds with one stone by showing how the same expression, which for unequal spins gives a magnon energy $\sim k^2$ at long wavelengths, will yield the antiferromagnon energy $\sim k$. The mathematics is based on work by Nakamura and Bloch,[19] and consists of a straightforward expansion of the square roots in the Holstein-Primakoff representation. For large spins, the agreement of even the linearized theories with the classical equations of motion gives some confidence in this procedure, for which there is no other formal mathematical justification. (The reader should now solve Problem 2 of Chapter 5 if he has not done so already.)

Let $s_A \geqslant s_B$, let there be N of each, and put

$$s_A = (1 + \alpha)s \qquad s_B = (1 - \alpha s) \tag{179}$$

Except for the unequal spins, the Hamiltonian is precisely that of Eq. (168) in the preceding section. We keep the first three terms in an expansion of the Hamiltonian in powers of s:

$$\mathcal{H} = \mathcal{H}_0 + \mathcal{H}_1 + \mathcal{H}_2 + o(s^{-2}) \tag{180}$$

They are,

$$\mathcal{H}_0 = \sum [\gamma_0(s_B a_k^* a_k + s_A b_k^* b_k)$$

$$+ \sqrt{s_A s_B} \; \gamma_k(a_k b_k + \text{H.c.})] - N\frac{z}{2} s_A s_B \tag{181A}$$

---

[18] For a comprehensive review and references to the literature, see, e.g., W. P. Wolf, "Ferrimagnetism," *Repts. Progr. Phys.*, XXIV: 212 (1961).
[19] T. Nakamura and M. Bloch, *Phys. Rev.*, **132**: 2528 (1963).

$$\mathscr{H}_1 = -\frac{1}{4N\sqrt{s_A s_B}} \sum_{k_1 k_2 k_3 k_4} (s_B \gamma_{k_1} b_{k_1} a^*_{k_2} a_{k_3} a_{k_4} + s_A \gamma_{k_1} a_{k_1} b^*_{k_2} b_{k_3} b_{k_4}$$

$$+ \sqrt{s_A s_B} \; \gamma_{k_1 - k_3} a^*_{k_1} a_{k_3} b^*_{k_4} b_{k_2}) \Delta(k_1 + k_2 - k_3 - k_4) + \text{H.c.} \qquad (181\text{B})$$

with $\mathbf{V}(\mathbf{k})$ defined on p. 158; and finally,

$$\mathscr{H}_2 = -\frac{1}{2(4N)^2 (s_A s_B)^{\frac{3}{2}}} \sum_{k_1 \ldots k_6} (s_A^2 \gamma_{k_1} a^*_{k_1} b^*_{k_4} b^*_{k_5} b_{k_2} b^*_{k_6} b_{k_3}$$

$$- 2s_A s_B \gamma_{k_1 + k_2 - k_4} a^*_{k_1} a^*_{k_2} a_{k_4} b^*_{k_5} b^*_{k_6} b_{k_3}$$

$$+ s_B^2 \gamma_{k_6} a^*_{k_1} a^*_{k_2} a_{k_4} a^*_{k_3} a_{k_5} b^*_{k_6}) \Delta(k_1 + k_2 + k_3 - k_4 - k_5 - k_6) + \text{H.c.} \quad (181\text{C})$$

where

$$a_{\mathbf{k}} = \frac{1}{\sqrt{N}} \sum_{j \subseteq A} a_j e^{-i\mathbf{k}\cdot\mathbf{R}_j} \quad \text{and} \quad b_{\mathbf{k}} = \frac{1}{\sqrt{N}} \sum_{i \subseteq B} b_i e^{+i\mathbf{k}\cdot\mathbf{R}_i} \qquad (182)$$

and

$$\gamma_{\mathbf{k}} = \sum_{\delta} e^{i\mathbf{k}\cdot\delta} \qquad \gamma_0 = z \qquad (183)$$

Next, $\mathscr{H}_0$ is diagonalized by the Bogolubov-like transformation,

$$a_{\mathbf{k}} \to a_{\mathbf{k}} \cosh u_{\mathbf{k}} + b^*_{\mathbf{k}} \sinh u_{\mathbf{k}}$$

$$b_{\mathbf{k}} \to a^*_{\mathbf{k}} \sinh u_{\mathbf{k}} + b_{\mathbf{k}} \cosh u_{\mathbf{k}} \qquad (184)$$

which mixes operators of the A and B sites. The degeneracy of the magnon spectrum in antiferromagnetism is lifted for $\alpha \neq 0$, and the following two magnon branches are found:

$$\varepsilon_a(\mathbf{k}) = \gamma_0 s (f_{\mathbf{k}} - \alpha) \qquad \text{and} \qquad \varepsilon_b(\mathbf{k}) = \gamma_0 s (f_{\mathbf{k}} + \alpha) \qquad (185)$$

where

$$f_{\mathbf{k}} = \sqrt{1 - (1 - \alpha^2)\left(\frac{\gamma_{\mathbf{k}}}{\gamma_0}\right)^2} \qquad (186)$$

provided the transformation parameter, $u_{\mathbf{k}}$, is chosen so as to eliminate $a_{\mathbf{k}} b_{\mathbf{k}} + \text{H.c.}$ from the Hamiltonian:

$$\tanh 2u_{\mathbf{k}} = -\frac{\gamma_{\mathbf{k}}}{\gamma_0} \sqrt{1 - \alpha^2} \qquad (187)$$

In the long wavelength approximation, the magnon energies are

$$\varepsilon_a(\mathbf{k}) \approx (\sqrt{\alpha^2 + (1 - \alpha^2)(ka)^2} - \alpha)\gamma_0 s \propto \frac{1 - \alpha^2}{2\alpha}(ka)^2$$

$$(188)$$

$$\varepsilon_b(\mathbf{k}) \approx (\sqrt{\alpha^2 + (1 - \alpha^2)(ka)^2} + \alpha)\gamma_0 s$$

from which it is easy to see the range dependent on α, over which the lower branch is quadratic, as in ferromagnets, before becoming approximately linear, as in antiferromagnets.

The ground-state energy, in this linear approximation, is

$$E_0 = -\frac{z}{2}(2N)s^2(1-\alpha^2)\left(1+\frac{\gamma}{zs}\right) \tag{189}$$

(it must be noted that there is a total of $2N$ spins in the present calculation) with

$$\gamma = zs\left(1-\frac{1}{N}\sum f_k\right) \tag{190}$$

This quantum-mechanical correction is smaller in ferrimagnets than in antiferromagnets, which is not too surprising in view of the resemblance with ferromagnets, for which $\gamma \equiv 0$.

The nonlinearities are handled in the following manner. *First*, $\mathscr{H}_1$ and $\mathscr{H}_2$ are both transformed by the rules of Eqs. (184) and (187). *Then*, the diagonal terms in $\mathscr{H}_1$ are combined with the now entirely diagonal $\mathscr{H}_0$ to give a first-order diagonal Hamiltonian which we may denote $\mathscr{H}_D$, by analogy with the treatment of ferromagnetism. *Finally*, the off-diagonal matrix elements of $\mathscr{H}_1$ are eliminated by a canonical transformation, such as T in the ferromagnetic case. The resulting additional diagonal terms, combined with the diagonal parts of $\mathscr{H}_2$, form the second-order correction to $\mathscr{H}_D$. The remaining nondiagonal terms are discarded, for their contribution is $o(s^{-2})$. These calculations are undertaken in the paper of Nakamura and Bloch[20] but are too lengthy to be reproduced here. They also analyze the temperature dependence of the magnon energies (a subject which is treated here for ferromagnets only, in a separate chapter). Some of their results at $T = 0°K$ are as follows:

1. There is a small s-independent shift in the magnon energies as given in Eqs. (185) and (187), but even for $s = \frac{1}{2}$ it is relatively quite small at all wavelengths.

2. There is a nonlinear diagonal magnon energy, of the form

$$\sum_{k,\,k'}[\tfrac{1}{2}\Gamma_{aa}(k,\,k')(a_k^* a_k)(a_{k'}^* a_{k'}) - \Gamma_{ab}(k,\,k')(a_k^* a_k)(b_{k'}^* b_{k'})$$
$$+ \tfrac{1}{2}\Gamma_{bb}(k,\,k')(b_k^* b_k)(b_{k'}^* b_{k'})] \tag{191}$$

which, together with the linear magnon terms, makes up $\mathscr{H}_D$. One significant property of the nonlinear Hamiltonian is that the coefficient of $a_k^* a_k$ turns out to vanish for $k = 0$, regardless of the occupation numbers of the other modes. This expresses the rotationally invariant nature of the approximations leading to $\mathscr{H}_D$. But differences with the analogous treatment of the ferromagnet can be noted, due to the presence of two spin-wave branches with different properties; for example, an increase in the occupation numbers of either branch *increases* the magnon energies in that branch and *decreases* the magnon energies of the other branch. [However, this appears to be a consequence of the nearest-neighbor model, and is not a law of universal validity; (see the discussion following Eq. (120).] The formulas for the coefficients and further details of the theory are in the Nakamura and Block paper cited earlier.

---

[20] *Op. cit.*

CHAPTER 7

MAGNETISM AND
MAGNONS IN METALS

All the electrons in a metal do not participate in the electrical conduction, nor in other physical, chemical, or magnetic processes. The reason is that some are core electrons, belonging to filled shells tightly bound to the nucleus and unaware of the metallic environment. Electrons in unfilled shells have a range of behavior intermediate between that of tightly bound localized electrons and that of quasifree particles experiencing only a smooth periodic atomic potential and participating fully in the electrical conductivity.

It is easiest to discuss the theory of magnetism in such metals where the electrons can be clearly divided into distinct sets of tightly bound and quasifree particles. Hopefully, the results still have qualitative merit when the carriers have properties intermediate between these two extremes.

The simplest model of magnetism in metals is the following: electrons in well-localized magnetic d or f shells interact with one another via a Heisenberg nearest-neighbor exchange mechanism, whilst an entirely distinct set of (quasifree) electrons in Bloch states accounts for the metallic properties without partaking of the magnetic ones. *Unfortunately, this model is purely fictional;* X-ray data, optical experiments, measurements of specific heat all indicate that the d electrons in the iron transition series metals are essentially conduction electrons, in bands several electron volts wide. Whereas in the rare earths, on the contrary, the magnetic shells are *so* well localized (~ 0.3 Å) that the overlap between atoms (at a distance of approximately 3 Å) must be negligibly small, and there is therefore *no* Heisenberg nearest-neighbor exchange to a good approximation. The observed magnetism in such a case must involve the conduction electrons, which alone are capable of sustaining correlations over several interatomic distances.

For these and other reasons,[1] it is not possible to ignore the band structure in any sensible theory of magnetism in metals. In the present chapter we start with a review of the band theory in the one-electron approximation,[2] with emphasis on *tight binding*, which is the simplest approximation of any value in the investigation of magnetic properties. Proceeding from there, we shall see what gives rise to strong

---

[1] See the indictment of the Heisenberg and Heitler-London theories in J. C. Slater, "Ferromagnetism and the Band Theory," *Rev. Mod. Phys.*, **25**: 199 (1953).

[2] For a more comprehensive treatment see any text on theory of solids or specialized treatise such as J. Callaway, *Energy Band Theory*, Academic, New York, 1964. See also Sir Nevill Mott's very comprehensive "Electrons in Transition Metals," *Advances in Phys.*, **13**: 325 (1964).

magnetic properties, such as ferromagnetic or antiferromagnetic behavior. We shall even show that the Heisenberg Hamiltonian for insulators can be derived on the basis of a band picture entirely analogous to the band theory of metals. Finally, we shall derive the theory of magnons in metals for the various models considered.

What will be found, is roughly this: For a material to be *magnetic*, the Hund's rule energy $O(1 \ eV)$ which is responsible for the existence of atomic magnetic moments must be larger than the banding energy, as measured by the density of states or by the Fermi energy. (It is normally only in transition and rare-earth materials that such a condition can be fulfilled and that the tendency of the bonding orbitals to have their spins paired can be partially frustrated.) We shall also find that the long-range order is *ferro*magnetic when $2k_F \ll K_n$, and *antiferro*magnetic when $2k_F \sim K_n$, where $k_F =$ Fermi wavevector of the majority spin band and $K_n =$ any reciprocal lattice vector. The energy which stabilizes such long-range order is $O(kT_c) \ll O(1 \ eV)$. Estimated orders of magnitudes of the various energies are listed in Table 7.3.

To start, it is necessary to recapitulate the Hartree-Fock theory of one-electron states in solids. As an example we shall show how the weak para- and diamagnetic properties shared by all metals are calculated from a knowledge of the important one-electron density of states parameter, $N(E)$.

BLOCH AND WANNIER FUNCTIONS

In the one-electron band approximation, the Hamiltonian is

$$\mathscr{H} = \frac{\mathbf{p}^2}{2m} + \sum_i V(\mathbf{r} - \mathbf{R}_i) \tag{1}$$

where $V(\mathbf{r} - \mathbf{R}_i)$ is the averaged potential due to the nucleus and all other electrons except the one under consideration. In the simple cubic structure, lattice spacing a, the translation $\mathbf{r} \to \mathbf{r} + a(n_1, n_2, n_3)$ commutes with Eq. (1) for integer n_i; and so the translation operator can be used to provide the eigenfunctions of $\mathscr{H}$ with an important quantum number, the crystal momentum $\mathbf{k}$. In other lattices, the translations $\mathbf{R}_\alpha$ take a different form, but a crystal momentum can always be defined and, together with the band index t, it provides the quantum numbers for the *Bloch functions*,

$$\psi_{t,\mathbf{k}}(\mathbf{r}) = e^{i\mathbf{k}\cdot\mathbf{r}} u_{t,\mathbf{k}}(\mathbf{r}) \tag{2}$$

which are the eigenfunctions of $\mathscr{H}$. The function $u_{t,\mathbf{k}}(\mathbf{r})$ has periodicity of the lattice and obeys the eigenvalue equation,

$$e^{-i\mathbf{k}\cdot\mathbf{r}} \mathscr{H} e^{+i\mathbf{k}\cdot\mathbf{r}} u_{t,\mathbf{k}}(\mathbf{r}) = \left[\frac{(\mathbf{p} + \hbar\mathbf{k})^2}{2m} + \sum_i V(\mathbf{r} - \mathbf{R}_i) \right] u_{t,\mathbf{k}}(\mathbf{r}) = E_t(\mathbf{k}) u_{t,\mathbf{k}}(\mathbf{r}) \tag{3}$$

subject to the boundary condition $u_{t,\mathbf{k}}(\mathbf{r} + \mathbf{R}_\alpha) = u_{t,\mathbf{k}}(\mathbf{r})$, with $\mathbf{R}_\alpha \equiv$ a translation vector of the lattice (see below).

The meaning of the band index t is best understood in connection with the Fourier transform of the Bloch functions, viz., the *Wannier functions*

$$\psi_{t,\,i}(\mathbf{r}) = \frac{1}{\sqrt{N}} \sum_{\mathbf{k}} e^{-i\mathbf{k}\cdot\mathbf{R}_i}\psi_{t,\,\mathbf{k}}(\mathbf{r}) \tag{4}$$

which like the Bloch functions, form a complete, orthonormal set of functions in the Hilbert space of the Hamiltonian, Eq. (1). The sum over $\mathbf{k}$ is restricted to the *first Brillouin zone*, i.e., to the range of $\mathbf{k}$'s obeying the inequality

$$|\mathbf{k}\cdot\mathbf{R}_\alpha| < \pi$$

where $\mathbf{R}_\alpha$ = any one of the smallest translation vectors of the lattice (primitive translation vectors). In the limit of infinite interatomic separation, the Wannier functions reduce to ordinary atomic orbitals. In that limit, i identifies the atom, and t the set of atomic quantum numbers (principal, orbital, azimuthal, spin; the use of a single index is for typographical simplicity). When atoms are brought close together, the atomic levels identified by t broaden into a band, unless, as in the f shell of the rare earths and the $1s$ helium core common to all metallic atoms, the electrons are still so tightly bound to the nucleus at the observed interatomic separation that the very concept of one-electron bands remains inapplicable. But this is not the case of the $3d$ states, and we note that the first metal to have a filled $3d$ band (Cu), and the elements immediately following it in the periodic table (Zn, Ga, etc.) are nonmagnetic; whereas the iron series just preceding these, noted for the unfilled d shell in the atom and d band in the metal, form materials with varied and interesting magnetic properties. One may rightly suspect the d-band electrons of being particularly important in the study of magnetism, and the unfilled d band of containing "magnetically active" electrons.

Before making these notions more precise it is necessary to review some of the properties shared by all electrons, including the nonmagnetic ones. Some of these can be studied in the "plane wave approximation," in which we set $V(\mathbf{r} - \mathbf{R}_i) = 0$, and $u_{t,\,\mathbf{k}} = 1$. But we do not wish to sacrifice the band structure, the qualitative features of which are retained in the tight-binding approximation which we study next.

TIGHT-BINDING

The basic premise in this theory is that it is easier to estimate matrix elements involving Wannier functions (because of their supposed localization about specified atoms) than to solve the differential equations for the Bloch functions. We illustrate this, using the Hamiltonian $\mathcal{H}$ defined in Eq. (1), and form the Wannier matrix elements

$$H(\mathbf{R}_{ij})_{n,\,n} = \int \psi_{n,\,i}^*(\mathbf{r})\mathcal{H}\psi_{n,\,j}(\mathbf{r})\,d_3r \tag{5}$$

so that Schrödinger's equation reduces to the determinantal eigenvalue problem,

$$\mathrm{Det}\,\|H(\mathbf{R}_{ij})_{n,\,n} - E\delta_{ij}\| = 0 \tag{6}$$

Evidently it does not matter which representation we solve Schrödinger's equation in, and the eigenvalues E will coincide exactly with the Bloch energies $E_n(\mathbf{k})$. Moreover, the eigenfunctions necessarily turn out to be precisely the proper linear combination,

$$\psi_{n,\,\mathbf{k}}(\mathbf{r}) = \frac{1}{\sqrt{N}} \sum_{i=1}^{N} e^{i\mathbf{k}\cdot\mathbf{R}_i}\psi_{n,\,i}(\mathbf{r}) \qquad (7)$$

which make up the Bloch functions, Eq. (4).

If one uses *approximate* Wannier functions, however, the *interband* $(n \neq m)$ matrix elements $H(\mathbf{R}_{ij})_{n,\,m}$ need not vanish. It is common practice to use atomic orbitals instead of Wannier orbitals as a first approximation, and therefore this method is often known as the LCAO method, for the initials of *linear combination of atomic orbitals*. The mixing of different orbitals to form the bands in the solid expresses the well-known fact that angular momentum is "quenched" (not conserved) due to the lowering of symmetry from spherical to cubic, hexagonal, or whatever.

It is standard practice to limit the matrix elements $H(\mathbf{R}_{ij})_{n,\,m}$ to nearest-neighboring (in extreme cases, perhaps as far as second- and third-nearest-neighboring) atomic distances R_{ij}. It is not sensible to consider more distant interactions, for if they become important the tight-binding procedure itself becomes unwieldy, and other methods such as the quasifree electron approximation are then simpler and more appropriate.

Consider the band structures derived in the following simple examples. The determinantal equation yields the energy at all points in $\mathbf{k}$-space, with only the constant parameters (overlap integrals) required to be numerically calculated. And if we do not know the atomic orbitals, nor trust them in the particular crystal under consideration, these constants may be taken as adjustable parameters to be fitted either by experiment or by comparison with a few calculated points given by more accurate band structure calculations. *Assume a simple cubic structure* and consider:

s bands: By symmetry, the matrix elements to the six nearest neighbors are all equal, so that only two parameters enter the problem:

$$A \equiv H(\mathbf{0}) = \int \psi^*(r)\mathscr{H}\psi(r)\,d_3r$$

and $\qquad -B \equiv H(0,0,a) = \cdots = H(a,0,0) = \int \psi^*(|\mathbf{r} + (0,0,a)|)\mathscr{H}\psi(r)\,d_3r$

In terms of these, the energy eigenvalues are

$$E(\mathbf{k}) = A - 2B(\cos k_x a + \cos k_y a + \cos k_z a) \qquad (8)$$

Problem 1:

(a) Assuming nearest-neighbor overlap, prove that in the body-centered cubic structure the s bands have the form

$$E(\mathbf{k}) = A - B\cos k_x a \cos k_y a \cos k_z a$$

and that in the face-centered cubic structure the appropriate formula is

$$E(\mathbf{k}) = A - B(\cos k_x a \cos k_y a + \cdots + \cos k_y a \cos k_z a)$$

(b) Derive the s-band structure for the hexagonal close-packed lattice.

p bands: Again in the simple cubic structure, with nearest-neighbor interactions only, the threefold degeneracy of the atomic orbitals is not lifted. We write the orbitals as

$$\psi_n(\mathbf{r}) = x\phi(r),\ y\phi(r),\ z\phi(r)$$

instead of using the spherical harmonics; for example, $\cos\theta = z/r$. A first parameter,

$$A \equiv H(0)_{n,n} = \int x\phi^*(r)\mathscr{H}x\phi(r)\, d_3r$$

is the same for all three bands. A second parameter,

$$-B = \int x\phi^*(|\mathbf{r} + (0, 0, a)|)\mathscr{H}x\phi(r)\, d_3r = \int y\phi^*(|\mathbf{r} + (0, 0, a)|)\mathscr{H}y\phi(r)\, d_3r$$

and finally a third one

$$-C = \int \cdot(z + a)\phi^*(|\mathbf{r} + (0, 0, a)|)\mathscr{H}z\phi(r)\, d_3r$$

are required. All other integrals may be obtained from the above, except those for $m \neq n$; these vanish by symmetry, subject to the restriction to nearest-neighbor overlap. When the Hamiltonian eigenvalue equation (6) is finally solved, we find three degenerate bands:

$$E_1(\mathbf{k}) = A - 2B(\cos k_x a + \cos k_y a) - 2C(\cos k_z a) \tag{9A}$$

$$E_2(\mathbf{k}) = A - 2B(\cos k_y a + \cos k_z a) - 2C(\cos k_x a) \tag{9B}$$

and $$E_3(\mathbf{k}) = A - 2B(\cos k_z a + \cos k_x a) - 2C(\cos k_y a) \tag{9C}$$

The three *p* bands are related to one another by those rotations in **k**-space, which permute the Cartesian components $k_{x, y, z}$. In each band, the contours of constant energy have less than cubic symmetry, and even at small **k**, these contours are not spherical but are ellipsoids of revolution with principal nonequivalent axes along the $k_{x, y, z}$ directions.

Had we chosen the axes of quantization of the three *p* functions along other than a crystal axis, the interband matrix elements $H(0, 0, a)_{n, m}$ for $n \neq m$ would not have vanished so conveniently. The eigenvalue equation, Eq. (6), which held for the exact Wannier functions, must be replaced in the general case by the *r*-dimensional equation,

$$\boxed{Det\ \|H(\mathbf{k})_{n, m} - E\delta_{n, m}\| = 0} \tag{10}$$

where r = number of interacting bands; $n,\ m = 1,\ 2,\ \dots,\ r$. Here we have taken advantage of translational invariance to form the Fourier transforms, and to define

$$(n/m) \equiv H(\mathbf{k})_{n, m} = \frac{1}{N}\sum_{i, j} e^{i\mathbf{k}\cdot\mathbf{R}ij} \int \psi_{n, i}^* \mathscr{H}\psi_{m, j}\, d_3r \tag{11}$$

TABLE 7.1
Matrix Elements of Eqs. (10) and (11) in Tight-Binding (LCAO) Approximation

(s/s)	$H(000)_{s,s} + 2H(100)_{s,s}(X + Y + Z) + 4H(110)_{s,s}(XY + XZ + YZ)$ $+ 8H(111)_{s,s}XYZ$
(s/x)	$2iH(100)_{s,x}\tilde{X} + 4iH(110)_{s,x}\tilde{X}(Y + Z) + 8iH(111)_{s,x}\tilde{X}YZ$
(s/xy)	$-4H(110)_{s,xy}\tilde{X}\tilde{Y} - 8H(111)_{s,xy}\tilde{X}\tilde{Y}Z$
$(s/x^2 - y^2)$	$\sqrt{3}H(001)_{s,3z^2-r^2}(X - Y) + 2\sqrt{3}H(110)_{s,3z^2-r^2}(Y - X)Z$
$(s/3z^2 - r^2)$	$H(001)_{s,3z^2-r^2}(2Z - X - Y) - 2H(110)_{s,3z^2-r^2}(-2XY + XZ + YZ)$
(x/x)	$H(000)_{x,x} + 2H(100)_{x,x}X + 2H(100)_{y,y}(Y + Z)$ $+ 4H(110)_{x,x}X(Y + Z) + 4H(011)_{x,x}YZ + 8H(111)_{x,x}XYZ$
(x/y)	$-4H(110)_{x,y}\tilde{X}\tilde{Y} - 8H(111)_{x,y}\tilde{X}\tilde{Y}Z$
(x/xy)	$2iH(010)_{x,xy}\tilde{Y} + 4iH(110)_{x,xy}X\tilde{Y} + 4iH(011)_{x,xy}\tilde{Y}Z$ $+ 8iH(111)_{x,xy}\tilde{Y}XZ$
(x/yz)	$-8iH(111)_{x,yz}\tilde{X}\tilde{Y}\tilde{Z}$
$(x/x^2 - y^2)$	$\sqrt{3}iH(001)_{z,3z^2-r^2}\tilde{X} + 2\sqrt{3}iH(011)_{z,3z^2-r^2}(\tilde{X}Y + \tilde{X}Z)$ $+ 2iH(011)_{z,x^2-y^2}\tilde{X}(Y - Z) + 8iH(111)_{x,x^2-y^2}\tilde{X}YZ$
$(x/3z^2 - r^2)$	$-iH(001)_{z,3z^2-r^2}\tilde{X} - 2iH(011)_{z,3z^2-r^2}\tilde{X}(Y + Z)$ $+ 2\sqrt{3}iH(011)_{z,x^2-y^2}\tilde{X}(Y - Z) - (8/\sqrt{3})H(111)_{x,x^2-y^2}\tilde{X}YZ$
$(z/3z^2 - r^2)$	$2iH(001)_{z,3z^2-r^2}\tilde{Z} + 4iH(011)_{z,3z^2-r^2}\tilde{Z}(X + Y)$ $+ (16/\sqrt{3})iH(111)_{x,x^2-y^2}XY\tilde{Z}$
(xy/xy)	$H(000)_{xy,xy} + 2H(100)_{xy,xy}(X + Y) + 2H(001)_{xy,xy}Z$ $+ 4H(110)_{xy,xy}XY + 4H(011)_{xy,xy}(X + Y)Z + 8H(111)_{xy,xy}XYZ$
(xy/xz)	$-4H(011)_{xy,xz}\tilde{Y}\tilde{Z} - 8H(111)_{xy,xz}X\tilde{Y}\tilde{Z}$
$(xy/x^2 - y^2)$	Zero
$(xy/3z^2 - r^2)$	$-4H(110)_{xy,3z^2-r^2}\tilde{X}\tilde{Y} - 8H(111)_{xy,3z^2-r^2}\tilde{X}\tilde{Y}Z$
$(xz/x^2 - y^2)$	$2\sqrt{3}\,H(110)_{xy,3z^2-r^2}\tilde{X}\tilde{Z} + 4\sqrt{3}\,H(111)_{xy,3z^2-r^2}\tilde{X}\tilde{Z}Y$
$(xz/3z^2 - r^2)$	$2H(110)_{xy,3z^2-r^2}\tilde{X}\tilde{Z} + 4H(111)_{xy,3z^2-r^2}\tilde{X}\tilde{Z}Y$
$(x^2 - y^2/x^2 - y^2)$	$H(000)^* + \frac{3}{2}H(001)^*(X + Y) + 2H(001)^\S(\frac{1}{4}X + \frac{1}{4}Y + Z)$ $+ 3H(110)^*(X + Y)Z + 4H(110)^\S(XY + \frac{1}{4}XZ + \frac{1}{4}YZ)$ $+ 8H(111)^*XYZ$
$(3z^2 - r^2/3z^2 - r^2)$	$H(000)^* + 2H(001)^*(\frac{1}{4}X + \frac{1}{4}Y + Z) + \frac{3}{2}H(001)^\S(X + Y)$ $+ 4H(110)^*(XY + \frac{1}{4}XZ + \frac{1}{4}YZ) + 3H(110)^\S(XZ + YZ)$ $+ 8H(111)^*XYZ$
$(x^2 - y^2/3z^2 - r^2)$	$\frac{1}{2}\sqrt{3}H(001)^*(-X + Y) - \frac{1}{2}\sqrt{3}H(001)^\S(-X + Y)$ $+ \sqrt{3}H(110)^*(X - Y)Z - \sqrt{3}\,H(110)^\S(X - Y)Z$

---

* $H(LMN)^* \equiv H(LMN)_{3z^2-r^2,3z^2-r^2}$.

§ $H(LMN)^\S \equiv H(LMN)_{x^2-y^2,\,x^2-y^2}$.

NOTE: Assuming nearest-neighbor interactions only, in the **simple cubic** structure retain only terms in (100), (010), and (001). For **face-centered** cubic retain only (110), (011), and (101). For **body-centered** cubic retain only (111).

KEY: $X = \cos k_x a$
$Y = \cos k_y a$
$Z = \cos k_z a$
$\tilde{X} = \sin k_x a$
$\tilde{Y} = \sin k_y a$
$\tilde{Z} = \sin k_z a$

The band parameter constants are the integrals $H(LMN)_{m,n} = \int \psi_m^*[\mathbf{r} + a(L, M, N)]\mathscr{H}\psi_n(\mathbf{r})\, d_3r$ where $L, M, N = 0, 1, \dots$.

SOURCE: Based on Table II in J. Slater and G. Koster, *Phys. Rev.*, **94**: 1498 (1954).

In Table 7.1 are reproduced results by Slater and Koster, who have calculated these matrix elements out to third nearest neighbor in the simple cubic structure. This is sufficient also for obtaining nearest-neighbor interactions in face- and body-centered cubic structures (and with some manipulations, next nearest neighbors also, but we shall not be interested in these). Note that $H(\mathbf{k})_{n,m}$ is abbreviated (n/m) in Table 7.1 for typographical simplicity. The matrix elements $H(\mathbf{k})_{n,m}$ are given, abbreviated as (n/m), among s-like functions (s); p-like functions (x, y, and z); and d-like functions (xy, xz, yz, $3z^2 - r^2$, and $x^2 - y^2$).

It is sensible to consider these matrix elements as empirical constants; they can be estimated by performing the appropriate two-center integrals, but for greater accuracy should be fitted either to experiment or to one of the more precise band structure calculations. Conversely, the LCAO method provides useful interpolation formulas, which permit functions, integrals, and derivatives of the band structure parameters to be calculated with relative ease.

Consider five d bands in the simple cubic structure, ignoring s and p bands as well as non-nearest-neighbor interactions. Looking up Table 7.1, extract the following special case of the eigenvalue equation, Eq. (10):

$$
\text{Det}
\begin{array}{c|ccc:cc}
 & (xy) & (xz) & (yz) & x^2 - y^2 & 3z^2 - r^2 \\
\hline
(xy) & F_1(k) - E & 0 & 0 & 0 & 0 \\
(xz) & 0 & F_2(k) - E & 0 & 0 & 0 \\
(yz) & 0 & 0 & F_3(k) - E & 0 & 0 \\
\hdashline
x^2 - y^2 & 0 & 0 & 0 & F_4(k) - E & V(k) \\
3z^2 - r^2 & 0 & 0 & 0 & V(k) & F_5(k) - E
\end{array} = 0 \qquad (12)
$$

The definitions of the F's and $V(k)$, and some features of the solutions, are discussed in Problem 2.

Problem 2:

(a) In the example of Eq. (12) in the text, find $F_i(k)$ and $V(k)$ by referring to Table 7.1. Show that the solutions of the eigenvalue equation describe three degenerate d bands with ellipsoidal contours of constant energy much like the p bands of Eq. (9) and two nondegenerate s-like bands. Obtain the contours of constant energy of the latter near $k = 0$. Plot the energy as a function of k along the three principal directions, (100), (110), and (111).

(b) Calculate the first-order effect of an infinitesimal next-nearest-neighbor interaction on the band structures calculated in part (a).

Making some assumptions about the relative and absolute magnitudes of the band-structure parameters, Slater and Koster calculated the histogram *density of states* curve (number of eigenvalues per unit energy) which includes all five d bands in the body-centered cubic structure, such as in Fe. This is reproduced in Fig. 7.1. The lower peak belongs to the *bonding orbitals* in the chemical terminology, and, according to Slater and Koster, explains the anomalously great binding energies of some metals in the first half of the iron transition series.

What the histogram could not show are the so-called *Van Hove singularities*. Whenever an $E(\mathbf{k})$ curve has a minimum, maximum, or simply a saddle point, its contribution to the density of states becomes excessive. [For example, a totally constant $E(\mathbf{k}) = E_0$ contributes a delta-function singularity to the density of states

FIG. 7.1. Density-of-states histogram for d bands in bcc structure. $N(E)$ is plotted versus E (Rydbergs), and is equal to the number of eigenvalues $E_n(k)$ within $\pm.025$ Ry of the energy E, normalized such that the total area under curve equals 5. (From J. Slater and G. Koster.)

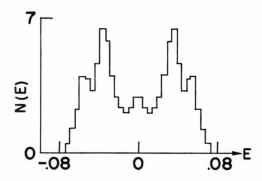

function.] Some years after the Slater-Koster work, Wohlfarth and Cornwell published the curve reproduced in Fig. 7.2, giving the density of states

$$N(E) \propto \sum_{n,\,k} \delta[E - E_n(\mathbf{k})] \tag{13}$$

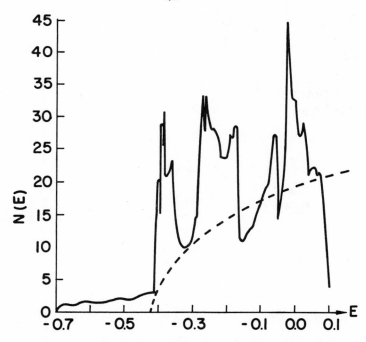

FIG. 7.2. Density-of-states curve $N(E)$ plotted versus E (Rydbergs) for bcc iron. (According to E. Wohlfarth and J. Cornwell.) Dashed line is average free-electron approximation $N(E) \propto \sqrt{E}$; and note how at several points (for example, $E = 0$ or -0.4) the computed density of states can exceed the average curve by a large factor.

as the output of a computer calculation in which the Van Hove singularities were scrupulously preserved. The peaky nature of this new curve is evident, with the principal maxima occurring whenever an energy band touches the Brillouin zone. Note also the revision upwards of the estimated effective width of the bands over the earlier work, by a factor approximately 3.

As we shall see subsequently, it is of crucial importance in the theory of magnetism in metals whether the density of states is high or low, particularly in the vicinity of the Fermi level (μ).[3]

WEAK MAGNETIC PROPERTIES

All metals share some weak magnetic characteristics. The study of these has enjoyed great vogue lately, because of the very detailed information on the band structure and Fermi surface parameters which it divulges. As some examples of important dynamic properties, we list the Hall effect, magnetoresistance, and cyclotron resonance. Some important static properties of the electrons include Pauli spin paramagnetism, Landau diamagnetism, and the De Haas-Van Alphen effect. All these are well known and abundantly discussed in standard texts on solid-state or metal physics.[4] Therefore, here we shall be content with a qualitative discussion of the physical basis of the static phenomena listed, without emphasizing the mathematics which can become rather complicated. The principal purpose is to display the important role of the density of states function $N(E)$ in the magnetic properties of electrons, and to introduce the concepts of Fermi energy and Fermi distribution.

In the ground state of a normal metal ($T = 0°K$) all the one-electron states of energy less than μ are occupied, all those above are empty. μ is the chemical potential or Fermi energy. Moreover, in the absence of magnetic fields or spin-orbit coupling to lift the Kramers' degeneracy, every state of given $(n, \mathbf{k})$ below the Fermi level is *doubly* occupied by an electron with spin up and one with spin down.

At finite temperature, states within $\pm kT$ of the Fermi level are partly occupied, as may be seen from the Fermi distribution function

$$f(E_{\mathbf{k}}) = \frac{1}{e^{(E_{\mathbf{k}} - \mu)/kT} + 1} \tag{14}$$

which gives the thermal-average probability that the state of energy $E_{\mathbf{k}}$ is occupied (absorbing band and spin indices into $\mathbf{k}$). In a weak magnetic field, the spins of the electrons within the $\pm kT$ neighborhood of the Fermi energy will be free to orient themselves parallel to the field; and according to the laws of Langevin and Curie, each will contribute a magnetization proportional to the applied field, to Curie's constant (given on p. 227), and to the inverse temperature, viz.,

$$\delta\mathcal{M} \sim H \frac{C}{T}$$

---

[3] The band structure of some magnetic metals is now known fairly well. Perhaps the best understood is nickel. H. Ehrenreich et al., *Phys. Rev.*, **131**: 2469 (1963); and J. C. Phillips, *Phys. Rev.*, **133**: A1020 (1964). See also L. F. Mattheiss, "Energy Bands for the Iron Transition Series," *Phys. Rev.*, **134**: A970 (1964).

[4] Less known but equally interesting is the subject treated by E. Fawcett, "High Field Galvanomagnetic Properties of Metals," *Advances in Phys.* (*Phil. Mag. Suppl.*),**13**:139 (1964).

The number of participating electrons is $\sim 2kT \, N(\mu)$, and therefore the total para-magnetic spin susceptibility is

$$\chi_p = 2CkN(\mu) \tag{15}$$

This agrees with more rigorous derivations of Pauli's spin paramagnetism of free electrons and is correct to $O[(kT/\mu)^2]$ at finite temperatures. ($kT/\mu \ll 10^{-2}$ at room temperature for most nonmagnetic metals.) Note the dependence on $N(\mu)$, the density of states *at* the Fermi energy. This susceptibility is smaller by a factor $2kTN(\mu)/\mathcal{N}$ than that of $\mathcal{N}$ free spins.

The De Haas-Van Alphen effect is not so easy to explain nor to understand; nevertheless it also reflects the dependence of the thermodynamic properties of the metal on the density of states. In this case, the density of states is affected by a magnetic field, and therefore the thermodynamic functions will depend on the field. For illustrative purposes, consider the wavefunctions in the free-electron approximation,

$$\psi_\mathbf{k} = e^{i\mathbf{k}\cdot\mathbf{r}} \qquad \mathscr{H} = \frac{\mathbf{p}^2}{2m^*} = -\frac{(\hbar\nabla)^2}{2m^*} \tag{16}$$

The effective mass m^* may differ from the free-electron mass $m_0 = 9.1 \times 10^{-28}$ gram by one or more orders of magnitude (greater or smaller). The effective mass approximation used here may be quite successful for describing s bands, but it does not lead to a realistic density of states for the d bands, as shown in Fig. 7.2; so the following derivation must be taken with a grain of salt.

In a weak electromagnetic field, described by the vector potential $\mathbf{A}(\mathbf{r}, t)$, the electron momenta $\mathbf{p}$ become $\mathbf{p} - e\mathbf{A}/c$, and the Schrödinger equation becomes

$$\frac{[\mathbf{p} - (e/c)\mathbf{A}]^2}{2m^*} \, \psi(\mathbf{r}, t) = \hbar i \frac{\partial}{\partial t} \, \psi(\mathbf{r}, t) \tag{17}$$

For a static magnetic field, $\mathbf{A}(\mathbf{r}) = (0, Hx, 0)$ does not depend on the time and satisfies the two equations

$$\nabla\mathbf{x}\mathbf{A} = (0, 0, H) \qquad \text{and} \qquad -\frac{1}{c}\frac{\partial\mathbf{A}}{\partial t} = \mathbf{E}(\mathbf{r}, t) = 0 \tag{18}$$

Therefore we write $\psi(\mathbf{r}, t) = e^{i(k_y y + k_z z)}\phi(x) \, e^{-iEt/\hbar}$, find that $\phi(x)$ obeys a harmonic-oscillator equation, so that the total energy is given by

$$E = \frac{\hbar^2 k_z^2}{2m^*} + (n + \tfrac{1}{2})\hbar\omega_c \qquad n = 0, 1, 2, \ldots \tag{19}$$

with the "cyclotron frequency" ω_c defined by

$$\omega_c = \frac{eH}{m^*c} \tag{20}$$

Problem 3: Derive Eqs. (19) and (20) of the text, by solving Schrödinger's equation in the manner described.

The expression for the energy may be interpreted as the result of quantization on the classical circular motion of a charge in a magnetic field.

The density of states is obtained by differentiating the function which gives the total number of states lying below energy E. Thus,

$$N(E) \propto 2 \frac{d}{dE} \sum_{m=1}^{M(E)} \int_{0}^{\sqrt{E-(m+\frac{1}{2})\hbar\omega_c}} \hbar dk_z (2m^*)^{-\frac{1}{2}}$$

$$\propto \sum_{m=1}^{M(E)} \frac{1}{\sqrt{E - (m + \frac{1}{2})\hbar\omega_c}} \tag{21}$$

where $M(E)$ = largest positive integer for which the radicand is positive. A plot of this function is given in Fig. 7.3(a); it is similar to the free-electron function $N(E) \sim E^{\frac{1}{2}}$ except for narrow, integrable, square-root singularities at half-odd-integer multiples of the cyclotron energy $\hbar\omega_c$.

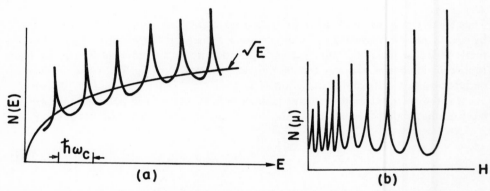

FIG. 7.3.   (a) Density-of-states $N(E)$ versus E in constant magnetic field. Averaging the singularities would lower curve below its zero-field value $\sqrt{E}$. Therefore the energy of a constant number of electrons in weak magnetic fields is higher than in zero field, and the Landau motional susceptibility is diamagnetic. (b) Density of states at the Fermi energy, $N(\mu)$, as function of strong applied magnetic field. The oscillatory behavior results in De Haas-Van Alphen effect. Note that μ is itself a function of H, and is determined by the requirement $\mathcal{N} = \int^{\mu} dE N(E) = \text{constant}$.

The most interesting behavior occurs in the neighborhood of the Fermi energy μ as the magnitude of H is increased. Whenever $(\mu - \frac{1}{2}\hbar\omega_c)$ becomes an integer multiple of $\hbar\omega_c$, the above sums start to include a new integer $M(\mu)$, and the density of states $N(\mu)$ itself acquires a square-root singularity. This is shown in Fig. 7.3(b). Clearly, this must lead to fluctuating, quasiperiodic behavior of all the thermodynamic properties of the metal: the specific heat, magnetic susceptibility, electrical resistance, etc., must all be oscillatory functions of the maximum integer, $M(\mu) \propto 1/H$.

The weak-field limit occurs either when $\hbar\omega_c \ll kT$ or when scattering results in a mean free path smaller than the radius of the cyclotron orbit. In either case it is permissible to expand the free energy and other thermodynamic quantities in powers of H.

For example, a method due to Peierls[5] is based on the Poisson summation formula,

$$N(E) \propto \sum_{p=-\infty}^{+\infty} (-1)^p \int_0^{E/\hbar\omega_c} \frac{e^{2\pi i p x}}{\sqrt{E - x\hbar\omega_c}}\, dx$$

and some partial integrations to evaluate the leading terms in the free energy. As an example, the internal energy to leading order is

$$E_{tot}(H) = \int dE N(E) E f(E) \cong E_{tot}(0) - \tfrac{1}{2}\chi_d H^2 \tag{22}$$

with $-\chi_d$ a positive quantity. Because the increase in energy can result in a force tending to repel the material from an applied field, this corresponds to a diamagnetic susceptibility.

Finally, the total susceptibility, combining the Pauli spin paramagnetism with the Landau orbital diamagnetism can be shown to have the value

$$\chi = 2CkN(\mu)\left[1 - \frac{1}{3}\left(\frac{m_0}{m^*}\right)^2\right] \tag{23}$$

which explains the weak net paramagnetism of most metals (where $m^* \sim m_0$) and, on the other hand, the strong diamagnetism of bismuth, in which the carriers have an effective mass more than two orders of magnitude smaller than is usual in metals.

In common with other magnetic phenomena studied in this book, the Landau diamagnetism is a purely quantum mechanical effect, which disappears in the correspondence limit by virtue of the oft-invoked Bohr-Van Leeuwen theorem. Also the diamagnetic increase in energy, Eq. (22), is extensive, i.e., every unit volume of the material contributes equally to the diamagnetic current density.

Note: It is possible to view the nonvanishing diamagnetism as a direct consequence of the uncertainty principle; for if the electrons have perfectly sharp momenta **p**, the vector potential $\mathbf{A} = (0, Hx, 0)$ cannot be simultaneously specified nor removed by a gauge transformation and vice versa. Therefore for small H, the energy is raised above the ground state value it had in the absence of the field. This point of view has been carried through by an expansion of the partition function and free energy in powers of $\hbar$ in a review by Van Vleck of the weak magnetic properties of metals and of the effects of exchange and correlation on the calculated quantities.[6]

A tendentious explanation of the Landau diamagnetism which is often given is that it is caused by the inability of surface currents to cancel volume currents, due to quantum mechanical effects. But this is only a half-truth; for it obscures the physically significant fact that χ_d depends only on the bulk properties, and is independent of the surface geometry, boundary conditions, scattering, etc.

---

[5] R. E. Peierls, *Quantum Theory of Solids*, Oxford, 1955, p. 148. See also M. Glaser, "Note on the evaluation of some Fermi integrals," *J. Math. Phys.*, **5**: 1150 (1964).

[6] J. H. Van Vleck, *Nuovo Cimento*, vol. 6, ser. X, suppl. 3, p. 857 (1957).

EXCHANGE IN SOLIDS: A UNIVERSAL HAMILTONIAN $\mathcal{H}_{eff}$

In solids as in atoms, the really strong magnetic phenomena are electrostatic in origin, the powerful Coulomb forces being "triggered" by the spins of the electrons under the regulation of the Pauli principle. This is well demonstrated in second quantization, to which an introduction is provided in this section. Specific applications to insulators and metals will be the subject of the remainder of the chapter. In second quantization, it is possible for a unique Hamiltonian to apply to all the various sorts of solids, with only numerical parameters and the occupation of the various bands remaining to be specified. Thus there is no need to deal differently with insulators or metals at the present stage.

First, let us reformulate the theory of noninteracting electrons, starting with the operator $c_{j, n, m}$ which destroys an electron at the jth Wannier site, in the nth band, with spin index $m(=\uparrow$ or $\downarrow)$. The operator which creates an electron in precisely the same state is the Hermitean conjugate operator $c_{j, n, m}^*$. The band Hamiltonian of Eq. (1) can be written in terms of these operators as

$$\mathcal{H}_0 = \sum_{i, j, n, m} H(R_{ij})_{n, n} c_{i, n, m}^* c_{j, n, m} \tag{24}$$

This represents quite graphically the "hopping" of an electron from site j to site i, with the matrix element previously calculated in Eq. (5), and displays the conservation laws obeyed by true Wannier functions in the present (one-electron) approximation. These are the conservation of the spin index, and of the band index (which may also be considered as an "isotopic" spin), ensuring that the one-electron bands are well defined.

The Fermion operators above obey the usual *anti*commutation relations:

$$c_r c_s + c_s c_r \equiv \{c_r, c_s\} = 0 \qquad \{c_r^*, c_s^*\} = 0$$

therefore $\qquad (c_r)^2 = (c_r^*)^2 = 0 \qquad$ and $\qquad \{c_r, c_s^*\} = \delta_{r, s}$ $\qquad$ (25)

and the occupation number operator $\mathfrak{n}_r = c_r^* c_r$ has eigenvalues 0, 1 only; r or s stand for any set of quantum numbers, for example, (i, n, m).

The band Hamiltonian is diagonal in the Bloch representation. We show this by means of a canonical transformation, which in turn is equivalent to choosing a linear combination of Wannier operators as follows:

$$c_{\mathbf{k}, n, m} = \frac{1}{\sqrt{N}} \sum_{i=1}^{N} e^{-i\mathbf{k} \cdot \mathbf{R}_i} c_{i, n, m}$$

and $\qquad c_{\mathbf{k}, n, m}^* = \frac{1}{\sqrt{N}} \sum_{i=1}^{N} e^{+i\mathbf{k} \cdot \mathbf{R}_i} c_{i, n, m}^* \qquad$ (26)

The $c_{\mathbf{k}}$'s and $c_{\mathbf{k}}^*$'s also obey the anticommutation relations, Eq. (25). The inverse linear combinations are simply

$$c_{i, n, m} = \frac{1}{\sqrt{N}} \sum_{\substack{k \text{ in} \\ \text{first B.z.}}} e^{+i\mathbf{k}\cdot\mathbf{R}_i} c_{\mathbf{k}, n, m}$$

and $$c_{i, n, m}^* = \frac{1}{\sqrt{N}} \sum_{\substack{k \text{ in} \\ \text{first B.z.}}} e^{-i\mathbf{k}\cdot\mathbf{R}_i} c_{\mathbf{k}, n, m}^*$$

(26A)

Therefore let us substitute these expressions into $\mathcal{H}_0$, and obtain

$$\mathcal{H}_0 = \frac{1}{N} \sum_j e^{i(\mathbf{k}-\mathbf{k}')\cdot\mathbf{R}_j} \sum_i H(\mathbf{R}_{ij})_{n, n} e^{i\mathbf{k}\cdot\mathbf{R}_{ij}} \sum_{n, m} c_{\mathbf{k}', n, m}^* c_{\mathbf{k}, n, m}$$

$$= \sum_{k, n, m} E_n(\mathbf{k}) c_{\mathbf{k}, n, m}^* c_{\mathbf{k}, n, m} = \sum_{k, n, m} E_n(\mathbf{k}) \mathfrak{n}_{\mathbf{k}, n, m}$$

(27)

using the definition of the energy of a Bloch electron $E_n(\mathbf{k})$ given previously.

Because $\mathcal{H}_0$ is diagonal in the Bloch operator representation ($n_{\mathbf{k}, n, m} = 0$ or 1), an eigenstate of this Hamiltonian is specified by stating which states labeled by $\mathbf{k}$, n, m are occupied, and which are not. For example, the no-particle *vacuum* state $|0)$ is annihilated by *every* $c_{\mathbf{k}}$: $c_{\mathbf{k}}|0) = 0$ therefore $\mathfrak{n}_{\mathbf{k}}|0) = 0$; and $\mathcal{H}_0$ must also have zero eigenvalue in this state. A more important eigenfunction is the *Fermi sea*, defined to be the state of lowest energy among all the eigenstates containing precisely $\mathcal{N}$ electrons. In terms of the Fermi energy μ (below which there are precisely $\mathcal{N}$ one-electron states $\mathbf{k}$, n, m) the Fermi sea can be written as

$$|F) \equiv \Pi\, c_{\mathbf{k}, n, m}^* |0)$$

(28)

where the product extends over all $\mathbf{k}$, n, m for which $E_n(\mathbf{k}) < \mu$. Cf. p. 105 *et seq.*

The eigenvalue of $\mathcal{H}_0$ in this state will be the "unperturbed" ground state energy W_0,

$$W_0 = \sum E_n(\mathbf{k}) = \int_{-\infty}^{\mu} dE\, N(E) E \quad \text{where } \mathcal{N} \equiv \int_{-\infty}^{\mu} dE\, N(E)$$

(29)

and where the sum over $\mathbf{k}$, n, m again extends only over the states in the Fermi sea. It is the principal object of the theory of magnetism in metals to explain precisely how the electronic interactions modify the Fermi sea, and perturb the ground state energy.

One possible result of the interactions, and of thermal excitations as well, is to create any number of *elementary excitations*. These are constructed by removing a single electron from the Fermi sea and placing it above in one of the unoccupied states. For example, letting b stand for a set of quantum numbers *within* $|F)$, and a for a set of quantum numbers *outside* $|F)$, the eigenfunction and eigenvalue of a single elementary excitation are

$$\psi_{ab} = c_a^* c_b |F) \quad \text{and} \quad W_{ab} = W_0 + E_a - E_b$$

(30)

As an alternative to the above description, we may conceive the elementary excitation of Eq. (30) as the creation of two *quasiparticles*: both a quasielectron of energy

$E_a - \mu$, and a quasihole of energy $\mu - E_b$ are added to the ground state. The energy of each quasiparticle, and of the elementary excitation as well, must be positive (by definition of the *ground* state).

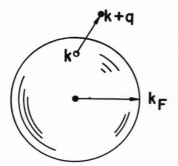

FIG. 7.4. Fermi sphere of radius k_F with an elementary excitation indicated: electron taken to $(\mathbf{k} + \mathbf{q})$, leaving hole at $\mathbf{k}$.

The elementary excitations occupy a continuum (in the limit $L \to \infty$, naturally) of energy levels even when restricted to a specific total momentum. In the free electron approximation $E(\mathbf{k}) = \mathbf{k}^2$ in some appropriate units, with the Fermi level at $\mu = k_F^2$, the Fermi sea is represented in $\mathbf{k}$ space as a sphere of radius k_F (Fig. 7.4), with total momentum, total current, total spin all zero. The elementary excitations are $c_{\mathbf{k}+\mathbf{q}}^* c_{\mathbf{k}} |F\rangle$, with $k < k_F$ and $|\mathbf{k} + \mathbf{q}| > k_F$, omitting spin indices. Even if $\mathbf{q}$ is fixed, there is a continuum of elementary excitations corresponding to the possible angles between $\mathbf{k}$ and $\mathbf{q}$, and the energy of these is bounded by two parabolas and the horizontal axis, as shown in Fig. 7.5. Brillouin zone and magnetic field effects on the spectrum of elementary excitations are discussed in Problem 4.

Problem 4:
a. Discuss the double spectrum of elementary excitations + spin flip,

$$\psi_{\mathbf{k}, \mathbf{q}}^{\pm} = c_{\mathbf{k}+\mathbf{q}\uparrow}^* c_{\mathbf{k}\downarrow} |F_H\rangle \quad \text{and} \quad c_{\mathbf{k}+\mathbf{q}\downarrow}^* c_{\mathbf{k}\uparrow} |F_H\rangle$$

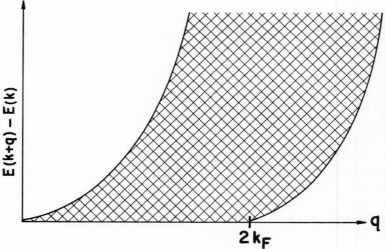

FIG. 7.5. Continuum of elementary excitations in nonmagnetic Fermi sea of noninteracting electrons.

for free electrons whose spins, only, are interacting with a magnetic field (e.g., an exchange field); that is, for which $E_m(\mathbf{k}) = \mathbf{k}^2 + m\mu_B H$, where $m = \pm 1$, and $|F_H\rangle$ is the Fermi sea appropriate to this situation. Plot the continua in the manner of Fig. 7.5, and notice that since $|F_H\rangle$ is the ground state, all excitation energies are required to be positive.

b. Neglecting spin (as in the text above), show the effects of the Brillouin zone by plotting qualitatively the elementary excitation spectrum of a half-filled s band in the simple cubic structure. Pay special attention to the effects of *umklapp* ($\mathbf{k}$ is necessarily in first B.z. but $\mathbf{k} + \mathbf{q}$ is not), and to the maximum energy cutoff in the spectrum.

Besides all one-body potentials, the band-theoretic Hamiltonian $\mathscr{H}_0$ can include the averaged effects of two-body forces. Let us see why this is the case; the most general two-body matrix element is, in the Wannier representation,

$$\mathscr{H}' = \sum V(i, j, n', n; i', j', t', t) c_{i't'm'}^* c_{in'm}^* c_{jnm} c_{j'tm'} \tag{31}$$

where $$V(i, j, n', n; i', j', t', t) = \frac{1}{2} \int d_3 r \int d_3 r' \psi_{t', i'}^*(\mathbf{r}') \psi_{t, j'}(\mathbf{r}') \frac{e^2}{|\mathbf{r} - \mathbf{r}'|} \psi_{n', i}^*(\mathbf{r}) \psi_{n, j}(\mathbf{r}) \tag{32}$$

These matrix elements will connect states which differ only by a change in the quantum numbers of two electrons, from jnm and $j'tm'$ to $in'm$ and $i't'm'$, and so long as we use orthogonal Wannier functions and two-body potentials (such as the physically important Coulomb repulsion), *there are no further matrix elements*, and *the total Hamiltonian consists of* $\mathscr{H}_{\text{tot}} = \mathscr{H}_0 + \mathscr{H}'$. As stated above, some of the terms in $\mathscr{H}'$ can be incorporated in $\mathscr{H}_0$; consider as one possible example the terms with $i' = j'$ and $t' = t$,

$$\left[\sum V(i, j, n', n; i', i', t, t) \mathfrak{n}_{i'tm'} \right] c_{in'm}^* c_{jnm} \tag{33}$$

Although the factor which multiplies $c_{in'm}^* c_{jnm}$ is an operator, its average value in the Fermi sea serves as a useful estimate of its magnitude. We must incorporate into $\mathscr{H}_0$ the terms,

$$\delta\mathscr{H}_0 = \sum \delta H(\mathbf{R}_{ij})_{n, n'} c_{in'm}^* c_{jnm} \tag{34}$$

with $$\delta H(\mathbf{R}_{ij})_{n, n'} \equiv \sum_{i'tm'} V(F|\mathfrak{n}_{i'tm'}|F)$$

and subtract them from $\mathscr{H}'$. This is the sort of procedure which was already anticipated in Eq. (1) and those following, when it was stated that $V(\mathbf{r} - \mathbf{R}_i)$ is the *averaged* potential due to the nucleus, and all other electrons except the one under consideration. Thus the transfer of all the averaged effects of $\mathscr{H}'$ into $\mathscr{H}_0$ has the result that what remains of the former has vanishing expectation value in the Fermi sea:

$$(F|\mathscr{H}' - (F|\mathscr{H}'|F)|F) \equiv 0$$

This procedure "renormalizes" the band structure $E_n(\mathbf{k})$ in a self-consistent way. Note that the self-consistent one-electron band picture must be altered somewhat if we consider a different state, such as the ferromagnetic state instead of $|F\rangle$); but the resultant changes are ignored in zeroth order. We may therefore imagine $\mathscr{H}_0$ to have constant parameters, to include a priori all the important electron-electron interactions (on the average), as well as all the interactions of the electrons with nuclei and their kinetic energy. From $\mathscr{H}'$ we shall extract for present consideration only a significant subset of two-body terms. Using as a guiding principle the consideration of only those interactions which matter most when the atoms are very far apart (the intra-atomic terms) or when they are very close (the long-ranged Coulomb interaction), we can extract from $\mathscr{H}_{tot} = \mathscr{H}_0 + \mathscr{H}'$ the features of greatest physical significance and provide a starting point for future more ambitious investigations.

The first of the interactions to be retained is the genuine two-particle *Coulomb repulsion* obtained from $\mathscr{H}'$ by setting $in' = jn$ and $i't' = j't$. After a change of dummy indices, it is

$$\mathscr{H}_c = \sum_{\substack{i,\,j,\,n,\,t \\ m,\,m'}} V(\mathbf{R}_{ij})_{n,\,t}\, \mathfrak{n}_{i,\,n,\,m}[\mathfrak{n}_{j,\,t,\,m'} - (F|\mathfrak{n}_{j,\,t,\,m'}|F)] \tag{35}$$

where the simplified notation is used,

$$V(\mathbf{R}_{ij})_{n,\,t} \equiv V(i,\,i,\,n,\,n;\,j,\,j,\,t,\,t) = \frac{1}{2}\int d_3r \int d_3r'\, \psi_{t,\,j}^*(\mathbf{r}')\psi_{t,\,j}(\mathbf{r}')\frac{e^2}{|\mathbf{r} - \mathbf{r}'|}\, \psi_{n,\,i}^*(\mathbf{r})\psi_{n,\,i}(\mathbf{r}) \tag{36}$$

and the factor $\frac{1}{2}$ prevents double-counting. At large distances the leading term in a multipole expansion of this integral is

$$2V(\mathbf{R}_{ij})_{n,\,t} \sim \frac{e^2}{\mathbf{R}_{ij}} \qquad i \neq j \tag{37}$$

and this may be accurate even as close as nearest-neighbor separation. (As an estimate of the *intra*-atomic integral $V(0)_{n,\,t}$, the above is, however, inapplicable. For large though it might be, this integral is nevertheless finite.) The terms subtracted in Eq. (35) ensure that

$$(F|\mathscr{H}_c|F) = 0$$

as required.

The next important class of terms are the *exchange interactions*, which are the subset of terms in Eq. (31) for which $i = j'$, $n' = t$ and $i' = j$, $t' = n$. Because $c_{in'm}^*$ and c_{jnm} *anticommute*, the interchange of these two operators to properly associate the pairs in the manner indicated, results in a minus sign. Except for the operator formalism, this then is the ordinary exchange interaction discussed repeatedly in this volume. It acts as a correction to the Coulomb repulsion of *two electrons in a relative triplet state*, and lowers the energy of this state as compared to the singlet configuration. By grouping pairs of Fermions into spin operators, even the operators can be organized so as to provide the natural and obvious generalization to the Bartlett exchange operator $(1 + 4\,\mathbf{S}_i\cdot\mathbf{S}_j)$, including the variable occupation-number feature of the second quantization. Associating the indices as prescribed, one extracts from Eq. (31) the exchange Hamiltonian,

$$\mathscr{H}_{ex} = - \sum_{\substack{n, n' \\ i, j \\ (n, j) \neq (n', i)}} J(\mathbf{R}_{ij})_{n, n'} \{\mathbf{S}_{n, j} \cdot \mathbf{S}_{n', i} + \tfrac{1}{4} \mathfrak{n}_{n, j} [\mathfrak{n}_{n', i} - (F|\mathfrak{n}_{n', i}|F)]\} \tag{38}$$

where

$$\mathfrak{n}_{n, j} \equiv \mathfrak{n}_{n, j, \uparrow} + \mathfrak{n}_{n, j, \downarrow} \tag{39}$$

and the spin operators,

$$S_p^z = \tfrac{1}{2}(\mathfrak{n}_{p\uparrow} - \mathfrak{n}_{p\downarrow}) = \tfrac{1}{2}(c_{p\uparrow}^* c_{p\uparrow} - c_{p\downarrow}^* c_{p\downarrow})$$

$$S_p^+ = S_p^x + iS_p^y = c_{p\uparrow}^* c_{p\downarrow} \quad \text{and} \quad S_p^- = S_p^x - iS_p^y = c_{p\downarrow}^* c_{p\uparrow} \tag{40}$$

are recognized as the Fermion representation of the spin one-half operators, with $\hbar = 1$, and $p = (n, j)$, etc.

The exchange constant, in the simplified notation, is the *positive-definite* integral:

$$J(\mathbf{R}_{ij})_{n, n'} = 2 V(i, j, n', n; j, i, n, n')$$

$$= \int d_3 r \int d_3 r' \psi_{n, j}^*(\mathbf{r}') \psi_{n', i}(\mathbf{r}') \frac{e^2}{|\mathbf{r} - \mathbf{r}'|} \psi_{n', i}^*(\mathbf{r}) \psi_{n, j}(\mathbf{r}) \tag{41}$$

The largest exchange integral is the familiar intra-atomic Hund's rule integral to which we assign a special symbol,

$$J_{n, n'}^{Hu} \equiv J(0)_{n, n'}$$

$$= \int d_3 r \int d_3 r' \psi_{n, i}^*(\mathbf{r}') \psi_{n', i}(\mathbf{r}') \frac{e^2}{|\mathbf{r} - \mathbf{r}'|} \psi_{n', i}^*(\mathbf{r}) \psi_{n, i}(\mathbf{r}) \tag{42}$$

and in most cases it will not be necessary to consider any other exchange contribution. The reason for this is that $J(\mathbf{R}_{ij})$ decreases *much* faster than the Coulomb integral $V(R_{ij})$, so that when Eq. (42) does not vanish by symmetry or for any other reason, the nearest-neighbor exchange will be small in comparison, and the non-nearest-neighbor contributions completely negligible. (Such a reason *might* be, that there is only one band; then two electrons can be in a triplet state only if they are on different Wannier sites, and the leading exchange integral would be for nearest-neighbor distances.)

The designation of the exchange forces has a certain degree of arbitrariness, so it is useful to conclude this section with a review of the choice which was exercised. One traditional approach which was implicitly discarded, was the one-band, free electron approximation, with Bloch electrons interacting solely via the long-range Coulomb repulsion, Eq. (35). While this idea might have appeared plausible at the time Bloch first proposed it,[7] it had to be discarded in the face of strong theoretical and experimental evidence. "... those causes of the magnetical motions ... we relinquish to the moths and the worms."[8] Obviously, experiment cannot disprove a correct theory; the fact that metals with simple nondegenerate bands are never found to

[7] F. Bloch, *Z. Phys.*, **57**: 545 (1929).
[8] W. Gilbert, *De Magnete*, p. 64.

possess strong magnetic properties should merely have been a spur to the experimentalists to look harder, had it not been for wiser counsel, notably Wigner's arguments[9] showing that correlations among the charged particles keep electrons both of parallel spin *and* of antiparallel spin apart (see also Chapter 1, p. 28). In fact when the Coulomb interaction is strong enough, the ground state has to be a singlet as in the hydrogen molecule. *The key to magnetic behavior must therefore be the existence of degenerate bands:* the fact that various mobile electrons in a given band are constrained by the imposed density of carriers in that band to be on the same or neighboring atoms means that they cannot escape the Coulomb repulsion even by elaborate correlations. The fact is that the same forces which are present in the individual atoms to produce Hund's rule "atomic magnetism" cannot suddenly be nullified in the solid state.[10] Compelling as these arguments may be, they do not constitute a rigorous proof. Such a general proof is available only in one dimension; it was shown[11] that the ground state of $\mathscr{H}_0$ + any interaction Hamiltonian $\mathscr{H}_c$, is *always* a nonmagnetic singlet state, regardless of the number of electrons or the nature of the interaction (see also Chapter 4). The proof breaks down, of course, in face of the degeneracy of three-dimensional atoms, as symbolized by the exchange Hamiltonian of Eq. (38). This adds plausibility to the choice of a single effective Hamiltonian for use in all solids which includes Eq. (38), viz.,

$$\boxed{\mathscr{H}_{\text{eff}} = \mathscr{H}_0 + \mathscr{H}_c + \mathscr{H}_{\text{ex}}} \qquad (43)$$

defined in Eqs. (27), (35) and (38). *The retention of that part of $\mathscr{H}'$ which is explicitly spin-dependent, namely $\mathscr{H}_{\text{ex}}$, is what gives rise to the possibility of magnetic behavior.*

Unfortunately, the eigenfunctions and eigenvalues of $\mathscr{H}_{\text{eff}}$ cannot be found exactly because the three constituent terms do not commute with one another and therefore cannot be simultaneously diagonalized. If we average $\mathscr{H}_{\text{ex}}$ somewhat, *à la* Stoner, a simpler Hamiltonian results, which is denoted $\mathscr{H}_{00}$ [Eq. (77)]. It is this simpler version which we shall examine later, with a view to determining what the threshold magnitude of the exchange coupling must be in order for magnetism to exist in metals.

$\mathscr{H}_{\text{eff}}$ itself is only part of the total Hamiltonian,

$$\boxed{\mathscr{H}_{\text{tot}} = \mathscr{H}_0 + \mathscr{H}'} \qquad (44)$$

defined in Eqs. (27) and (31), which contains corrections to the band picture, to the vector-coupling model of the atom, etc. Due to its complexity and the lack of present-day theoretical refinement, the exact Hamiltonian of the interacting electrons is essentially useless. Also for simplicity, the electron-phonon interaction is not included in the present theory.

---

[9] E. P. Wigner, *Trans. Faraday Soc.*, **205**: 678 (1938).

[10] The credit for this idea belongs to J. C. Slater, *Phys. Rev.*, **49**: 537, 931 (1936); **52**: 198 (1937).

[11] E. Lieb and D. Mattis, "Theory of Ferromagnetism and Ordering of Electronic Energy Levels," *Phys. Rev.*, **125**: 164 (1962). See also Chapter 4.

PERTURBATION-THEORETIC DERIVATION OF HEISENBERG HAMILTONIAN

To illustrate the uses of $\mathcal{H}_{\text{eff}}$, we shall obtain the Heisenberg Hamiltonian valid in an insulating magnetic material. This derivation is an extension to the many-body problem of the method used in Problem 1, Chapter 2; but nevertheless, it is not a general theory of magnetism in insulators, a complicated and rather specialized subject when investigated in appropriate detail. According to the theory, the larger contributions will mostly be the antiferromagnetic ones, in accordance with experiment. But there do exist exceptions to this prevalent antiferromagnetism in insulators:

... a europium oxide of the formula EuO becomes truly ferromagnetic at 77°K with a saturation moment of close to 7 Bohr magnetons. This is thus the first rare earth oxide to be found to become ferromagnetic, and with the exception of CrO_2 the only oxide to our knowledge that has true ferromagnetic coupling.[12]

In the insulator, $\mathcal{H}_c + \mathcal{H}_{\text{ex}}$ is the *big* part of $\mathcal{H}_{\text{eff}}$, and $\mathcal{H}_0$ is the perturbation. However, $\mathcal{H}_{\text{ex}}$ may be further decomposed; the Hund's rule part is retained in lowest order, whereas the nearest-neighbor exchange is treated by first-order perturbation theory. The starting Hamiltonian is, therefore,

$$\mathcal{H} = \mathcal{H}_c + \mathcal{H}_{\text{ex}}^{\text{Hu}} \tag{45}$$

and is supposed to describe the ground and excited states of noninteracting Wannier "atoms," each of net spin $\mathbf{S}_i$ of magnitude $s_i = \frac{1}{2}$ times the number of electrons in unfilled shell. (It is assumed that a crystal field quenches the angular momentum, or else the appropriate quantities are $\mathbf{J}_i$ and j_i.) The ground-state eigenfunctions of $\mathcal{H}$ are highly degenerate, in fact they number N_0, where

$$N_0 \equiv \prod_i (2s_i + 1)$$

and it is the perturbation $\mathcal{H}_0$ which will lift this degeneracy. The perturbation $\mathcal{H}_0$ can be seen from Eq. (24) to transfer an electron from one site to a neighboring site, this virtual transition occurring in second-order perturbation theory with matrix element $H(\mathbf{R}_{ij})_{n,n}$ and an increase of energy $U > 0$ in the intermediate state due to the creation of two ionized sites: a positively ionized ion at $\mathbf{R}_i$ and a negatively ionized one at $\mathbf{R}_j$. Let one of the neutral ground states be $|\alpha\rangle$ and one of the excited ionized states be $|\beta\rangle$; then $U = (\beta|\mathcal{H}|\beta) - (\alpha|\mathcal{H}|\alpha)$ and the second-order perturbation theoretic change in the energy of $|\alpha\rangle$ equals

$$\delta E_\alpha = -\sum_\beta \frac{|(\beta|\mathcal{H}_0|\alpha)|^2}{U}$$

$$= \frac{(\alpha|\mathcal{H}_0|\alpha)^2 - (\alpha|\mathcal{H}_0^2|\alpha)}{U} \tag{46}$$

with the second line obtained by closure $[\Sigma_\beta|\beta)(\beta| \equiv 1]$. $\mathcal{H}_0$ has vanishing ground state expectation value in the insulator (as opposed to a metal) and therefore $(\alpha|\mathcal{H}_0|\alpha)$

---

[12] B. T. Matthias et al., *Phys. Rev. Letters*, **7**: 160 (1961). The nature of the "insulating state" is the subject of Walter Kohn's "Theory of the Insulating State," *Phys. Rev.*, **133**: A171 (1964).

vanishes. In writing out the second term, one immediately isolates from the product of four Fermion operators such terms as

$$-H^2(\mathbf{R}_{ij})_{n,\,n} c^*_{in\uparrow} c_{in\downarrow} c^*_{jn\downarrow} c_{jn\uparrow} = -H^2(\mathbf{R}_{ij})_{n,\,n} S^+_{i,\,n} S^-_{j,\,n} \tag{47}$$

and others corresponding to $S^z_i S^z_j$, as well as terms which do not depend on the relative orientation of two spins. The latter have the same magnitude for all states $|\alpha\rangle$ and therefore contribute only an unimportant shift in the overall energies. The degeneracy of the ground state is lifted and the energies δE_α are described precisely by eigenvalues of the effective interaction

$$\mathscr{H}_{\text{Heis}} = \sum_{i,\,j \neq i} \sum \left[\frac{2}{U} H^2(\mathbf{R}_{ij}) - J(\mathbf{R}_{ij}) \right] \mathbf{S}_i \cdot \mathbf{S}_j \tag{48}$$

It is important to note that the vectors $\mathbf{S}_i$ are the *total atomic* spin operators and *not* individual electron components such as $\mathbf{S}_{i,\,n}$, which cannot be specified in any of the N_0 ground states. Therefore the quantities $H^2(\mathbf{R}_{ij})$ and $J(\mathbf{R}_{ij})$ are appropriate averages of the corresponding quantities in the various bands. Note that the non-Hund's rule nearest-neighbor exchange has been reintroduced at this point by means of first-order perturbation theory.

Thus the total Heisenberg Hamiltonian in nonconducting media must be considered as the sum of two effects: an invariably antiferromagnetic interaction due to the virtual "hopping" of an electron from $\mathbf{R}_i$ to $\mathbf{R}_j$ (and back), which is a "one-body" or "kinetic" exchange mechanism. It is antiferromagnetic because the hopping is greatly enhanced when the spins are antiparallel, the exclusion principle prohibiting certain hops when the spins are parallel. The second, ferromagnetic, contribution arises from the exchange of two electrons not on the same atom; its matrix elements among the degenerate ground states may be described by first-order perturbation theory; it is always ferromagnetic because $J > 0$.

As in the Heitler-London theory, the net interaction is the difference between two positive contributions and can have either sign. (Estimates of the various integrals indicate that the result is usually antiferromagnetic.) However the present derivation is free from some of the undesirable features of the H-L derivation discussed in an earlier chapter. The natural expansion parameter here is U^{-1}, a physically measurable quantity; whereas in the older theory, the parameter l is not, in fact, an observable. The use of orthogonalized functions removes an element of arbitrariness from the theory, and the usual mathematical analysis of Hamiltonian mechanics can now be applied systematically.

In real materials (e.g., magnetite) the hopping occurs via an intermediary non-magnetic ion, such as O^{-2}. This is called *superexchange*, a mechanism first proposed by Kramers[13] 30 years ago. The detailed theory of magnetism in insulators, including the theory of superexchange, is discussed by Anderson,[14] who has contributed much towards the development of this field.

[13] H. A. Kramers, *Physica*, **1**: 182 (1934).
[14] P. W. Anderson, review articles in *Solid State Physics*, **14**: 99 (1963), and in G. Rado and H. Suhl (eds.), *Magnetism*, Academic, New York, 1964, vol. I, chap. 2.

HEISENBERG HAMILTONIAN IN METALS

The indirect exchange theory of magnetism in metals is another example where an effective interatomic Heisenberg Hamiltonian can be derived by second-order perturbation theory. The relative importance of the various energies is here completely reversed over the previous section, for we may now imagine U to vanish and $\mathscr{H}_0$ to be the principal Hamiltonian, with $\mathscr{H}_c$ and $\mathscr{H}_{ex}$ the perturbations.

The theory developed below was first invented in connection with nuclear magnetic resonance by Ruderman and Kittel[15] and independently, by Bloembergen and Rowland[16]; these authors studied the effective long-ranged interaction between nuclear spins due to the hyperfine coupling with the common sea of conduction electrons. The extension of their analysis to the s-d or s-f interaction[17] permitted the explanation of some significant experiments by Zimmerman[18] on the long-ranged interaction between Mn atoms dissolved in Cu. Briefly, the Mn impurity atom retains part of its Hund's rule magnetization in the solute state and by this same mechanism polarizes the spins of the conduction electrons in its neighborhood. The conduction electrons, constrained by the Pauli exclusion principle, respond with a characteristic wavelength

$$\lambda_F = \pi/k_F \tag{49}$$

and the resultant spin polarization is not well localized in the vicinity of the impurity but is oscillatory and long-ranged. A second manganese atom at an arbitrary distance from the first, suffers a ferromagnetic or an antiferromagnetic interaction with it, depending upon whether it is in the trough or on the crest of the polarization wave. But the magnitude of the interaction gradually decreases with distance, in a manner we shall calculate.

Assume a pair of solute magnetic atoms at $\mathbf{R}_1$ and $\mathbf{R}_2$, in an otherwise ideal non-magnetic metal characterized by an s-band Hamiltonian $\mathscr{H}_0$. Internal Hund's rule coupling maintains the magnitudes of the solutes' spins fixed at s_1 and s_2 respectively, but the *relative orientation* of the two spins will be governed by the interaction which is derived below. The exchange coupling of the localized electrons with the conduction electrons is the perturbation,

$$\mathscr{H}_{ex}^{Hu} = -J^{Hu}[\mathbf{S}_1 \cdot \mathbf{s}_c(\mathbf{R}_1) + \mathbf{S}_2 \cdot \mathbf{s}_c(\mathbf{R}_2)] \tag{50}$$

with the conduction-band spin operators $\mathbf{s}_c(\mathbf{R}_i)$ given by Eq. (40). The substitution of Bloch operators for the Wannier operators, given in Eq. (26A), results in the following:

$$s_c(\mathbf{R}_i)^z = \frac{1}{2N} \sum_{\mathbf{k},\mathbf{q}} e^{-i\mathbf{q}\cdot\mathbf{R}_i}(c_{\mathbf{k}+\mathbf{q}\uparrow}^* c_{\mathbf{k}\uparrow} - c_{\mathbf{k}+\mathbf{q}\downarrow}^* c_{\mathbf{k}\downarrow}) \tag{51}$$

$$s_c(\mathbf{R}_i)^+ = \frac{1}{N} \sum_{\mathbf{k},\mathbf{q}} e^{-i\mathbf{q}\cdot\mathbf{R}_i}(c_{\mathbf{k}+\mathbf{q}\uparrow}^* c_{\mathbf{k}\downarrow}) \quad \text{and} \quad s_c(\mathbf{R}_i)^- = \frac{1}{N}\sum_{\mathbf{k},\mathbf{q}} e^{-i\mathbf{q}\cdot\mathbf{R}_i}(c_{\mathbf{k}+\mathbf{q}\downarrow}^* c_{\mathbf{k}\uparrow})$$

[15] M. A. Ruderman and C. Kittel, *Phys. Rev.*, **96**: 99 (1954).

[16] N. Bloembergen and T. J. Rowland, *Phys. Rev.*, **97**: 1679 (1955).

[17] K. Yosida, *Phys. Rev.*, **106**: 893 (1957).

[18] See review of theory and experiments by W. Marshall et al., *Rev. Mod. Phys.*, **36**: 399 (1964) and see also G. S. Rushbrooke, "Theory of Randomly Dilute Ising and Heisenberg Ferromagnetics," *J. Math. Phys.*, **5**: 1106 (1964).

With this definition in mind, let us calculate the eigenvalues and eigenfunctions of

$$\mathscr{H} = \sum_{m=\uparrow,\downarrow} E(\mathbf{k})\mathfrak{n}_{\mathbf{k},m} - J^{\text{Hu}} \sum_{i=1}^{2} \{s_c(\mathbf{R}_i)^z S_i^z + \tfrac{1}{2}[s_c(\mathbf{R}_i)^+ S_i^- + \text{H.c.}]\} \tag{52}$$

by ordinary perturbation theory. In particular, we wish to see how the perturbation lifts the degeneracy of the $r \equiv (2s_1 + 1) \times (2s_2 + 1)$ states of orientations of the two solute spins. The conduction electrons will be assumed to be in their ground state, except for the resultant polarization effects.

The first-order correction to the energy,

$$\delta E^{(1)} = (t; F|\mathscr{H}_{\text{ex}}^{\text{Hu}}|F; t) = 0 \tag{53}$$

is seen to vanish. We use the notation $|F; t)$ to indicate the product state of Fermi sea with the two solute spins, with the index t spanning the range $t = 1, \ldots, r$.

The conduction-band spin operators c^*c create elementary excitations of energy $E(\mathbf{k} + \mathbf{q}) - E(\mathbf{k})$; their matrix elements are unity if $k < k_F$ and $|\mathbf{k} + \mathbf{q}| > k_F$, and zero otherwise. Therefore, by second-order perturbation theory

$$\delta E_t^{(2)} = -\left(\frac{J^{\text{Hu}}}{2N}\right)^2 \sum_{\substack{t', k < k_F \\ |\mathbf{k}+\mathbf{q}|>k_F}} \frac{(t|e^{i\mathbf{q}\cdot\mathbf{R}_1}\mathbf{S}_1 + e^{i\mathbf{q}\cdot\mathbf{R}_2}\mathbf{S}_2|t')\cdot(t'|e^{-i\mathbf{q}\cdot\mathbf{R}_1}\mathbf{S}_1 + e^{-i\mathbf{q}\cdot\mathbf{R}_2}\mathbf{S}_2|t)}{E(\mathbf{k}+\mathbf{q}) - E(\mathbf{k})}$$

$$= -\left(\frac{J^{\text{Hu}}}{2N}\right)^2 \sum_{\substack{k < k_F \\ |\mathbf{k}+\mathbf{q}|>k_F}} \frac{(t|s_1(s_1 + 1) + s_2(s_2 + 1) + 2\mathbf{S}_1\cdot\mathbf{S}_2 \cos \mathbf{q}\cdot\mathbf{R}_{12}|t)}{E(\mathbf{k}+\mathbf{q}) - E(\mathbf{k})} \tag{54}$$

The second line is the result of using closure on the intermediate states $|t')$. It is convenient to separate this formula into two parts: a self-energy

$$\delta E^{(2)} = -K \sum_i s_i(s_i + 1) \tag{55}$$

with

$$K = \left(\frac{J^{\text{Hu}}}{2N}\right)^2 \sum_{\substack{k < k_F \\ |\mathbf{k}+\mathbf{q}|>k_F}} \frac{1}{E(\mathbf{k}+\mathbf{q}) - E(\mathbf{k})} \tag{55A}$$

and an interaction energy, which is the eigenvalue of the effective Hamiltonian

$$\mathscr{H}_{IE} = -\sum_{(i,j)} J(\mathbf{R}_{ij})_{IE}\mathbf{S}_i\cdot\mathbf{S}_j \tag{56}$$

where the indirect exchange coupling constant is

$$J(\mathbf{R}_{ij})_{IE} = +\left(\frac{J^{\text{Hu}}}{2N}\right)^2 \sum_{\substack{k < k_F \\ |\mathbf{k}+\mathbf{q}|>k_F}} \frac{2 \cos \mathbf{q}\cdot\mathbf{R}_{ij}}{E(\mathbf{k}+\mathbf{q}) - E(\mathbf{k})} \tag{56A}$$

If instead of only two impurities there are N_I, the sum in Eq. (55) runs over all N_I spins and the interaction, Eq. (56), over all $\tfrac{1}{2}N_I(N_I - 1)$ distinct pairs.

For a useful estimate of the indirect exchange coupling, one uses the effective mass approximation, $E(\mathbf{k}) = \hbar^2 \mathbf{k}^2/2m^*$ and $\mu = \hbar^2 k_F^2/2m^*$, and introduces an imaginary part $\hbar i/\tau$ to the denominator to account for a finite electronic mean free path.

$$J(\mathbf{R}_{ij})_{IE} = \left(\frac{J^{\mathrm{Hu}}}{2}\right)^2 \left(\frac{a_0}{2\pi}\right)^6 \int_{[\underset{<\mu}{E(k)}]} d_3k \int_{[\underset{>\mu}{E(k')}]} d_3k' \frac{2\cos(\mathbf{k} - \mathbf{k}')\cdot\mathbf{R}_{ij}}{(\hbar^2/2m^*)(\mathbf{k}'^2 - \mathbf{k}^2 + i2m^*/\hbar\tau)}$$

$$= \frac{+(J^{\mathrm{Hu}})^2}{2} \left(\frac{a_0}{2\pi}\right)^6 \frac{m^*}{2\hbar^2} \left(\frac{4\pi}{R_{ij}}\right)^2 \int_0^{k_F} dk\,k \int_{-\infty}^{\infty} dk'\,k' \frac{\sin kR_{ij} \sin k'R_{ij}}{k'^2 - k^2 + i2m^*/\hbar\tau}$$

$$= \frac{-(J^{\mathrm{Hu}})^2}{\mu} \frac{(k_F a_0/2)^6}{2\pi^3} \left[\frac{\sin 2k_F R_{ij} - 2k_F R_{ij} \cos 2k_F R_{ij}}{(2k_F R_{ij})^4}\right] e^{-R_{ij}/\lambda} \tag{56B}$$

where λ = mean free path = $\hbar k_F \tau/m^*$ and $a_0^{-3} \propto$ volume of Brillouin zone. In the second line, the symmetry of the integrand with respect to k' is used to extend the integral to negative values, so that a convenient contour integration yields the result in the third line, assuming $k_F\lambda \ll 1$. This result was first published by Ruderman and Kittel[19] (without the mean free path factor) and is universally referred to as the *Ruderman-Kittel interaction*.

The effective Heisenberg Hamiltonian, with Ruderman-Kittel interactions linking the spins, is valid under the following three conditions.

1. $(J^{\mathrm{Hu}}N_{\mathrm{I}}/\mu\mathscr{N}) \ll 1$.

Even if perturbation theory provides only an asymptotic expansion in the parameter of smallness J^{Hu}, such an inequality ensures that the leading nontrivial term, Eq. (56), yields a reasonable approximation to the magnitude and ordering of the energy levels of the magnetic degrees of freedom.

2. *There must be no level crossing in the electronic system.*

By this is meant, that the assumed Fermi sea $|F\rangle$ remains the ground state and is not replaced by some other state $|F'\rangle$ having some kind of long-range order. Detailed (unpublished) calculation has shown that the reason $|F\rangle$ is generally stable as compared to some polarized configuration $|F'\rangle$ is that any *decrease* of the energy $\delta E^{(1)}$, Eq. (53), in the state $|F'\rangle$ is overcompensated by a greater *increase* in the self-energy $\delta E^{(2)}$. However, this is not necessarily always the case, particularly when $N_{\mathrm{I}} \sim N$; so that even when the indirect exchange theory is applicable, the Ruderman-Kittel interaction may not be. [It is not difficult to repeat the procedures of this section and to derive new results correct to second order when a state $|F'\rangle$ other than $|F\rangle$ is found to be the electronic ground state.]

3. *The elementary excitations must be free-particle-like; there must be no incipient long-range ordering in the conduction gas caused by the Coulomb repulsion $\mathscr{H}_c$.* This is certainly the case in such "normal" metals as Cu, but it need not always be true, e.g., in semimetals. Overhauser has argued that if the correlation energy in an

---

[19] *Op. cit.* A derivation is also given in C. P. Slichter, *Principles of Magnetic Resonance*, Harper & Row, New York, 1963. Also, cf. C. Froidevaux and M. Weger, "Direct Measurement of the Ruderman-Kittel Interaction in Platinum Alloys," *Phys. Rev. Letters*, **12**: 123 (1964).

electron gas can be neglected, the Hartree-Fock ground state is not the usual Fermi sea, but is likely a spiral spin configuration,[20] which he has dubbed "spin density wave." This ordering would be somewhat different from that discussed above (2) because it would exist even in the absence of the paramagnetic impurity atoms; the Ruderman-Kittel interaction would be that much more inapplicable. As Overhauser neglects Hund's rule exchange, his theory does not apply to the ordered magnetic materials, so we shall not discuss it further.

ORDERED MAGNETIC METALS

Some of the most interesting applications of the indirect exchange theory are to metals containing elements in the gadolinium rare-earth series (*lanthanides*). Generally the f-shell radii of the rare-earth atoms are so small that even nearest neighboring atoms do not have significant direct overlap and the interaction is assumed to be principally the Ruderman-Kittel indirect exchange mechanism derived in the preceding section (with crystal field anisotropy the principal correction).[21] Ordered alloys containing transition elements are also described by this theory if the magnetic atoms are sufficiently far apart for the d-shell overlaps to be unimportant.

Therefore we are led to consider the Hamiltonian

$$\mathscr{H}_{IE} = -\sum J_{ij}\mathbf{S}_i \cdot \mathbf{S}_j \tag{57}$$

and to calculate its eigenstates and eigenvalues in cases where the spins $\mathbf{S}_i$ occupy points on a regular lattice. For convenience, we shall assume it to be one of the Bravais lattices, and particularly one of the three principal cubic lattices. There is no exact method known to obtain the ground state, but the following procedure avoids unnecessary complications, and appears reliable. First, we construct the product wavefunction

$$\Psi = \Pi \phi_i \tag{58}$$

in which the ϕ_i are, as yet, unspecified but normalized states of the spins $\mathbf{S}_i$. The variational energy in this configuration is

$$E = (\Psi|\mathscr{H}_{IE}|\Psi) = -\sum J_{ij}(\phi_i|\mathbf{S}_i|\phi_i)\cdot(\phi_j|\mathbf{S}_j|\phi_j) \tag{59}$$

where $\qquad\qquad (\phi_i|\mathbf{S}_i|\phi_i)^2 \leqslant s_i^2 \tag{60}$

In the remainder, assume all N_I magnetic atoms to belong to the same species, so that $s_i = s$. The well known *method of Luttinger and Tisza* (also known as the "spherical model") can then be used to find the lowest energy attainable with a trial function of

[20] A. W. Overhauser, *Phys. Rev.*, **128**: 1437 (1962).
[21] Discussed in R. J. Elliott, *Phys. Rev.*, **124**: 346 (1961); and H. Miwa and K. Yosida, *Progr. Theoret. Phys. (Kyoto)*, **26**: 693 (1961).

the type in Eq. (58). It consists mainly of relaxing the inequality above, requiring only

$$\sum_i (\phi_i|\mathbf{S}_i|\phi_i)^2 \leqslant N_I s^2 \tag{61}$$

which is a weaker constraint. *The lowest energy (59) subject to the weaker constraint (61) must be lower than the lowest energy (59) subject to the more rigorous constraint,* (60). E is calculated by Fourier transforms, letting

$$(\phi_i|\mathbf{S}_i|\phi_i) = \sum_\mathbf{k} e^{i\mathbf{k}\cdot\mathbf{R}_i}\mathbf{S}_\mathbf{k} \tag{62}$$

substituting it into Eq. (59) and obtaining,

$$E = -N_I \sum_\mathbf{k} J(\mathbf{k})|\mathbf{S}_\mathbf{k}|^2 \tag{63}$$

where

$$J(\mathbf{k}) = \frac{1}{2N_I}\sum_{i,j} J_{ij}e^{i\mathbf{k}\cdot\mathbf{R}_{ij}} \tag{64}$$

The weak inequality (61), by substitution of the Fourier transform, is found to be

$$\sum_\mathbf{k} |\mathbf{S}_\mathbf{k}|^2 \leqslant s^2 \tag{65}$$

and if we define $\mathbf{q}_0$ to be the wavevector for which $J(\mathbf{q}_0)$ attains its largest value (or one of the wavevectors which have this property if there are more than one) then

$$E(\mathbf{q}_0) = -N_I J(\mathbf{q}_0)s^2 \tag{66}$$

is certainly the lowest energy subject to the weak constraint. Now choose the wave-functions ϕ_i such that

$$(\phi_i|\mathbf{S}_i|\phi_i) = s(\cos\mathbf{q}_0\cdot\mathbf{R}_i, \sin\mathbf{q}_0\cdot\mathbf{R}_i, 0) \tag{67}$$

which is called a *spiral* configuration of pitch $\mathbf{q}_0$. Inserting this variational *ansatz* into Eq. (59) leads to precisely the energy $E(\mathbf{q}_0)$ calculated above; and being an upper bound as well as a lower bound to the ground-state energy (in the Hartree product wave-function approximation), $E(\mathbf{q}_0)$ must itself be the Hartree ground-state energy.

When $\mathbf{q}_0 = 0$, all spins are parallel and the ground state is ferromagnetic. When $\mathbf{q}_0$ is a wavevector on one of the points of symmetry of the Brillouin zone boundary, for example, $\pi/a(\pm1, \pm1, \pm1)$ in the simple cubic structure, the ground state is an antiferromagnetic configuration of some sort (the Néel state in the example given). If $\mathbf{q}_0$ is none of these special wavevectors, the ground state is a spiral spin configura-tion, as these screw structures are known in general. The various possible configura-tions can be found from group theory or by matrix methods, even in non-Bravais lattices, particularly in insulators when J_{ij} is limited to the Heisenberg nearest-neighbor forces.[22] Note that in the present derivation the range of the interaction does

---

[22] E. F. Bertaut, in G. Rado and H. Suhl (eds.), *Magnetism*, Academic, New York, 1963, vol. III, chap. 4.

not matter, therefore the proof holds equally well for the short-ranged Heisenberg interaction in insulators. In the case of the long-ranged Ruderman-Kittel interaction, numerical calculation is required to obtain $J(\mathbf{k})$, and to determine $\mathbf{q}_0$.

The numerical calculation of $J(\mathbf{0})$ is particularly interesting, because according to the theory developed in the next chapter, it is proportional to the paramagnetic Curie temperature θ. A negative θ necessarily precludes ferromagnetism; a positive θ is a likely indication of ferromagnetism, but it is still possible for $\mathbf{q}_0 \neq 0$ to be the ground state solution, and for a spiral configuration to be the stable ground state at low temperatures. Therefore it is also necessary to study the spin-wave spectrum,

$$\hbar\omega(\mathbf{k}) = 2s[J(\mathbf{0}) - J(\mathbf{k})] \tag{68}$$

to determine that all $\hbar\omega(\mathbf{k})$ are positive, if the ferromagnetic state is to be stable. This is a necessary but *not sufficient* condition for ferromagnetism.[23] The minimizing wavevector $\mathbf{q}_0$ can also be found at the minimum of the function $\hbar\omega(\mathbf{q}_0)$.

As an example, we calculate $\hbar\omega(\mathbf{k})$ for the Ruderman-Kittel interaction, in the limit $k_F a \to 0$, where the lattice sums can be replaced by integrals. Let us define $(x_i \equiv 2k_F R_i, \quad a = 1)$

$$\epsilon(\mathbf{k}) \equiv \sum a^3 \frac{\sin x_i - x_i \cos x_i}{5 x_i R_i^3} e^{-R_i/\lambda} (1 - \cos \mathbf{k} \cdot \mathbf{R}_i) \tag{69}$$

which is the magnon energy with constant factors eliminated, for tabular convenience; and

$$WMF \equiv \sum_{R_i \neq 0} a^3 \frac{\sin x_i - x_i \cos x_i}{5 x_i R_i^3} e^{-R_i/\lambda} \tag{70}$$

is the paramagnetic Curie temperature θ with similar constant factors removed. The limiting values are elementary integrals:

$$\lim_{k_F \to 0} WMF = \frac{8\pi}{10} \left(1 + \frac{1}{32 k_F \lambda} - \frac{1}{16\pi k_F \lambda} \tan^{-1} \frac{1}{2 k_F \lambda} \right) \tag{71}$$

and
$$\lim_{k_F \to 0} \epsilon(\mathbf{k}) = \frac{4\pi}{10} \left\{ 1 - \frac{(2k_F\lambda)^2 + 1 - (k\lambda)^2}{(4k\lambda)(2k_F\lambda)} \ln \frac{(2k_F\lambda + k\lambda)^2 + 1}{(2k_F\lambda - k\lambda)^2 + 1} \right.$$
$$\left. + \frac{1}{2k_F\lambda} \left[\tan^{-1} \frac{4k_F\lambda}{(2k_F\lambda)^2 - 1} - \tan^{-1} \frac{4k_F\lambda}{(2k_F\lambda)^2 - (k\lambda)^2 - 1} \right] \right\}$$
$$\tag{72}$$

These are the magnetic parameters for a "continuum" or "jellium" lattice. Note that they are both positive, indicating ferromagnetism.

Closely associated with k_F is the dimensionless parameter $n_{c/a} \equiv$ number of conduction electrons per magnetic atom. (If there is one conduction electron per unit cell,

---

[23] Cf. D. Mattis, "Ground State of Interacting Spins," *Phys. Rev.*, **130**: 76 (1963) where it is shown that in some exceptional instances the ground state may be nonferromagnetic, even though the ferromagnetic state is stable against the emission of (any finite number of) spin waves.

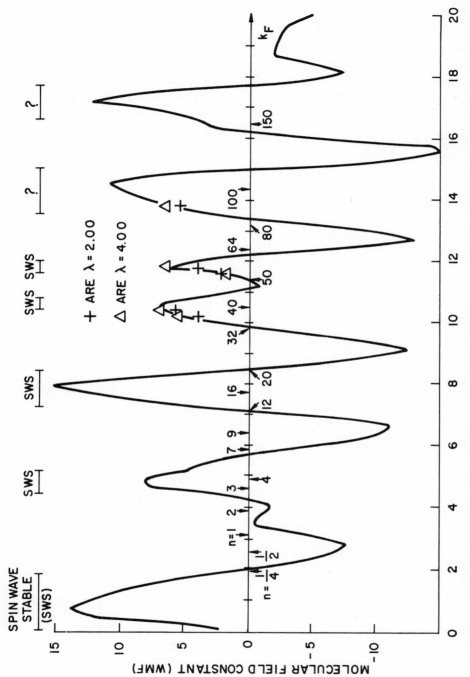

Fig. 7.6. *WMF* plotted versus k_F for sc lattice, a = spin lattice constant = 1. Values of $n = (8\pi/3)(k_F/2\pi)^3 \propto$ number of conduction electrons per spin are indicated by arrows. This curve and the indicated regions of spin-wave stable ferromagnetism (sws) are based on the same calculation as the tables in the Appendix. Main curve is for $\lambda = 3.00$, with some points for $\lambda = 2.00$ and 4.00 showing insensitivity of calculation to the precise value of this parameter.

but a magnetic atom is present only in every other cell, $n_{c/a} = 2$, etc. The "jellium" limit is equivalent to $n_{c/a} \rightarrow 0$.) As $n_{c/a}$ is raised, the paramagnetic Curie temperature goes through zero at approximately $n_{c/a} = \frac{1}{4}$ for the three principal cubic lattices. There is then an antiferromagnetic region as $n_{c/a}$ is increased further, until it exceeds the value $\frac{3}{2}$ for the bcc and fcc lattices, and $\frac{5}{2}$ for the sc lattice. At this point the paramagnetic Curie temperature becomes positive once more until $n_{c/a}$ is approximately doubled, whereupon a new antiferromagnetic region is encountered, etc.

A plot of WMF as a function of k_F and $n_{c/a}$, which displays the features just discussed, is given in Figs. 7.6 to 7.8 for the three cubic lattices. In Fig. 7.6 are also shown the spin-wave stable regions where $\hbar\omega(\mathbf{k}) > 0$; these are seen to be somewhat smaller than the regions of positive paramagnetic Curie temperature. To scale the results so that they correspond to the Ruderman-Kittel interaction of Eq. (56) with constant J^{Hu}, it is necessary to multiply the plotted and tabulated values by appropriate functions of k_F, a, and a_0. In the calculations, the value $a = 1$ is taken for convenience. Therefore, comparing Eqs. (56B), (68), and (69), we obtain the physical parameters θ and $\hbar\omega(\mathbf{k})$

$$[\theta, \hbar\omega(\mathbf{k})] \propto (J^{Hu})^2 (k_F a_0)(k_F a)^3 \left(\frac{a_0}{a}\right)^6 [WMF, \epsilon(\mathbf{k})] \tag{73}$$

in terms of WMF and $\varepsilon(\mathbf{k})$, the computed functions of the dimensionless variable $k_F a$, (k_F when $a = 1$).

Example: The tabulated value of WMF is seen in Figs. 7.6–7.8 to between more or less constant upper and lower bounds over a very large range of $k_F a$. Therefore we expect that the average over a range of concentrations of either $|WMF|$ or WMF^2 should be independent of $k_F a$. From this and Eq. (73) it follows that the magnitude of the paramagnetic Curie temperature, and possibly other thermodynamic functions of a dilute solution of paramagnetic atoms in a given metal (k_F and $a_0 =$ fixed) will vary in the ratio of $a^{-3} =$ concentration of the dilute magnetic impurity N_I. This is indeed experimentally the case (cf. Ref. 18).

In Fig. 7.9 we reproduce recent unpublished experimental results of S. Methfessel and collaborators, on the paramagnetic Curie temperature of certain ordered Eu–Gd–Se alloys, in which the electronic concentration could be varied from insulator to metallic, corresponding to the range $0 < k_F a < 2$ (the upper value is an order of magnitude estimate). These results are apparently in good qualitative agreement with the applicable portions of the theoretical curves.

A plot of $J(\mathbf{k})$ in the simple cubic lattice is given in Fig. 7.10. One observes the ferromagnetic state characterized by $\mathbf{q}_0 = 0$ being succeeded by antiferromagnetic configurations as k_F is increased from frame (a) to (b). The resulting configuration consists of alternating planes of parallel spins, the alternation being in the (100) direction. As one proceeds to frames (d), (e), and (f), he sees the alternation going into the (110) direction, and finally the (111) direction, the last being the Néel state.

Tables of the functions $\epsilon(\mathbf{k})$ and WMF for the sc, bcc, and fcc lattices are reproduced in the Appendix. These results were numerically computed on an IBM 7094 electronic calculator.[24] The high-accuracy numerical calculations have shown little dependence on the mean free path, which thus serves only as an ultimate cutoff and

---

[24] IBM, T. J. Watson Research Center, Yorktown Heights, New York. They have had some prior circulation: D. Mattis et al., "Tables for Theory of Magnetism," unpublished work (1963).

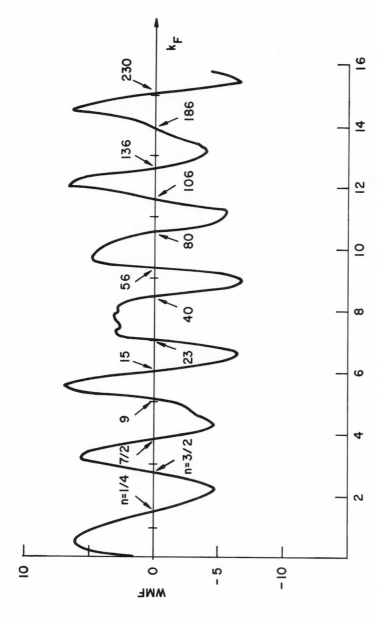

Fig. 7.7. *WMF* versus k_F for fcc lattice, with values of $n = (16\pi/3)(k_F/2\pi)^3$ indicated by arrows (cf. Appendix).

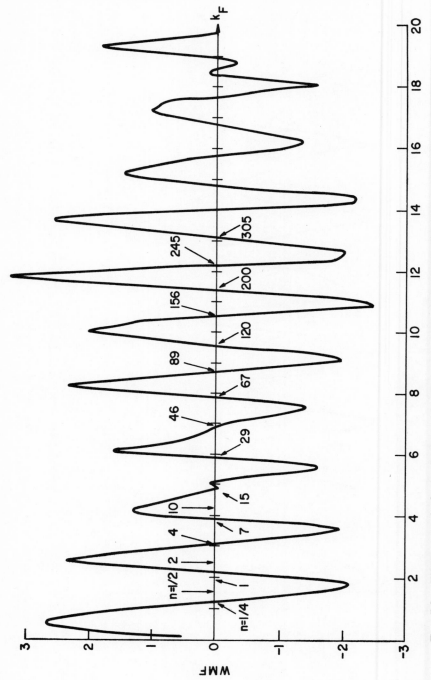

Fig. 7.8. W/MF versus k_F for bcc lattice, with values of $n = (32\pi/3)(k_F/2\pi)^3$ indicated by arrows (cf. Appendix).

convergence factor, but whose exact value is not important (provided it is finite). At small k_F, the computed values agree extremely well with the analytic calculations resulting in Eqs. (71) and (72), even as to the approximate isotropy of the magnon spectrum. Note that if the Ruderman-Kittel interaction is a valid one to use for small k_F, then the statistical mechanics will be very well described by the molecular field

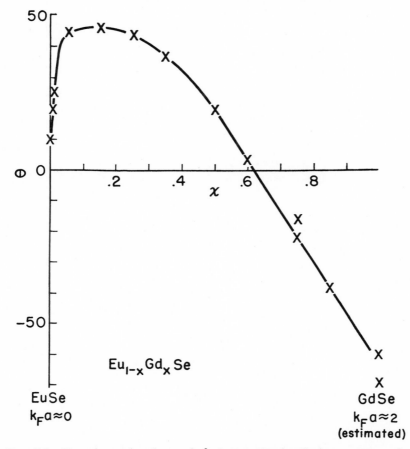

FIG. 7.9. Experimental values of θ (paramagnetic Curie temperature) versus composition (roughly, k_F^3) obtained by S. Methfessel et al. in a series of ordered rare-earth alloys. An order-of-magnitude estimate is that k_Fa varies in the range 0–2 over the range of compositions, and these results are in qualitative agreement with Ruderman-Kittel theory (cf. Figs. 7.6 to 7.8 over same range of k_F).

theory which we develop in the succeeding chapter. For then, the interaction is long-ranged and practically nodeless (J_{ij} is ferromagnetic out to distances $\sim 1/k_F$ and is very small beyond) and the criteria of the molecular field theory are met at all but the lowest temperatures, where spin-wave theory is applicable.

Because the indirect exchange theory is used mainly for the description of the magnetic properties of the rare-earth metals and alloys,[25] it is interesting to note that

---

[25] See T. A. Kaplan and D. H. Lyons, "Theory of Indirect Exchange Interactions in Rare Earth Metals," *Phys. Rev.*, **129**: 2072 (1963).

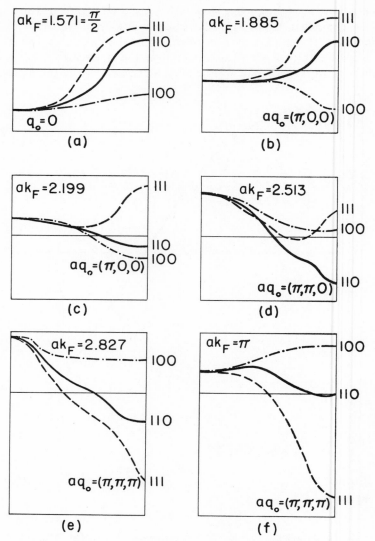

FIG. 7.10. Plot of $-J(\mathbf{k})$ for the Ruderman-Kittel interaction versus $\mathbf{k}$ in the three principal directions, sc lattice. In the range $0 < k_F a \leqslant \pi/2$ the ground state is ferromagnetic. However, as k_F is increased in frames (b) to (f), various antiferromagnetic states become stable, indicated by nonzero values of spiral pitch parameter $\mathbf{q}_0$. $J(\mathbf{k})$ is defined in Eqs. (56) and (64).

in many cases the angular momentum of the f shell in these ions is not quenched, and the total $\mathbf{J}_i$ angular momentum must be specified and not just the total spin $\mathbf{S}_i$. That is, the magnetic degrees of freedom of each rare earth are described by $2j_i + 1$ eigenfunctions, and not by $2s_i + 1$. But this is easily taken into account by using the definition of the Landé g factor. In the subspace of the $2j_i + 1$ eigenfunctions, the following equality defines the Landé factor g_i,

$$\mathbf{M}_i = \mathbf{J}_i + \mathbf{S}_i = g_i \mathbf{J}_i \tag{74}$$

where $\mathbf{M}_i$ is the magnetic moment operator of the ion. Subtracting $\mathbf{J}_i$ from both sides of the equation, we obtain the prescription useful in the present case:

$$\boxed{\text{replace } \mathbf{S}_i \text{ by } (g_i - 1)\mathbf{J}_i} \tag{75}$$

in $\mathscr{H}_{IE}$ for all rare earths *except* when $j = 0$, as in the case of Eu in some states. Because $(g_i - 1)$ can be positive or negative, a sort of "charge" is introduced into the indirect exchange theory: ions with opposite signs of $(g_i - 1)$ will interact antiferromagnetically for ferromagnetic J_{ij}, and vice versa, so that this gives to mixed rare-earth alloys yet another degree of freedom.

The indirect exchange Hamiltonian is thus,

$$\mathscr{H}_{IE} = -\sum J_{ij}(g_i - 1)(g_j - 1)\mathbf{J}_i \cdot \mathbf{J}_j \tag{76}$$

except when $j_i = 0$, when $\mathbf{S}_i$ is used. Table 7.2 lists the rare earths and their effective "spin charge" $g_i - 1$.

TABLE 7.2
g-Factor and Angular Momenta of Rare Earths

Number of electrons in f shell	Symbol	s	l	j	$g - 1$
0	La	0	0	0	$\cdots$
1	Ce	$\frac{1}{2}$	3	$\frac{5}{2}$	$-\frac{1}{7}$
2	Pr	1	5	4	$-\frac{1}{5}$
3	Nd	$\frac{3}{2}$	6	$\frac{9}{2}$	$-\frac{3}{11}$
4	Pm	2	6	4	$-\frac{2}{5}$
5	Sm	$\frac{5}{2}$	5	$\frac{5}{2}$	$-\frac{5}{7}$
6	Eu	3	3	0	$\cdots$
7	Gd	$\frac{7}{2}$	0	$\frac{7}{2}$	$+1$
8	Tb	3	3	6	$+\frac{1}{2}$
9	Dy	$\frac{5}{2}$	5	$\frac{15}{2}$	$+\frac{1}{3}$
10	Ho	2	6	8	$+\frac{1}{4}$
11	Er	$\frac{3}{2}$	6	$\frac{15}{2}$	$+\frac{1}{5}$
12	Tm	1	5	6	$+\frac{1}{6}$
13	Yb	$\frac{1}{2}$	3	$\frac{7}{2}$	$+\frac{1}{7}$
14	Lu	0	0	0	$\cdots$

NOTE: From the following formula: $g - 1 = [j(j+1) + s(s+1) - l(l+1)]/2j(j+1)$.

In transition metal ions the angular momentum is quenched because of strong crystal field effects on the relatively extensive d orbitals. This is reflected in experimentally measured g factors close to 2, the theoretical spin-only value. In those cases, the correct low-lying states are designated by m_s, and the correct vector operator is still $\mathbf{S}_i$.

MAGNETISM WITHOUT LOCALIZED SPINS

The strongly magnetic properties of the iron transition series metals and of their alloys must be explained by band theory. This would be required for the following two reasons alone: the number of Bohr magnetons per atom is generally far from being an integer, and both calculated and observed band widths are of the order of electron volts. Neither of these facts could be accorded with a scheme based on localized spins, and together with such additional evidence as the abnormally high specific heat (which can only be explained by a continuum of states for the magnetic carriers) they point instead to the need for associating the uncompensated spins with Bloch electrons rather than with their Wannier counterparts in the first approximation.

The band theory of magnetism is currently a very active field of research, and it is not yet possible to predict the degree of accuracy and sophistication it may attain. At present, it is far less developed than the relatively straightforward Heisenberg theory for insulators; but the physical mechanisms are established and some of the consequences therefrom approximately understood. Let us start by visualizing, inaccurately perhaps, localized spins in the indirect exchange theory being gradually modified so as to allow some overlap and the formation of "magnetic" electron bands. The energy gap against the excitation of electrons in the magnetic states disappears, and a finite density of states appears at the Fermi surface. This now allows charge fluctuations, hence the conduction of electricity by magnetic electrons; it permits them to contribute to the electronic specific heat, microwave absorption, etc. On the other hand, there is no particular reason why the inherently *magnetic* properties—such as the magnon spectrum—should be affected to leading order. As with indirect exchange, there is no universally valid reason that the long-range order in the ground state be ferromagnetic, and spiral or other antiferromagnetic configurations, such as are actually observed in Mn and in Cr, are not difficult to reconcile with this approach.

One salient difference with the indirect-exchange theory, is that nonmagnetic *s*-like bands can be ignored in the first approximation. Doubtless some indirect exchange still goes on, but the dominant, primary interactions are now *among* the magnetic bands themselves. An interesting point of view has been taken by Goodenough,[26] who has suggested that the *d* electrons (e.g., in Fe) effectively split into two sub-bands; one of which is narrow, so that the electrons it contains are well localized like the rare-earth *f* states, and the other is more like an ordinary conduction band. It is quite likely, that even were such a model describable by the indirect exchange Hamiltonian of Eq. (52), the perturbation-theoretic solution on which the Ruderman-Kittel interaction is based, would not be valid. A strong-coupling solution of that Hamiltonian would resemble the results which we shall derive in this and the following section, so that even Goodenough's model can be treated as a special case of the band theory. Note that the most spectacular feature of the band theory is that with neglect of the nonmagnetic electrons the remaining magnetic ones do not number any particular rational multiple of the number of atoms. Therefore, the occupation number of the magnetic bands is a vital, and often an adjustable, parameter in the theory.

For definiteness in this study, let us assume that whenever an ordered state exists, it is ferromagnetic. We then calculate the magnon spectrum,[27] and if some magnon

---

[26] J. B. Goodenough, *Phys. Rev.*, **120**: 67 (1960).
[27] The first such calculation, specifically for metals, is due to C. Herring and C. Kittel (in connection with theory of domains), *Phys. Rev.* **81**: 869 (1951).

has negative energy, the assumption is then surely false and the ground state must be antiferromagnetic. This procedure is simpler than calculating the energy of every possible ordered state, although as we saw in the indirect-exchange theory, it can lead to precisely the same results. The first fact we shall establish is that there is no magnetization unless the exchange exceeds a certain "critical" value.

The effective Hamiltonian which is assumed for the unfilled bands will be based on $\mathcal{H}_{\text{eff}}$ as given in Eq. (43), but we shall retain only the Hund's rule interaction in $\mathcal{H}_{\text{ex}}$ to keep the formulas simple. (It is good exercise for the reader to modify the results in the remainder of the chapter to include nearest-neighbor exchange coupling, and see how this affects the functional dependence of the formulas.) The restriction to Hund's rule intra-atomic coupling also makes visually clear the distinction between the forces involved in the metal, and those in the insulator. We slightly underestimate the exchange coupling by retaining only its averaged terms in the Bloch representation, and consider first the simplified Hamiltonian

$$\mathcal{H}_{00} \equiv \mathcal{H}_0 + \mathcal{H}_c - \frac{1}{N} \sum_{t,t'} J_{t,t'}^{\text{Hu}} \mathbf{S}_t \cdot \mathbf{S}_{t'} \tag{77}$$

with $\mathcal{H}_0$ given in Eq. (27), $\mathcal{H}_c$ in Eq. (35), $J_{t,t'}^{\text{Hu}}$ in Eq. (42), and

$$S_t^z = \tfrac{1}{2} \sum_{\mathbf{k}} (\mathbf{n}_{\mathbf{k},t,\uparrow} - \mathbf{n}_{\mathbf{k},t,\downarrow})$$

$$S_t^+ = S_t^x + iS_t^y = \sum_{\mathbf{k}} c_{\mathbf{k},t,\uparrow}^* c_{\mathbf{k},t,\downarrow} \qquad S_t^- = \sum_{\mathbf{k}} c_{\mathbf{k},t,\downarrow}^* c_{\mathbf{k},t,\uparrow} \tag{78}$$

the total spin operators for the individual bands, obtained, e.g., from the operators of Eq. (51) by averaging over all $\mathbf{R}_i$. Next, consider the usual Fermi sea, modified perhaps by $\mathcal{H}_c$ but nevertheless still populated equally by electrons with spins "up" and "down."

The minimum energy required to take n_t electrons of spin up near the Fermi surface of the tth band and change their spin to down, keeping them in the same band, is related to the density of states at the Fermi surface of the tth band, and is also just proportional to the Pauli spin susceptibility of this band. The Coulomb interaction $\mathcal{H}_c$ makes this a difficult object to calculate, so let us just assume that $N_t(\mu)$, the *exact* density of states appropriate for the spin susceptibility, is a *given* parameter. The total energy increase over the Fermi sea energy, assuming n_t to include only a small fraction of the electrons in each band, is

$$\delta E = \sum_t \frac{n_t^2}{N_t(\mu)} - \frac{1}{N} \sum_{t,t' \neq t} J_{t,t'}^{\text{Hu}} n_t n_{t'} \tag{79}$$

which includes all many-body effects by the appropriate definition of $N_t(\mu)$. Magnetism becomes possible when this energy is negative; and the threshold occurs when one of the eigenvalues of the matrix

$$M_{t,t'} = \frac{1}{N_t(\mu)} \delta_{t,t'} - \frac{1}{N} J_{t,t'}^{\text{Hu}} \tag{80}$$

vanishes. (It is assumed throughout that $J_{t,t}^{\text{Hu}} \equiv 0$ when $t' = t$ and that otherwise $J_{t,t'}^{\text{Hu}} \geqslant 0$.) When an eigenvalue vanishes the determinant vanishes also, so the eigenvalue condition can be manipulated into a more symmetrical form: *Magnetism occurs if*

$$\boxed{\text{Det } \|\delta_{t,t'} - \mathbb{I}_{t,t'}\| \leqslant 0} \tag{81}$$

where

$$\mathbb{I}_{t,t'} = \frac{J_{t,t'}^{\text{Hu}}}{N} \sqrt{N_t(\mu)N_{t'}(\mu)} \tag{81A}$$

For example, in a two-band model, Eq. (81) predicts magnetism is possible when

$$J_{1,2}^{\text{Hu}} \geqslant \frac{N}{\sqrt{N_1(\mu)N_2(\mu)}} \tag{82}$$

It is believed that the metals in the Pd transition series just fail to obey such a criterion, whereas those in the Fe transition series do. Strictly speaking, the above is a criterion for magnetic moments to make their appearance, such as might be measured in neutron scattering experiments. But the ordered state may be antiferromagnetic rather than

TABLE 7.3
Scale of Energies

Order of Magnitude	Explanation
1–10 eV	(a) Atomic Coulomb integrals
	(b) Hund's rule exchange energy
	(c) Energy of electronic excitations violating Hund's rule
	(d) Electronic band widths
	(e) $\mathcal{N} \div$ (density of states at Fermi Surface)
0.1–1.0 eV	(a) Crystal field splittings
10^{-2}–10^{-1} eV	(a) Spin-orbit coupling
	(b) kT_C or kT_N
10^{-4} eV	(a) Magnetic spin-spin coupling
	(b) Interaction of a spin with external field 10 kG
10^{-6}–10^{-5} eV	(a) Hyperfine electron-nuclear coupling.

SOURCE: This Table is partly based on P.W. Anderson, *Theory of Magnetism* (Univ. of Tokyo lecture notes, 1953, unpublished), p. 111.

ferromagnetic, or there may be no long-range order at all. For the long-range order in the band theory is found to depend on particularities of the Fermi surface, the Brillouin zone, etc., just as sensitively as in the indirect exchange theory. Because the scale of energies is all-important, there is given in Table 7.3 a list of the various orders of magnitude, based on estimates by Philip W. Anderson.

MAGNONS IN THE BAND THEORY

We add to $\mathscr{H}_{00}$ the missing (nonaveraged) terms in the exchange, to recover $\mathscr{H}_{\text{eff}}$ of Eq. (43):

$$\mathscr{H}_{\text{eff}} = \mathscr{H}_{00} - \frac{1}{N} \sum_{\substack{t \neq t' \\ \mathbf{k}_1 \neq \mathbf{k}_2 \\ \mathbf{k}_3 \neq \mathbf{k}_4}} \Delta(\mathbf{k}_1 + \mathbf{k}_3 - \mathbf{k}_2 - \mathbf{k}_4) J_{t,t'}^{\text{Hu}}$$

$$\times (c_{\mathbf{k}_1 t \uparrow}^* c_{\mathbf{k}_2 t \downarrow} c_{\mathbf{k}_3 t' \downarrow}^* c_{\mathbf{k}_4 t' \uparrow} - c_{\mathbf{k}_1 t \uparrow}^* c_{\mathbf{k}_2 t \uparrow} c_{\mathbf{k}_3 t' \downarrow}^* c_{\mathbf{k}_4 t' \downarrow}) \quad (83)$$

where $\Delta(\mathbf{k}) = 1$ when $\mathbf{k} = \mathbf{0}$ or $\mathbf{K}_n$ (reciprocal lattice vector), and 0 otherwise; incorporating also into $\mathscr{H}_{00}$ certain spin-independent interactions of the form $V\mathfrak{n}_{t,j}$ or $V\mathfrak{n}_{t,j}\mathfrak{n}_{t',j'}$ [cf. Eqs. (38) and (39)].

Assuming J^{Hu} to be larger than the threshold magnitude as determined in Eq. (81), and the ground state of $\mathscr{H}_{00}$ to be a (partly or totally) ferromagnetic state with the majority of electrons having spin *down*, we can assume the spin raising operator to be a linear combination of the elementary excitations:

$$S^+(\hbar\omega_q) = \sum_{\mathbf{k},t} F_{\mathbf{k},t} c_{\mathbf{k}+\mathbf{q},t\uparrow}^* c_{\mathbf{k}t\downarrow} \quad (84)$$

Before studying this operator, it is convenient to eliminate J^{Hu} in favor of the *Stoner gap parameter* Δ_t, which measures the energy splitting between spin-up and spin-down bands. Therefore consider first the simpler operator

$$S_t^+ = \sum_{\mathbf{k}} c_{\mathbf{k}t\uparrow}^* c_{\mathbf{k}t\downarrow} \quad (85)$$

which commutes with both kinetic energy and direct Coulomb interactions $\mathscr{H}_0$ and $\mathscr{H}_c$, as proved in Problem 5. That is, if ψ is an arbitrary eigenfunction of $\mathscr{H}_0 + \mathscr{H}_c$

Problem 5: Prove that S_t^+ commutes with $\mathscr{H}_0$; then reexpress this operator in terms of Wannier creation and anihilation operators, to prove that it also commutes with $\mathscr{H}_c$, as well as with any arbitrary function of the occupation-number operators $\mathfrak{n}_{t,j} = \mathfrak{n}_{tj\uparrow} + \mathfrak{n}_{tj\downarrow}$.

with energy E, then $S_t^+ \psi$ is another eigenfunction belonging to the same E but orthogonal to ψ, *unless* $S_t^+ \psi$ happens to vanish. However, S_t^+ is a raising operator for S_t^z; therefore *we define the Stoner energy gap to be the* additional *variational energy* associated with exciting the state $S_t^+ \psi_0$, where ψ_0 is the ferromagnetic ground state of $\mathscr{H}_{00}$, energy E_0. By straightforward calculation,

$$\Delta_t \equiv \frac{(\psi_0 | S_t^- (\mathscr{H}_{00} - E_0) S_t^+ | \psi_0)}{(\psi_0 | S_t^- S_t^+ | \psi_0)} = \left| \frac{2}{N} \sum_{t' \neq t} J_{t,t'}^{\text{Hu}} (\psi_0 | S_{t'}^z | \psi_0) \right| \quad (86)$$

where $\qquad S_{t'}^z = \frac{1}{2} \sum (\mathfrak{n}_{\mathbf{k},t',\uparrow} - \mathfrak{n}_{\mathbf{k},t',\downarrow}) \qquad$ and $\qquad -(\psi_0 | S_{t'}^z | \psi_0) = \mathscr{M}_{t'} \quad (86\text{A})$

Thus the energy required to flip the spin of an average electron in the tth band depends on the magnetization of the *other* bands $t' \neq t$ and on the Hund's rule coupling with them, although it is independent of band structure, Fermi level, Coulomb integrals, etc. The Stoner gap parameters vary between zero [at the threshold indicated by the equality in Eq. (81)] and arbitrary large positive values; increasing slowly at first, and then linearly with increasing J^{Hu}, and obey the limiting law

$$\Delta_t(\text{lin}) = \frac{1}{N} \sum_{t' \neq t} J^{\text{Hu}}_{t,t'} \mathcal{N}_{t'} \tag{87}$$

once J^{Hu} is sufficiently large for all $\mathcal{N}_{t'}$ electrons in the t'th band to have parallel spins. The onset of the linear[28] dependence Eq. (87), and of maximum possible saturation magnetization marks the threshold of the *very strong* coupling regime, as shown schematically in Fig. 7.11. We use units such that $\mu_B = 1$.

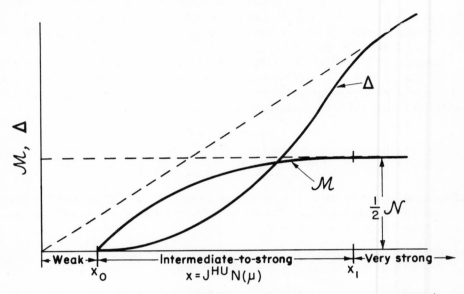

FIG. 7.11. Schematic plot of magnetization $\mathcal{M}$ and Stoner gap parameter Δ as functions of Hund's rule coupling strength $x = J^{Hu} N(\mu)$.

The ground state of $\mathcal{H}_{\text{eff}}$, ψ_0, and the excited states $S_t^+ \psi_0$, $t = 1, \dots, r$ are a set of $r + 1$ orthogonal states; and we may ask what are the best variational states which can be made out of these. One such state we infer from general invariance arguments; $S_{\text{tot}}^+ = \sum S_t^+$ is an operator which commutes with the *total* Hamiltonian, and consequently $S_{\text{tot}} \psi_0$ is an eigenstate, orthogonal to, but degenerate with, the ground state ψ_0. This and the other eigenstates can be found by solving the matrix equation for the r quantities F_t, where

$$\psi \equiv \Gamma \psi_0 \equiv (\sum F_t S_t^+) \psi_0 \tag{88}$$

is an assumed excited (unnormalized) eigenstate with energy γ above the ground state; and therefore Γ obeys the equation

$$[\mathcal{H}_{\text{eff}}, \Gamma] = \gamma \Gamma \tag{89}$$

---

[28] Experimental evidence that Fe is in the linear range has been provided by the experiments of R. H. Walmsley, "Linear Shift of the Fermi Level of Iron with applied Magnetic Field," *Phys. Rev. Letters*, **8**: 242 (1962).

which is denoted the "equation of motion" of the operator Γ, although it is nothing more than the Schrödinger equation written in convenient, commutator, notation. $\mathscr{H}_{\text{eff}}$ is the Hamiltonian of Eqs. (83) and (43), but as Γ commutes with $\mathscr{H}_{00}$ (cf. Problem 5) we consider only the exchange terms which have been explicitly written out.

Two basic commutators enable the evaluation of this equation to be carried out forthwith:

$$\left[c^*_{\mathbf{k}_1 t \uparrow} c_{\mathbf{k}_2 t \downarrow} c^*_{\mathbf{k}_3 t' \downarrow} c_{\mathbf{k}_4 t' \uparrow}, \sum_{\mathbf{k}} c^*_{\mathbf{k} t'' \uparrow} c_{\mathbf{k} t'' \downarrow} \right] = \delta_{t', t''} c^*_{\mathbf{k}_1 t \uparrow} c_{\mathbf{k}_2 t \downarrow} (c^*_{\mathbf{k}_3 t' \downarrow} c_{\mathbf{k}_4 t' \downarrow} - c^*_{\mathbf{k}_3 t' \uparrow} c_{\mathbf{k}_4 t' \uparrow}) \quad (90)$$

and $\left[c^*_{\mathbf{k}_1 t \uparrow} c_{\mathbf{k}_2 t \uparrow} c^*_{\mathbf{k}_3 t' \downarrow} c_{\mathbf{k}_4 t' \downarrow}, \sum_{\mathbf{k}} c^*_{\mathbf{k} t'' \uparrow} c_{\mathbf{k} t'' \downarrow} \right]$

$$= c^*_{\mathbf{k}_1 t \uparrow} (\delta_{t, t''} c^*_{\mathbf{k}_3 t' \downarrow} c_{\mathbf{k}_2 t \downarrow} - \delta_{t', t''} c^*_{\mathbf{k}_3 t' \uparrow} c_{\mathbf{k}_2 t \uparrow}) c_{\mathbf{k}_4 t' \downarrow} \quad (91)$$

Finally,

$$[\mathscr{H}_{\text{eff}}, \Gamma] = \sum_t \sum_{t' \neq t} (F_t - F_{t'}) \frac{2 S^z_t}{N} J^{\text{Hu}}_{t, t'} S^+_{t'} + \cdots \quad (92)$$

The dots indicate corrections involving more than one elementary excitation:

$$\sum c^*_{\mathbf{k} + \mathbf{q}, t \uparrow} c_{\mathbf{k} t \downarrow} c^*_{\mathbf{k}' t' m} c_{\mathbf{k}' - \mathbf{q} t' m} \quad (93)$$

which cannot be expressed in terms of the original operators, and which are neglected in the "random phase approximation." (We return to this point subsequently.) The terms which are retained define an eigenvalue equation for the eigenvector components, F_t, and eigenvalue, γ. The macroscopic operator

$$S^z_t = \frac{1}{2} \sum_{\mathbf{k}} (\mathfrak{n}_{\mathbf{k} t \uparrow} - \mathfrak{n}_{\mathbf{k} t \downarrow})$$

can be replaced by its expectation value, which is the negative quantity $-\mathscr{M}_t$ where $\mathscr{M}_t \equiv$ magnetization of the tth band. Using the definition of Δ_t, we readily obtain from Eqs. (92) and (89) the following determinantal condition:

$$\boxed{\text{Det} \, \| \delta_{t, t'} - \mathbb{K}_{t, t'} \| = 0} \quad (94)$$

where $\mathbb{K}_{t, t'} = 2 J^{\text{Hu}}_{t, t'} \dfrac{\mathscr{M}_t}{\Delta_t - \gamma}$ and $\mathbb{K}_{t, t} = 0$ (94A)

The F_t are related to the eigenvectors G_t, which are the solutions of the equation

$$\sum_{t'} \mathbb{K}_{t, t'} G_{t'} = G_t, \quad \text{by the relation} \quad F_t = \frac{G_t}{\gamma - \Delta_t} \quad (95)$$

The determinantal equation *always* admits the solution $\gamma = 0$ by virtue of the definition, Eq. (86), of Δ_t. The other solutions are not so discernible in general. Again in the soluble example of a two-band model discussed in Eq. (82), we find

$$\gamma = 0, \Delta_1 + \Delta_2 \tag{96}$$

where $F_1 = F_2$ for the lower solution (as expected), and $F_1/F_2 = -1$, for the higher solution. They are the $\mathbf{q} = 0$ limit of the "acoustic" and "optic" magnon spectra, respectively, as we shall soon discover.

MAGNONS AT $\mathbf{q} \neq 0$

We calculate the magnon spectra for $\mathbf{q} \neq 0$ in the same approximation as at $\mathbf{q} = 0$. The general form of the operator $S^+(\hbar\omega_\mathbf{q})$ was already suggested in Eq. (84), and if we are to apply to the study of it the same technique that was used for Γ, we must first write the equation of motion,

$$[\mathcal{H}_{\text{eff}}, S^+(\hbar\omega_q)] = \hbar\omega_q S^+(\hbar\omega_q) \tag{97}$$

and solve it in the random phase approximation, retaining only such terms as are identifiable with $S^+(\hbar\omega_q)$ itself or with $S_{\mathbf{k},t}^z$. An eigenvalue equation must then be solved for the amplitudes $F_{\mathbf{k},t}$ and the eigenvalues $\hbar\omega_q$, with integrals replacing the constants as matrix elements in Eq. (94).

Previously, $c_{\mathbf{k}t\uparrow}^* c_{\mathbf{k}t\downarrow}$ commuted with $\mathcal{H}_{00}$. The corresponding term in $S^+(\hbar\omega_q)$ is $c_{\mathbf{k}+\mathbf{q},t\uparrow}^* c_{\mathbf{k}t\downarrow}$, which creates elementary excitations in the Fermi sea. It is not strictly a raising operator of $\mathcal{H}_{00}$ because of the Coulomb interaction; but some of the correction may be taken into account by defining the energy of the elementary excitation, $E_t(\mathbf{k} + \mathbf{q}) - E_t(\mathbf{k})$, such as to yield the exact density of states when $\mathbf{q} \to 0$. Other (operator) corrections will be assigned to the ellipsis; thus,

$$[\mathcal{H}_{\text{eff}}, S^+(\hbar\omega_q)] = \sum_{\mathbf{k},t} (E_t(\mathbf{k} + \mathbf{q}) - E_t(\mathbf{k})) F_{\mathbf{k},t} c_{\mathbf{k}+\mathbf{q},t\uparrow}^* c_{\mathbf{k}t\downarrow}$$
$$+ \sum_{t,\mathbf{k}} \sum_{\substack{t' \neq t \\ \mathbf{k}'}} (F_{\mathbf{k},t} - F_{\mathbf{k}',t'}) \frac{\mathfrak{n}_{\mathbf{k}+\mathbf{q}t\uparrow} - \mathfrak{n}_{\mathbf{k}t\downarrow}}{N} J_{t,t'}^{\text{Hu}} c_{\mathbf{k}'+\mathbf{q},t'\uparrow}^* c_{\mathbf{k}',t'\downarrow} + \cdots \tag{98}$$

Combining the two equations above, *one arrives at precisely the previous eigenvalue equation*, Eq. (94), with, however, a new definition of the matrix elements:

$$\boxed{\mathbb{K}_{t,t'} = \frac{J_{t,t'}^{\text{Hu}}}{N} \sum_{\mathbf{k}} \frac{\mathfrak{n}_{\mathbf{k}t\downarrow} - \mathfrak{n}_{\mathbf{k}+\mathbf{q}t\uparrow}}{\Delta_t - \hbar\omega_q - E_t(\mathbf{k}) + E_t(\mathbf{k} + \mathbf{q})}} \tag{99}$$

in which $\mathfrak{n}_{\mathbf{k}tm}$ may be replaced by its thermal expectation value,

$$\langle \mathfrak{n}_{\mathbf{k},t,\downarrow} \rangle = f[E_t(\mathbf{k})] \quad \text{and} \quad \langle \mathfrak{n}_{\mathbf{k},t,\uparrow} \rangle = f[E_t(\mathbf{k}) + \Delta_t] \tag{99A}$$

for the purpose of the calculation. In view of the sharpness of the Fermi distribution at $T = 0°K.$, once Δ_t exceeds μ, then all $n_{\mathbf{k}t\uparrow} = 0$. This occurs for J^{Hu} at, or larger than, the threshold of the very strong coupling regime indicated in Fig. 7.11; note that *it is entirely possible that one or the other of the thresholds is exceeded in one band but not in another*, although this cannot conveniently be shown in the figure.

By the nature of the discrete sums above, scattering solutions of the determinantal equations must interlace the unperturbed continuum of states

$$\Delta_t - E_t(\mathbf{k}) + E_t(\mathbf{k} + \mathbf{q})$$

throughout the volume of momentum space where $\mathbf{k}$ satisfies

$$f[E_t(\mathbf{k})] = 1 = \{1 - f[E_t(\mathbf{k} + \mathbf{q}) + \Delta_t]\}$$

Bound state solutions can exist *above* the highest energy in the continuum, or *below* the lowest energy in it. Arguments of continuity indicate that for small $\mathbf{q}$ there are r bound state solutions, corresponding to r distinct magnon branches having energies at $\mathbf{q} = \mathbf{0}$, given by the eigenvalues γ of Eqs. (94) and (94A). As $\mathbf{q}$ is increased in magnitude (and depending upon its orientation relative to the reciprocal lattice vectors insofar as these affect the electronic band structure), eventually the bound-state solutions merge with the continuum and disappear.

Therefore, magnons do not exist at every value of $\mathbf{q}$ in the Brillouin zone, except in the very strong coupling limit and for k_F sufficiently large, as will be seen directly by means of the following soluble example and in Fig. 7.12.

Example:

Two degenerate bands in the effective mass approximation $E(\mathbf{k}) = \mathbf{k}^2$. Unit of energy is taken to be $\mu = k_F^2 = 1$. The determinantal equation, Eq. (94), with matrix elements, Eq. (99), is readily solved after the sums are converted to integrals in the standard manner. When $\Delta \geqslant 1$, we find the following transcendental equation:

$$\pm \frac{2}{3\Delta} = \frac{1}{2q} L(Q) \tag{100}$$

where

$$Q = \frac{2q}{\Delta + q^2 - \hbar\omega_q} \tag{101A}$$

and

$$L(Q) = \frac{1}{Q^2} \left[\frac{1}{2}(Q^2 - 1) \ln \left| \frac{Q+1}{Q-1} \right| + Q \right] \tag{101B}$$

For $\Delta \leqslant 1$, $n_{\mathbf{k}t\uparrow} \neq 0$, and we obtain a slightly more complicated equation:

$$\pm \frac{2}{3} \left[\frac{1 - (1 - \Delta)^{\frac{3}{2}}}{\Delta} \right] = \frac{1}{2q} [L(Q) - (1 - \Delta)L(Q')] \tag{102}$$

where

$$Q' = \frac{2q(1 - \Delta)^{\frac{1}{2}}}{\Delta - q^2 - \hbar\omega_q} \tag{103}$$

and Eqs. (101) define the other parameter and the function $L(Q)$.

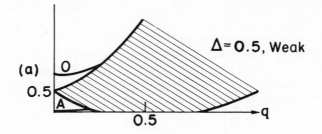

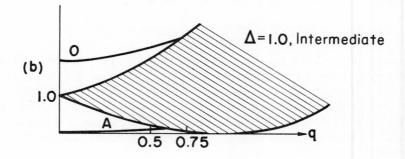

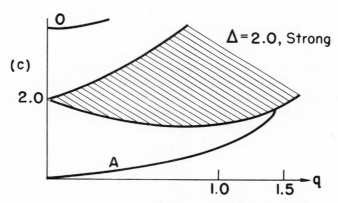

FIG. 7.12. Acoustic (A) and optical (O) magnons in the band theory, for $k_F = 1$, $a^{-1} \gg 1$ and various values of Δ. See Eqs. (100) ff. for details. Continuum indicated (shading) is for elementary excitations with spin flip; continuum for elementary excitations without spin flip remains the same as shown in Fig. 7.5, p. 188.

The optical magnon mode $(-)$ starts at 2Δ for $q = 0$ and increases somewhat before merging with the continuum. The acoustic $(+)$ branch starts at $\hbar\omega_0 = 0$ for $q = 0$ and increases approximately $\sim Dq^2 + O(q^4)$, with the parabolic approximation $\hbar\omega_q \sim Dq^2$ increasing in relative accuracy as Δ is increased. Expansion of the equations leads to a formula for D:

$$D = \frac{1 + (1 - \Delta)^{\frac{1}{2}} - \frac{4}{5}[1 - (1 - \Delta)^{\frac{1}{2}}]/\Delta}{1 - (1 - \Delta)^{\frac{1}{2}}} \qquad \text{for } \Delta \leqslant 1 \qquad (104\text{A})$$

and
$$D = 1 - \frac{4}{5\Delta} \qquad \text{for } \Delta \geqslant 1 \tag{104B}$$

The acoustic branch enters the continuum and "dies" at $q_{max} = 0.75\Delta$ for $\Delta \geqslant 1$. In the parabolic approximation, which we now want to test, the energy is

$$\hbar\omega^{ac}_{q\,max} \approx \left(1 - \frac{4}{5\Delta}\right)\left(\frac{9\Delta^2}{16}\right) = \frac{\Delta}{2}\left(\frac{9\Delta}{8} - 0.9\right)$$

whereas the exact energy at this value of q can be obtained by setting $Q = 1$ in Eq. (101). The result of the exact calculation is

$$\hbar\omega^{ac}_{q\,max} = \frac{\Delta}{2}\left(\frac{9\Delta}{8} - 1\right) \tag{105}$$

which is remarkably close. For $\Delta < 1$, q_{max} is not given by such a simple expression; also numerical calculations indicate that terms $O(q^4)$ become relatively more important as Δ is diminished.

Plots of the magnon spectra for three different values of Δ are shown in Fig. 7.12. The continuum of scattering modes is indicated by shading.

Antiferromagnetism occurs, according to the present Hund's rule 2-band model, when spin-down electrons start to fill the Brillouin zone,[29] as may be seen in strong coupling. Assume $\Delta \geqslant 1$, and every state in the spin-down zone is filled, every state in the spin-up zone is empty. The eigenvalue equation, Eq. (94), with appropriate matrix elements, Eq. (99), can be expanded in powers of $E_t(\mathbf{k} + \mathbf{q}) - E_t(\mathbf{k}) \equiv w(\mathbf{k}, \mathbf{q}, t)$, a procedure certainly valid for small $\mathbf{q}$. We make use of the assumption $E_t(-\mathbf{k}) = E_t(\mathbf{k})$ to prove,

$$\sum_{\mathbf{k}} w^{2p+1} \equiv 0 \qquad p = 0, 1, 2, \ldots, \qquad \text{all } \mathbf{q}, \tag{106}$$

which together with the identity $\sum w^{2p} \geqslant 0$ readily establishes the desired result:

$$\hbar\omega_0 = 0 \geqslant \hbar\omega_{\mathbf{q}} \qquad \text{all } \mathbf{q} \neq 0 \tag{107}$$

Not only does a collective magnon mode exist at every $\mathbf{q}$ in the Brillouin zone, but the $\mathbf{q} = 0$ mode is a *maximum*, and the ferromagnetic state must be unstable against the emission of any number and any type of magnons. The new ground state must then be an antiferromagnetic, or a spiral spin configuration of the type previously discussed.

The antiferromagnetic behavior sets in even before the spin-down Brillouin zone is completely filled by electrons, in the neighborhood of a half-filled zone, but the precise point at which it occurs must be calculated numerically. It is akin to the antiferromagnetism of insulators. Whereas the exclusion principle has the effect in the ferromagnetic state of preventing the kinetic motion of electrons from atom to atom, such motion is not prohibited in the antiferromagnetic configurations. The difference with insulators, is that the "hopping" (band, or kinetic, energy) represents real

[29] M. Tachiki and T. Nagamiya, "Helical Spin Arrangement of Band Electrons," *Phys. Letters,* 3: 214 (1963).

transitions in the metallic state, but only virtual transitions in the insulator [this is the importance of the large energy denominator U in Eq. (46)].

Connection between the band theory and the indirect exchange theory is very natural and easy to establish. For when one band is supposed narrow, the Hund's rule splitting of Kramers' degeneracy usually will send the entire spin-up band above the Fermi level, whereas the entire spin-down band will remain below this energy. This explains why narrow bands most likely lead to integral numbers of Bohr magnetons, just as in a localized electron theory. If this narrow band interacts with a broader band, as in Goodenough's model (*supra*), the broader band will be only slightly polarized. Whenever perturbation theory is applicable, something like the Ruderman-Kittel formula must result therefrom. If perturbation theory is not applicable, then the formulas derived in this section and the previous one provide a fair initial approximation to a strong-coupling theory, and should be used instead.

OTHER PROBLEMS AND REVIEW

Long-range order, the magnon spectrum, and many other magnetic properties are quite similar in the band theory, the indirect exchange theory, and the Heisenberg or Heitler-London theories. But there is a tremendous difference in the physical mechanisms involved in every one of these cases, and if use is to be made of these individual physical mechanisms, it is important to understand the distinction. We shall recapitulate:

In insulators, the electrons are well localized, have a definite spin, and interact with a limited number of neighbors. In the indirect exchange theory, the localized electrons provide the definite spin; the conduction electrons are polarized by them and provide the interaction between them. Finally in the band theory, all the magnetically interacting bands concurrently are partly responsible for the magnetization, and also partly responsible for the long-range ordering. This long-range ordering could be expressed in terms of the magnon spectrum which was calculated. A steeply rising spectrum with a minimum at $\mathbf{q} = \mathbf{0}$, which would result in a high Curie temperature, cannot occur in half-filled bands because of Brillouin zone effects. The situation is more complex when the interacting bands are of unequal width. However, this complexity is but a mathematical shadow of the tremendous diversity of properties which the magnetic metals and their alloys have displayed, and the trend is for the theory of magnetism in metals to become more complicated before it ever becomes simple again. It has been only ten years since Philip Anderson wrote, "The antiferromagnetic metals ... seem to represent a real challenge to the theory ... the greatest challenge to our present qualitative understanding of exchange phenomena."[30] Certainly, the reader who has arrived at the present point in this book has achieved some qualitative understanding of the ferromagnetic and antiferromagnetic metals, and insulators as well. Today the real defect in the theory of metals—as opposed to the theory of insulators—is a quantitative one, for it is desirable that experimental work be pegged on more solid theoretical foundations. Let us review some of the salient approximations made so far.

There has been no attempt to maintain approximate charge neutrality on each

---

[30] Philip W. Anderson, *Theory of Magnetism*, lecture notes, University of Tokyo, 1953 (unpublished).

atom, although Van Vleck[31] has emphasized that this must be done if the correct magnitude of exchange and correlation effects are to be obtained from the theory.

Besides the ferromagnetic state (partial or total), and the one-magnon states, we have not investigated any of the other possible magnetic states. Most important among these are the antiferromagnetic ground states and magnon states. It is likely that antiferromagnetic magnons in metals will have many similarities to those in insulators; but it is also likely that some new features will be found, as was the case in ferromagnetism.

It is desirable to go beyond the random phase approximation so as to study the effects of magnon-magnon interactions. None of the methods in this chapter can be reliably extended, but this problem has been investigated in the strong-coupling regime by other means.[32] These involve principally the use of Green functions, recently established as a powerful tool in solid-state physics. This method has the advantage that otherwise very complicated problems can be handily organized. Spatially inhomogeneous systems can be dealt with almost as readily as homogeneous ones. The extension of the random phase approximation, or the inclusion of effects such as emphasized by Van Vleck, i.e., treating $\mathcal{H}_0$ and $\mathcal{H}_c$ on an equal basis so as to truly minimize the ground-state energy, these are *difficult computational* problems in the Green function method, but not *impossible conceptual* ones as they are in standard approximation schemes. For these reasons, we include in the Bibliography a list of works detailing the modern approach to many-body theory.

Outstanding problems still to be resolved include the thermodynamics of magnetism in the band theory, particularly near and above the Curie temperature. Early calculations of Stoner and others[33] based upon a simplified band theory assumed that the magnetism evanesced at the Curie temperature. The theory developed in the present chapter shows that in metals as in insulators the principal elementary excitations of interest in magnetism are the spin waves. Therefore one must consider the possibility that the Curie temperature is attained when a sufficient number of spin waves have destroyed the long-range order, but *before* the magnetic moment is affected on the atomic level.[34] Even in the Heisenberg model, it is generally very difficult to calculate thermodynamic functions with any precision, and many elaborate approximative procedures have been developed for this purpose. So in the band theory, if we do not accept Stoner's simplified hypothesis, the calculations will be even more difficult and subject to error and therefore represent the greatest challenge. An introduction to the elementary theory of thermodynamics in magnetism given in the following chapter is, however, restricted to exactly soluble models or approximations.

Another interesting modern field of study is the theory of localized states in metals, particularly magnetically polarized localized states. From these may well come the source of the deepest understanding of the band theory of magnetism, and therefore we have included in the Bibliography some of the recent work on this subject.

---

[31] J. H. Van Vleck, "Models of Exchange Coupling in Ferromagnetic Media," *Rev. Mod. Phys.*, **25**: 220 (1953). Calculations based on these ideas have lately been carried out by M. Gutzwiller, *Phys. Rev. Letters*, **10**: 159 (1963); by J. Hubbard, *Proc. Roy. Soc.* (1964); and by J. Kanamori, to be published.

[32] T. Izuyama, *Phys. Rev. Letters*, **12**: 585 (1964); T. Nakamura, *ibid*, 279 (1964); cf. also T. Izuyama and R. Kubo, *J. Appl. Phys.*, pt. 2, **35**: 1074 (1964).

[33] See the review by E. P. Wohlfarth, *Rev. Mod. Phys.*, **25**: 211 (1953).

[34] For a classification of many metals and alloys according to the remnant magnetic moment, see P. Rhodes and E. P. Wohlfarth, *Proc. Roy. Soc.*, A273: 247 (1963). An approach to the thermodynamics is given in E. D. Thompson et al., *Proc. Phys. Soc.*, **83**: 59 (1964), and J. F. Cornwell, *Proc. Roy. Soc.*, A279: 346 (1964).

PART III

THERMODYNAMICS AND STATISTICAL MECHANICS

When a liquid is heated it is changed to a gas. When a liquid is cooled it changes to a solid. I had thought some times that I felt a solid object that was hotter than gas. It is wonderful that education can teach me the truth.

—*A Child's Garden of Misinformation*
(collected by Art Linkletter).

CHAPTER 8

ELEMENTARY STATISTICAL MECHANICS

When a piece of iron has been touched by a loadstone, if it be placed in a hot fire until it is perfectly red hot and remain in the fire some considerable time, it will lose that magnetick strength it had acquired. Even a loadstone itself through a longish stay in the fire, loses the powers of attracting implanted and innate in it, and any other magnetick powers ... Just as by the rigour of the surrounding air, water is changed from its nature into ice; so iron, glowing in fire, is destroyed by the violent heat, and has its nature confused and perturbed.[1]

* * * * * *

This chapter will provide an introduction to some problems of statistical mechanics. It begins with a particularly simple example, in terms of which various thermodynamic functions can be derived: U, the internal energy; F, the free energy; etc.; and a meaning assigned to T, the temperature.

SPINS IN A MAGNETIC FIELD

We consider a spin one-half, which interacts only with an external, constant magnetic field. For the purposes of statistical mechanics and thermodynamics, it is advantageous to consider an assembly of such spins, each statistically independent of the others, and to calculate their properties on the average. Let the energy of each spin parallel to the field be $-h$, and of each spin antiparallel to the field be $+h$, where

$$h = \tfrac{1}{2}g\mu_B H \tag{1}$$

($g = 2$ for spin and 1 for orbital angular momentum; μ_B = Bohr magneton = $e\hbar/2mc$ = $.927 \times 10^{-20}$ erg/gauss; this corresponds to a splitting of $2h = 1$ cm^{-1} when $g = 2$ and $H = 11,000$ gauss). If on the "average" n spins are parallel and $N-n$ are antiparallel to H, then the "average" energy of each spin, u, and the total energy U, are

$$u = \frac{U}{N} = \frac{1}{N}(N - 2n)h = (1 - 2p)h \qquad \text{with } p \equiv \frac{n}{N} \tag{2}$$

---

[1] William Gilbert, *De Magnete*, p. 66.

We have indicated by quotation marks that the notion of average has yet to be defined. Indeed at first we shall be concerned with the *most probable* value of n rather than the strict average. A strict postulational basis is really required in statistical mechanics, but for the present, a heuristic approach provides the best sort of introduction for the uninitiated.

The probability of attaining the configuration of Eq. (2) is $Q(n)$,

$$Q(n) = P(U) \cdot \frac{N!}{n!(N-n)!} \cdot 2^{-N} \tag{3}$$

where $P(U)$ is the yet-to-be-determined thermal (Maxwell-Boltzmann) factor; the second factor is the binomial coefficient (which gives the number of distinct arrangements which have the correct value of n) which is normalized by the last factor, the inverse of the *total* number of arrangements. Therefore Q = product of two independent probabilities: $P(U)$, the thermal a priori probability of the system having energy U; and the remaining factors, which give the statistical probability appropriate to that value of U or n. Further, by use of Stirling's approximation

$$\ln N! \sim N \ln N - N \tag{4}$$

it is readily seen that the entire statistical probability factor varies exponentially with N. The logarithm of Q is then an extensive variable—that is, one which scales with the size of the system—and $\ln Q$ is therefore the proper object of study.

$$\ln Q = \ln P(U) - N[\ln 2 + p \ln p + (1-p) \ln (1-p)] \tag{5}$$

setting $p = n/N$. Next, to determine $P(U)$ there are the following reasonable criteria:

1. $\ln P(U)$ must be extensive.
2. It must be dimensionless.
3. It must maximize the overall probability Q.

Requirement 1 is met by $\ln P \propto \pm U$; requirement 2 is satisfied by multiplying $\pm U$ by an intensive quantity (independent of N) of dimensions (energy)$^{-1}$. Requirement 3 is met by recognizing that in nature the lowest energies are always preferred, which eliminates $+U$ in favor of $-U$. And therefore

$$P(U) = e^{-\beta U} \tag{6}$$

where β is the intensive quantity chosen to be,

$$\beta = \frac{1}{kT} \tag{7}$$

k = Boltzmann's constant = 1.38×10^{-16} erg/$^\circ K$, and T = temperature, $^\circ K$. This derivation implies that two systems in thermal equilibrium with each other have the same value of T (see Problem 1). However, the problems of the establishment of a *scale* of temperature and other interesting thermodynamic refinements are beyond the scope of this section, and are found in standard books on the subject.

Problem 1: Divide the N spins into sets of n_1, n_2, ... spins, with $\Sigma n_i = N$. Assign temperatures T_1, T_2, ... to these sets and a total energy v. Show that Q is maximum when $T_1 = T_2 = \dots$, i.e., prove that for fixed U there is a *unique* temperature at thermodynamic equilibrium. Then derive Eq. (14), p. 182, for Fermions.

By analogy with the definition of $P(U)$, it is convenient to define the *free energy* F, and the free energy per spin f,

$$Q = e^{-\beta F} = e^{-\beta N f} \tag{8}$$

Eliminating Q one finds:

$$f = (1 - 2p)h + kT[\ln 2 + p \ln p + (1 - p) \ln (1 - p)] \tag{9}$$

From the preceding, we know that f must be a minimum, and therefore we seek the appropriate solution of

$$\frac{\partial f}{\partial p} = 0 \tag{10}$$

which is readily found to be

$$p = \frac{1}{1 + e^{-2\beta h}} \tag{11}$$

Substitution of this value into Eq. (2) gives the correct internal energy, and into Eq. (9) the correct free energy for thermodynamic equilibrium, given below by another method.

The same results can be obtained somewhat more simply, and in more generality, by dividing an arbitrary system into a large number of subsets, each with energy e_i and probability p_i. Assume that the total free energy is the sum of such terms as

$$F_i \equiv e_i p_i + kT p_i \ln p_i = (e_i p_i) - T\left(k p_i \ln \frac{1}{p_i}\right) \tag{12}$$

The quantities in parentheses are $(e_i p_i)$, the *internal energy* of the ith set, and $(k p_i \ln 1/p_i) = S(p_i)$, its *entropy*. Minimizing F with respect to the various p_i, one finds

$$p_i = \frac{e^{-\beta e_i}}{Z} \tag{13}$$

with Z chosen such that $\Sigma p_i = 1$. The normalizing factor Z is the partition function, or *Zustandsumme*,

$$\boxed{Z \equiv \sum_i e^{-\beta e_i} = Tr\{e^{-\beta \mathcal{H}}\}} \tag{14}$$

The second equality permits us to work in representations in which $\mathcal{H}$ is not diagonal, and this is often convenient. The quantity of which the trace is taken

$$\rho \equiv e^{-\beta \mathscr{H}} \tag{15}$$

is known as the *density matrix*; it is the quantum-mechanical operator generalization of the classical Boltzmann factor.

The partition sum Z has a physical significance closely akin to Q; and usually the evaluation of Z by the method of steepest descents yields exactly Q, provided N is a large number. Thus we define a new free energy by the relation

$$Z = e^{-\beta F} \tag{16}$$

It should in general be clear from the context whether one is using F derived from Z or from Q. In general it will not matter; however, there are some instances in quantum mechanics when it is exceedingly difficult to find an appropriate formula for Q, although Z is always well defined by Eq. (14). We therefore take the *partition sum* and Eq. (14) as the more fundamental starting point of statistical mechanics, abandoning the approach based on the most probable distribution with which we broached the subject. In addition to Eqs. (14) to (16), we must also have a prescription for calculating thermodynamic averages. Let **A** be an arbitrary operator. The thermal average $\langle \mathbf{A} \rangle_{TA}$ is given by the weighted average,

$$\langle \mathbf{A} \rangle_{TA} = \frac{Tr\{\mathbf{A}\rho\}}{Z} \tag{17}$$

The logarithm of Z is $-\beta F$, and thermal averages are equally conveniently expressed as derivatives of the free energy. For example, the correct generalization of the zero-temperature magnetization $\mathscr{M} = -\partial U/\partial H$ is

$$\mathscr{M}(T) = -\frac{\partial F}{\partial H} \tag{18}$$

The internal energy becomes (substituting $\mathscr{H}$ for **A** in Eq. (17))

$$U \equiv \frac{\partial(\beta F)}{\partial \beta} \tag{19}$$

In the following section we shall discuss the entropy, $S = (U - F)/T$, which is also expressible as a derivative of F.

It is interesting to calculate the thermodynamic properties of the noninteracting spins using the new formalism. The partition sum is

$$Z = (e^{\beta h} + e^{-\beta h})^N = (2 \cosh \beta h)^N \tag{20}$$

Therefore,

$$F = -\frac{N}{\beta} \ln (2 \cosh \beta h) \qquad (21)$$

and by Eq. (19)

$$U = \frac{\partial(\beta F)}{\partial \beta} = -Nh \tanh \beta h \qquad (22)$$

in perfect agreement with the elementary derivation based on Q. Also, by Eq. (18) we find a nonvanishing magnetization:

$$\mathscr{M} = N(\tfrac{1}{2}g\mu_B) \tanh \beta h = N(\tfrac{1}{2}g\mu_B) \tanh \tfrac{1}{2}\beta g\mu_B H \qquad (23)$$

The law of Langevin and Curie for the magnetic susceptibility χ of paramagnetic materials is

$$\chi \equiv \lim_{H \to 0} \left(\frac{\mathscr{M}}{H}\right) = \frac{C}{T} \qquad (24)$$

C = Curie's constant, and T = absolute temperature. This is in accord with the results above, provided

$$C = N\frac{(\tfrac{1}{2}g\mu_B)^2}{k} \qquad (25)$$

Problem 2: Find F, U, M, and C for the following: (a) spins 1 [eigenvalues $e_i = \tfrac{1}{2}g\mu_B H \cdot$ 1, 0, and -1]; (b) classical dipoles (eigenvalues $e = \tfrac{1}{2}g\mu_B H \cos \theta$, with $-\pi < \theta \leqslant \pi$).

Problem 3: *Adiabatic demagnetization*[2] is a method of achieving very low temperatures using the thermodynamic properties of spins in a magnetic field. As in any cooling process, the refrigeration cycle is carried out in two steps. First, the magnetization is increased iso-thermally by applying a magnetic field to a collection of spins in thermal equilibrium with a reservoir at temperature T. The amount of heat δE removed from the sample is (cf. Eq. (33))

$$\delta E = T dS$$

where dS = difference in entropy between the magnetized and unmagnetized states. In the second step, the contact to the reservoir is broken and the magnetic field is removed. The spins no longer have a preferred orientation, and quickly randomize, achieving thermal equilibrium at a new temperature T'. The lowest temperature which can be reached by ordinary methods (pumping on the vapor of liquid helium) is $0.7°K$. Assuming this value for T, calculate T', the temperature after one stage of adiabatic demagnetization, as function of the spin parameters and of magnetic field strength.

SPINS IN A MOLECULAR FIELD

In 1895, in his famous Mémoire *On the Magnetic Properties of Bodies at Various Temperatures*, Pierre Curie gave the first complete experimental study of the magnetization of a ferromagnet, iron, as a function of field and temperature. He concluded from the curves he

---

[2] See D. de Klerk, "Adiabatic Demagnetization," *Handbuch der Physik*, vol. XV, p. 38.

obtained, that "by analogy with the hypotheses about fluids, the rapid increase of magnetization occurs when the magnetic intensity of the particles is sufficiently strong to permit them to
interact." But he also cautions against attaching too much importance to this similarity.

There seem to be no reasons to doubt the truth of Pierre Curie's idea, nor that many
aspects of paramagnetism are to ferromagnetism what perfect gases are to dense fluids. The
theory of the molecular field is an outgrowth of this idea.[3]

Thus Weiss' main proposition was that all interactions of known or unknown
origins could be replaced by a single "molecular field" H_m, such that the total force on
each spin is the sum of an externally applied field H and of the molecular field H_m.
The equation determining the latter is the constitutive equation of the molecular field
theory.

The simplest assumption for a molecular field is that H_m is proportional to the
magnetization, i.e.,

$$H_m = H_0 \tanh \beta b(H + H_m) \tag{26}$$

H_0 = constant of proportionality, and $b = \frac{1}{2}g\mu_B$, by analogy with Eq. (23). [We deviate
from the standard practice of obtaining an equation for the magnetization. The
present approach ties in better with the independent spins of the preceding section, and
$\mathcal{M}(T)$ can be calculated from H_m.] Although more complicated constitutive equations
for H_m are easily imagined, the above is sufficient in the absence of any detailed knowledge about the interactions. Experiments give knowledge about the value of H_0 and b,
which are then the physical parameters which characterize a given material. It will
however become apparent in the course of this work that the molecular field hypothesis embodied in the equation above is valid only for very long-range physical
forces, and that the quantum mechanical forces truly responsible for magnetism are
not often of sufficiently long range to justify such a hypothesis. For short-range
forces the exact laws of the interaction will be required in order that the thermodynamic functions be calculable. However, if we imagine an idealized material in which
the forces are of sufficiently long range, the magnetization is the only possible physical
parameter of interest and Eq. (26) becomes a valid linear approximation to the true
constitutive equation *regardless of the actual details of the microscopic situation* (e.g.,
the indirect exchange interaction when $k_F \to 0$).

The constant of proportionality H_0, and the resulting molecular field H_m can be as
much as two or three orders of magnitude larger than the strongest laboratory fields
of some 10^5 gauss. It is therefore of some interest to solve for the thermodynamic
functions of the molecular field ferromagnet in the approximation that $H = 0$, and
later to take any existing applied fields into account by some sort of thermodynamic
perturbation theory. Therefore, we first solve the equation

$$H_m = H_0 \tanh \beta b H_m \tag{27}$$

which always possesses a trivial solution $H_m = 0$, but which in the temperature range

$$0 < kT < bH_0 \qquad (kT = \beta^{-1}) \tag{28}$$

is found to have a nontrivial solution. This is given graphically in Fig. 8.1.

---

[3] Pierre Weiss, 6th Solvay Congress, 1930.

How does one choose between the trivial and the nontrivial solution, in the range of temperature where they coexist? Recall requirement 1 in the previous section, stating that the overall probability should be maximal. This criterion is easily extended to the present case, by requiring Z to be maximal.

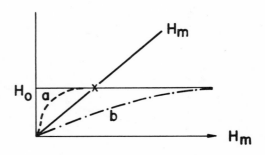

FIG. 8.1. Graphical solution of molecular field equations, Eq. (27). (a) $H_0 \tanh \beta b H_m$ for $\beta > \beta_c$. (b) $H_0 \tanh \beta b H_m$ for $\beta < \beta_c$ intersects H_m only at the origin (trivial solution).

The trivial solution immediately leads to a partition sum Z_{triv}.

$$Z_{\text{triv}} = 2^N \tag{29}$$

and the nontrivial one, to

$$Z_{\text{nontriv}} = (2 \cosh \beta b H_m)^N \tag{30}$$

These results are a direct application of Eq. (20). Comparing the two possibilities above, we see that the second one is always larger, and it is therefore always preferred in the range of temperatures where H_m exists. The special temperature T_c where the two solutions merge, at which $kT_c = bH_0$ and $H_m \to 0$, is known as the Curie temperature. Thus H_m starts from a maximum value of H_0 at $T = 0$, decreases to $H_m = 0$ at T_c, and remains zero above T_c. One finds a similar behavior for the internal energy,

$$U = -\frac{N}{2} b H_m \tanh \beta b H_m = -\frac{N}{2} (kT_c)\left(\frac{H_m}{H_0}\right)^2 \tag{31}$$

Note, however, that a factor of $\frac{1}{2}$ is introduced here into the formula, Eq. (22), to prevent double-counting.

Two other thermodynamic functions are of some interest. The first of these, the *specific heat*, is simply the thermal derivative of the internal energy;

$$c(T) \equiv \frac{1}{N} \frac{dU}{dT} \tag{32}$$

that is, in the present case,

$$c = \frac{2U}{N} \frac{d(\ln H_m)}{dT} \tag{32A}$$

The formula for c in terms of H_m is obtained by use of Eq. (31) for U, and is plotted as function of temperature in Fig. 8.2, lowest curve.

The second thermodynamic function of importance is the *entropy*, $S(T)$. Although this function is uniquely determined once $U(T)$ is known, often it is of interest to know S directly. The entropy is closely related to the second, statistical, term in Eq. (5) or (12), for the common textbook definition of S is, $S = k \ln W$, where W = total statistical

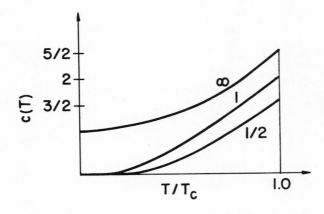

FIG. 8.2. Molecular field specific-heat curves, for $s = \frac{1}{2}, 1,$ and ∞.

weight of the most probable state. But it is not always convenient to obtain S from this definition and we may take as a more practical definition:

$$S(T) \equiv \frac{U - F}{T} = -\frac{\partial F}{\partial T} \qquad (33)$$

with U and F given by Eqs. (16) and (17). It may be useful to recall Nernst's law, the *third law of thermodynamics*, according to which S, hence c vanish at the absolute zero of temperature,

$$S(0) = c(0) = 0 \qquad (34)$$

The reader should verify the validity of this law in the present model (Problem 4).

DISCONTINUITY IN SPECIFIC HEAT

Because $U \to 0$ just at T_c and vanishes at all temperatures above it, there is no latent heat associated with the disappearance of the magnetization. Nevertheless a thermodynamical change has occurred, as may be seen by the discontinuous change in specific heat at T_c,

$$\Delta c|_{T_c} = \frac{3k}{2} \qquad (35)$$

(see Fig. 8.2). It is interesting to note that the magnitude of this discontinuity does not depend on the parameters H_m and b and therefore to speculate whether this should not be a universal property of all magnetic materials. But it is not, for at least two important reasons.

First, in physical materials it is always found that the magnetic specific heat does not vanish above T_c, but that a certain fraction of the maximum value persists to fairly high temperatures, so that $c(T)$ vanishes only at $T \gg T_c$. This should shake our faith in one of the physical premises of the molecular field theory, viz., that the forces causing the magnetism are sufficiently long ranged for the one-parameter theory to be accurate. (The Bethe-Peierls-Weiss method is a multiparameter refinement of molecular field theory which does allow for residual specific heat and short-range order above T_c.)[4]

Second, there is no reason to believe that the individual units of magnetic moment are elementary spins. Even within the context of the molecular field theory, we should test the effects of assuming $s = 1, \frac{3}{2}, 2, \ldots$ for the magnitude of the individual spins, to compare with our results for $s = \frac{1}{2}$.

Fortunately, there is no difficulty whatever in checking the second of these points, and repeating the calculation for $s \neq \frac{1}{2}$. Let us do this with the primary intent of recomputing the magnitude of Δc at T_c, and incidentally, so as to obtain the dependence of the Curie temperature T_c on the magnitude of the spins.

Below T_c, the partition sum for spins of magnitude s is

$$Z = (e^{2\beta bs(H + H_m)} + e^{2\beta b(s-1)(H + H_m)} + \cdots + e^{-2\beta bs(H + H_m)})^N$$

$$= \left(\frac{\sinh \beta b(H + H_m)(2s + 1)}{\sinh \beta b(H + H_m)} \right)^N \tag{36}$$

and therefore, in zero applied field, the magnetization is

$$\mathcal{M}(T) = \frac{\partial}{\partial H} \left[\frac{N}{\beta} \ln \frac{\sinh \beta b(H + H_m)(2s + 1)}{\sinh \beta b(H + H_m)} \right]_{H=0} \tag{37}$$

The constitutive equation, basically

$$\frac{H_m}{H_0} = \frac{\mathcal{M}(T)}{\mathcal{M}(0)} \tag{38}$$

takes on the following form:

$$H_m = H_0 2s \cdot B_s(\beta b H_m 2s) \tag{39}$$

where B_s is the Brillouin function,

$$B_s(y) = \frac{1}{2s} \left[(2s + 1) \coth\left(\frac{2sy + y}{2s} \right) - \coth \frac{y}{2s} \right] \tag{40}$$

A well-known function first derived by Langevin on the basis of classical statistics is just the limiting form of the above, $B_\infty(y)$, and so need not be considered separately. Note $B_s(\infty) = 1$.

Just near T_c the internal field H_m vanishes and we may expand the constitutive equation to $O(H_m^4)$ in a power series. We deduce that just below the Curie temperature,

$$\mathcal{M}(T) \propto (T_c - T)^{\frac{1}{2}} \tag{41}$$

---

[4] See P. R. Weiss, *Phys. Rev.,* **74**: 1493 (1948). Another method, due to Oguchi, has similar results. See J. S. Smart, *J. Phys. Chem. Solids,* **20**: 41 (1961).

a law obeyed by some, but by no means all, ferromagnets. As for the internal energy, we obtain the exact result

$$
U = \begin{cases} -\frac{1}{2}N \dfrac{kT_c}{\frac{4}{3}s(s+1)} \left(\dfrac{H_m}{H_0}\right)^2 & T \leqslant T_c \\[4mm] 0 & T \geqslant T_c \end{cases}
\tag{42}
$$

where

$$
kT_c = \tfrac{4}{3}s(s+1)H_0 b
\tag{43}
$$

A straightforward calculation yields the discontinuity in the specific heat

$$
\Delta c|_{T_c} = 5k\, \frac{s(s+1)}{s^2 + (s+1)^2}
\tag{44}
$$

which is the desired generalization of Eq. (35). As we see in Fig. 8.2, changes in the magnitude of s can account for specific heat discontinuities in the range between $3k/2$ and $5k/2$. Later we shall see that semiclassical spin-wave theory predicts $\Delta c = k$, and a linear decrease of the magnetization near T_c, $\mathcal{M}(T) \propto T_c - T$. The Ising model in two dimensions predicts yet another dependence of these quantities, $c = \infty$ at T_c, and $\mathcal{M}(T) \propto (T_c - T)^{\frac{1}{8}}$. The experimental situation is equally inconclusive.

A particularity of the molecular field theory, shared by the Ising model, is the exponential decrease of the specific heat near zero absolute. This feature, derived in Problem 4, is not in good agreement with experiment, which supports the spin-wave theory instead.

Problem 4: Show that in molecular field theory, $c(T) = A \exp - B/T$, in the limit $T \to 0$. Find A, B in terms of T_c, s. Discuss the anomalous limit $s \to \infty$ (see Fig. 8.2).

MAGNETIC SUSCEPTIBILITY

The response of magnetic materials to external magnetic fields is measured by the static susceptibility

$$
\chi = \lim_{H \to 0} \frac{\mathcal{M}}{H}
\tag{45}
$$

In ferromagnets a finite $\mathcal{M}$ exists without any applied field at all, and therefore χ must be infinite below the Curie temperature. Above T_c, the limit $H \to 0$ allows us to pose $H_m \to 0$ in Eq. (37). To leading order in these infinitesimals we find,

$$
H_m = \tfrac{1}{3}H_0 \beta b [(2s+1)^2 - 1](H + H_m)
$$

From the molecular field we can calculate the magnetization and finally the susceptibility which is

$$
\boxed{\chi = \frac{C}{T - \theta}}
\tag{46}
$$

the Curie-Weiss law. With $b = \frac{1}{2}g\mu_B$ by Eq. (26), we find (N = number of spins)

$$C = N\frac{4}{3}s(s + 1)\frac{b^2}{k}$$

as before, and θ, the "paramagnetic Curie temperature," is given by

$$k\theta = H_0 \frac{4b}{3} s(s + 1) \tag{47}$$

and is therefore numerically identical to T_c. According to the experimental evidence, however, and also according to more refined theories, this last result is only approximately correct.

It is only slightly more trouble to obtain the formula for the susceptibility of *antiferromagnetic* materials. In the simplest approximation, these consist of two types of spins which are oppositely oriented. Let us assume that if the A spins are pointed in any direction, they exert a molecular field on the B spins which tends to align them in the opposite direction. Therefore, above the critical temperature ($\tilde{N}$ = Weiss const),

$$\mathscr{M}_A = \frac{C}{T}(H - \tilde{N}\mathscr{M}_B)$$

and

$$\mathscr{M}_B = \frac{C}{T}(H - \tilde{N}\mathscr{M}_A) \tag{48}$$

are the two coupled equations. From these it follows that χ once more obeys the Curie-Weiss law, but with negative $\theta = -\tilde{N}C$. This is a very important result, suggesting the use of the high-temperature susceptibility to predict whether a material is ferromagnetic ($\theta > 0$), paramagnetic ($\theta = 0$), or antiferromagnetic ($\theta < 0$). When θ is negative, we may define $T_N = -\theta$ as the *paramagnetic Néel temperature*, named after one of the pioneers in this field. A magnetic field applied to an antiferromagnet at temperatures below T_N will align $\mathscr{M}_A$ and $\mathscr{M}_B$ perpendicular to itself, with a small component of each along the field. This results in the so-called perpendicular susceptibility $\chi_\perp = C/2T_N$ = constant independent of temperature. On the other hand, if anisotropy, or some other mechanism constrains the spins to point along a certain preferred direction and H is parallel to this direction, the parallel susceptibility which is then measured must vanish at $T = 0$, as the interaction energy $= H(\mathscr{M}_A + \mathscr{M}_B)$ vanishes when in the absence of thermal fluctuations $\mathscr{M}_A \equiv -\mathscr{M}_B$. In a powdered sample crystal orientations are randomized and the direction cosines average to $\frac{1}{3}$. Therefore the measured $\langle\chi\rangle$ at $T = 0$ will have the average value of $\frac{2}{3}(C/2T_N)$. This "two-thirds" law has been subjected to experimental verification. The constancy of $\chi_\perp$ is also in good accord with exact calculations on the Ising model[5] antiferromagnet (where, although $\chi_\perp$ is not perfectly constant below T_N, one finds ratios on the order of $(\chi_{\perp max}/\chi_{\perp 0}) = 1.183$, not far from unity). This feature may be a model-independent property of antiferromagnets.

---

[5] In a later chapter we deal with the Ising model, although not specifically with this result, quoted by M. E. Fisher, *J. Math. Phys.*, **4**: 278 (1963).

Customarily one plots χ^{-1} rather than χ, so as to observe agreement with, or deviations from, the Curie-Weiss law. Typical plots are given in Fig. 8.3.

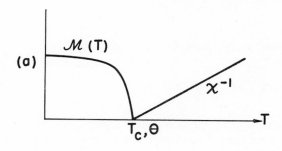

FIG. 8.3. Susceptibility and magnetization, or sublattice magnetization, of (a) ferromagnet and (b) antiferromagnet.

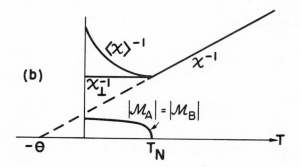

LANDAU'S THEORY OF SECOND-ORDER PHASE TRANSITIONS

Although the free energy must be continuous across any phase boundary, the first or higher derivatives of this function may be discontinuous or even infinite, and this gives rise to a variety of possible phase transitions. For example, the familiar transformation of water to ice is associated with a discontinuity in $U = \partial(\beta F)/\partial\beta$, that is, it involves a latent heat, and is a first-order phase transformation.

As we have seen in the Weiss molecular field theory, the disappearance of the magnetization is associated not with latent heat, but rather with a discontinuity in specific heat, a second derivative of F. Ehrenfest denoted this a second-order phase transition. The general theory for this was given by D. Landau, valid for a range of temperature just below T_c. Within this restricted range of temperature, it encompasses the molecular field theory or any other physical model of magnetism.

The free energy is decomposed into two parts, one of which is insensitive to the phase transition and the other of which depends explicitly on an order parameter. This order parameter, quite naturally, is a function of the *magnetization* in the present context, vanishing above T_c. Below T_c it must assume such a value as to minimize the free energy. Following Landau, let us denote the order parameter η, set $t = T_c - T$, and write

$$F = F_0 + F_1(t, \eta)$$

F_0 is the smooth, uninteresting part of the free energy and persists even above T_c. On the other hand, F_1 exists only below T_c (that is, $t > 0$) and vanishes above T_c (that is, $t < 0$). For sufficiently small positive t we expand in a power series:

$$F_1(t, \eta) = g_1(t)\eta + g_2(t)\eta^2 + \cdots \tag{49}$$

For sufficiently small η terms of $O(\eta^3)$ may be neglected; F_1 is then minimized with respect to η. This determines η as a function of t:

$$-\frac{\frac{1}{2}g_1(t)}{g_2(t)} = \eta(t) \tag{50}$$

But by assumption,

$$\eta(0) = 0 \tag{51}$$

and this provides a boundary condition.

So far, the treatment has been fairly general. Now let us particularize. The simplest solution of Eq. (50) to have the desired property of vanishing at $t = 0$ is

$$\eta(t) = At \qquad \text{therefore } At = -\frac{\frac{1}{2}g_1(t)}{g_2(t)} \tag{52}$$

That is, first we assume that the order parameter varies linearly with t (A is a constant), and then we use Eq. (50) to constrain the functions $g_{1,2}$ appearing in the expansion of F_1, which would otherwise be arbitrary. Finally, the simplest manner to satisfy this last equation is to set

$$g_2(t) = \text{constant} \qquad \text{and} \qquad g_1(t) = -2Atg_2 \tag{53}$$

One must also attribute a physical meaning to η. It can only involve an even power of the magnetization since the latter is a vector quantity, odd powers of which cannot appear in the free energy. Thus, making once more the simplest possible choice, one assumes

$$\eta = \mathcal{M}^2 \tag{54}$$

Problem 5: Check that Eqs. (49) to (54) agree with the calculations on the basis of the molecular field theory, including $\mathcal{M} \sim \sqrt{T_c - T}$; and calculate the discontinuity in the specific heat at T_c.

Evidently, the assumptions Eqs. (52), (53) and (54) are highly arbitrary, and although they lead to agreement with molecular field theory (cf. Problem 5) they are neither unique, nor of general validity. For example, in order to obtain agreement with the Ising model (in two dimensions), which we study later, the choices

$$g_2 = \ln t \qquad g_1 = -2Atg_2 \qquad \text{and} \qquad \eta = \mathcal{M}^8 \tag{55}$$

are required. In antiferromagnets, two or more order parameters may be required even under the simplest assumptions. This and other interesting applications of the

Landau theory, to inhomogeneous materials, for example, are outside the scope of our introduction.[6]

ONE-DIMENSIONAL ISING MODEL

The first of several exactly soluble models which we shall examine is the model of ferromagnetism (see p. 27 and Bibliography, p. 295). It provides an interesting example to study. Consider first the Ising Hamiltonian for a one-dimensional chain of spins in the absence of any external fields:

$$\mathscr{H}_0 = -J \sum_{n=1}^{N-1} \sigma_n^z \sigma_{n+1}^z - J\sigma_N^z \sigma_1^z \tag{56}$$

with σ^z a Pauli spin matrix,

$$\sigma^z = \begin{vmatrix} 1 & 0 \\ 0 & -1 \end{vmatrix} \tag{57}$$

with eigenvalues ± 1. Starting with this explicit Hamiltonian, it is desired to obtain first the partition function and then the various thermodynamic functions of interest. One simple way to do this is to use the fact that each bond has only two degrees of freedom, depending upon whether the spins are parallel or antiparallel. Formally, we can define a new set of N Pauli spin matrices,

$$\tau_n \equiv \sigma_n^z \sigma_{n+1}^z \qquad \tau_N \equiv \sigma_N^z \sigma_1^z \tag{58}$$

which have the same form as Eq. (57) and also have eigenvalues ± 1. The partition sum is thus

$$Z_0 = Tr\left\{ \prod_{n=1}^{N} e^{\beta J \tau_n} \right\} = \prod_{n=1}^{N} (e^{\beta J} + e^{-\beta J}) = (2 \cosh \beta J)^N \tag{59}$$

The above is extremely reminiscent of the noninteracting spins, with J replacing h in Eq. (20), that is, the exchange coupling parameter taking the place of the applied field. As in the case of the independent spins, the spontaneous magnetization of the one-dimensional chain vanishes. To see this, however, we shall have to resort to an alternate manner of calculating Z because the simple method given above does not work if there is an additional (applied) field H. So let us next consider

$$\mathscr{H} = \mathscr{H}_0 - h \sum_n \sigma_n^z \tag{60}$$

and the statistical mechanics which results therefrom.

Again, we try to express the partition sum as a product of 2×2 matrices; in this case

$$Z = \Pi V_n \qquad \text{with } V_n = e^{\beta(J\sigma_n^z \sigma_{n+1}^z + h\sigma_n^z)}, \ V_N = e^{\beta(J\sigma_N^z \sigma_1^z + h\sigma_N^z)} \tag{61}$$

---

[6] Cf. K. P. Belov, *Magnetic Transitions*, Consultants Bureau, New York, 1961, which is entirely based on the Landau theory of Eqs. (52) to (54).

The trace is equivalent to ordinary matrix multiplication. For example, the trace over σ_3^z contracts $V_2 V_3$ into a 2×2 matrix in σ_2^z, σ_4^z space:

$$\sum_{\sigma_3^z = -1}^{+1} V_2 V_3 = e^{\beta(-J\sigma_2^z + h\sigma_2^z)} e^{\beta(-J\sigma_4^z - h)} + e^{\beta(J\sigma_2^z + h\sigma_2^z)} e^{\beta(J\sigma_4^z + h)}$$

The matrix structure of V_n is given in Eq. (63) below. All matrices have the same basic structure (independent of n); therefore,

$$Z = Tr\{V^N\} = z_1^N + z_2^N = z_1^N (1 + e^{-N \ln z_1/z_2})$$

(62)

where z_1 and z_2 are the two eigenvalues of the *transfer matrix* V:

$$
V =
\begin{array}{cc}
 & \begin{array}{cc} \sigma_{n+1}^z = +1 & \sigma_{n+1} = -1 \end{array} \\
\begin{array}{c} \sigma_n^z = +1 \\ \sigma_n^z = -1 \end{array} &
\left\| \begin{array}{cc} e^{\beta(J+h)} & e^{\beta(-J+h)} \\ e^{\beta(-J-h)} & e^{\beta(J-h)} \end{array} \right\|
\end{array}
$$

(63)

Let us always choose z_1 to be the larger eigenvalue, so that in the limit of long chains $(N \to \infty)$, $Z \to z_1^N$.

The transfer matrix V, which is obviously of such great importance, derives its name from the following considerations. Let P and $1 - P$ be the probabilities, respectively, of the first spin, being up or down. Then the probabilities that the second one be up or down, Q and $1 - Q$, may be related to P by the equation:

$$z(Q, 1 - Q) = (P, 1 - P) \cdot \mathbf{V}$$

(64)

The parameter z is readily found, by the requirement that the probability vectors be normalized such that the total probability be unity, i.e., the sum of their components must add up to 1. As one knows from usual matrix theory, z must lie between the largest eigenvalue z_1 and the smallest one z_2, unless the probability vector is an eigenvector of V. In that case, $P = Q$, and what is more, an eigenvector of V is also an eigenvector of V^r, $r = 1, 2, \dots$, so that in an eigenstate, and *only* in an eigenstate, the rth spin also has exactly the same probability of being up as the first two. *This is one condition of thermodynamic equilibrium.* In a long chain (and of course one cannot apply thermodynamics except in very large assemblies) the various spins have identical surroundings and must therefore be indistinguishable in thermal equilibrium. This requirement is met by demanding that the probability vectors be eigenstates of V. But how to choose between z_1 and z_2, the two eigenvalues and the two corresponding eigenstates? Here too, the answer is unambiguous. In the case of the smaller eigenvalue, z_2, the eigenvector cannot be chosen so as to make both P and $1 - P$ positive. This is a serious defect, which prevents the interpretation of the eigenvector of V as a probability vector. On the other hand, because all the matrix elements of V are positive, it can be easily verified that the eigenvector belonging to the *largest* eigenvalue is necessarily composed of all entries of the same sign, and is therefore suitable as a probability vector. The conclusion is in accord with the general idea, that z should have the largest possible value.

The two eigenvalues are easily found by solving the usual determinantal equation, with the result:

$$z_{1,\,2} = e^{\beta J} \cosh \beta h \pm \sqrt{e^{2\beta J} \cosh^2 \beta h - 2 \sinh 2\beta J} \qquad (65)$$

But we have demonstrated that only the + branch is of interest. When $h = 0$, $Z = (z_1)^N$ is in perfect accord with the first calculation, Eq. (59).

The absence of long-range order in this one-dimensional model is discussed in Problem 6. It is closely related to the absence of spontaneous magnetization at any finite temperature $T > 0$ and to the lack of phase transitions in one dimension. The zero-field specific heat, $(N^{-1}dU/dT)_{h=0}$, is

$$c(T) = k\left(\frac{kT}{J} \cosh \frac{J}{kT}\right)^{-2} \qquad (66)$$

and the magnetic susceptibility $(d\mathcal{M}/dh)_{h=0}$ is

$$\chi \sim \frac{1}{T} e^{2J/kT} \qquad (67)$$

These quantities are plotted in Fig. 8.4, and may be seen to be continuous functions of T and thus to differ considerably from molecular field theory.

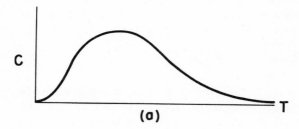

(a)

FIG. 8.4. (a) Specific heat and (b) susceptibility of one-dimensional Ising ferromagnet.

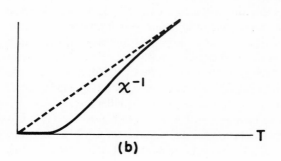

(b)

Problem 6: Show that V^n applied to the arbitrary probability vector $(P, 1 - P)$ of Eq. (64) yields z^n times another probability vector, and that z^n approaches z_1^n asymptotically [to $O(e^{-n})$]. Refer, if necessary, to the chapter on rotations in angular momentum. Show that the final probability vector is itself asymptotically *independent of P*, assuming only that $P > 0$ and $1 - P > 0$. Use these results to show that the spontaneous magnetization vanishes at any finite temperature.

Problem 7: Obtain the thermodynamic functions F, $c = N^{-1}dU/dT$, and χ for the Ising *antiferromagnetic chain*,

$$\mathcal{H} = +J \sum \sigma_n{}^z\sigma_{n+1}{}^z - h \sum \sigma_n{}^z \qquad J > 0$$

MAGNETOSTRICTION IN A LINEAR CHAIN

In spite of its physical limitations, the Ising model is simple enough that we may wish to study the effects on this model of nonmagnetic degrees of freedom. One example is magnetoelastic coupling. This does not lead to an effect related to the ordinary garden variety magnetostriction, for the latter is primarily related via spin-orbit coupling to the motion and orientation of domains and cannot be properly discussed in a one-dimensional model. But the effect of homogeneous magnetoelastic coupling, denoted *volume magnetostriction*, can be simulated by a simple model, based on the observation that the parameter which couples the neighboring spins can increase or decrease as the separation of the atoms is changed. The magnetic Hamiltonian can therefore be considered as an additional source of potential energy for the dynamic lattice vibrations, and changes in volume and even in the shape of the lattice are not unexpected. (However, in one dimension, shape does not matter.)

Given the position of the nth atom at $(na + x_n)$, with a = interatomic separation, the Hamiltonian for the elastic motion is

$$\sum_n \left[\frac{p_n^2}{2M} + \tfrac{1}{2}M\omega_0^2(x_{n+1} - x_n)^2 \right] \qquad \text{with } p_n = \frac{\hbar}{i} \frac{\partial}{\partial x_n} \tag{68}$$

and the Ising Hamiltonian is,

$$- \sum_n [J(a + x_{n+1} - x_n)\sigma_n^z\sigma_{n+1}^z - h\sigma_n^z] \tag{69}$$

It may be assumed that the thermal motion, typically, is smaller than a by one or more orders of magnitude, therefore the coupling parameter can be expanded to lowest order in the atomic displacements:

$$J(a + x_{n+1} - x_n) \cong J(a)\left(1 + \eta \frac{x_{n+1} - x_n}{a}\right) \tag{70}$$

with $$\qquad \eta \equiv \frac{\partial \ln J(a)}{\partial \ln a} \equiv \text{first order magnetostrictive coefficient} \tag{71}$$

Combining the two Hamiltonians, we obtain

$$\mathcal{H} = \sum_n \left[\frac{p_n^2}{2M} + \tfrac{1}{2}M\omega_0^2(x_{n+1} - x_n)^2 - J(a)\left(1 + \eta \frac{x_{n+1} - x_n}{a}\right)\sigma_z^n\sigma_{z+1}^n - h\sigma_n^z \right] \tag{72}$$

The eigenstates and the statistical mechanics of this Hamiltonian are exactly soluble by means of a canonical transformation. It is desired to remove the cross terms linking atomic displacements with spin coordinates, and this can be accomplished by shifting the origin for the motion of each atom in the following amount:

$$x_n \to x_n + \frac{J(a)\eta}{M\omega_0^2 a} \sum_{j<n} \sigma_j^z \sigma_{j+1}^z \tag{73}$$

The unitary transformation which accomplishes this is e^{iR}, with

$$R = -\sum_n p_n \frac{J(a)\eta}{a\hbar M\omega_0^2} \sum_{j<n} \sigma_j^z \sigma_{j+1}^z \tag{74}$$

so that every operator (including the Hamiltonian) is transformed as follows:

$$\text{op} \to e^{-iR} \, \text{op} \, e^{iR} \tag{75}$$

As every operator except the set of coordinates x_n commutes with R, the only effect is the linear shift, Eq. (73), which results in the new Hamiltonian:

$$\mathcal{H} \to \sum_n \left[\frac{p_n^2}{2M} + \tfrac{1}{2} M\omega_0^2 (x_{n+1} - x_n)^2 \right] - \left[J(a) \sum \sigma_n^z \sigma_{n+1}^z - h \sum \sigma_n^z \right] - \left[\tfrac{1}{2} N \frac{J^2(a)\eta^2}{M\omega_0^2 a^2} \right]$$
$$= \mathcal{H}_{ph} + \mathcal{H}_I - W \tag{76}$$

Just as the Hamiltonian can be written as the sum of three noninteracting parts, $\mathcal{H}_{ph}$ (phonons = lattice vibrations), $\mathcal{H}_I$ (ordinary Ising Hamiltonian), and $-W$ (constant interaction energy), the partition sum factors into three factors, and the free energy also becomes the sum of three noninteracting terms.

It is not out of place to indicate briefly how the partition sum for the phonons is obtained, because it is typical of the manner in which the statistical mechanics and quantum mechanics of Bosons is handled. First, it is desired to express p_n and x_n in terms of the operators a_n and a_n^*, the Boson destruction and creation operators defined by the commutation relations:

$$a_n a_m - a_m a_n \equiv [a_n, a_m] = 0 \qquad [a_n^*, a_m^*] = 0 \qquad [a_n, a_m^*] = \delta_{n,m} \tag{77}$$

In terms of these, we may write

$$x_n = \sqrt{\frac{\hbar}{2M\omega}} \, (a_n + a_n^*) \qquad p_n = \frac{1}{i}\sqrt{\frac{\hbar M\omega}{2}} \, (a_n - a_n^*) \tag{78}$$

with ω an arbitrary parameter of dimension $\sec^{-1}$, for example, $\omega = \omega_0$. Next, one effects a transformation to running waves:

$$a_n = \frac{1}{\sqrt{N}} \sum a_k e^{ikn} \qquad a_n^* = \frac{1}{\sqrt{N}} \sum a_k^* e^{-ikn} \qquad k = \frac{2\pi}{N} \times \text{integer} \tag{79}$$

with a_k, a_k^* a new set of Boson operators obeying commutation relations, Eq. (77).

Because of translational invariance, (that is, because $1/N \sum_n e^{i(k-k')n} = \delta_{k,k}$) the only terms in the Hamiltonian which survive these successive transformations are of the form of one of four operators:

$$a_k^* a_k = \mathfrak{n}_k \qquad a_k a_k^* = 1 + \mathfrak{n}_k \qquad a_k a_{-k} \quad \text{and} \quad a_k^* a_{-k}^* \tag{80}$$

The following transformation is canonical, and can be used to eliminate the last two (nondiagonal) terms:

$$a_k \to a_k \cosh f_k + a_{-k}^* \sinh f_k \qquad a_k^* \to a_k^* \cosh f_k + a_{-k} \sinh f_k \qquad \text{with } f_k = f_k^* = f_{-k} \tag{81}$$

[cf. Eq. (171), p. 169]. The function f_k must be chosen so as to diagonalize $\mathscr{H}_{ph}$, which is then finally in the form,

$$\mathscr{H}_{ph} = \sum \hbar \omega_k (\mathfrak{n}_k + \tfrac{1}{2}) \tag{82}$$

For small k, a calculation shows that

$$\omega_k \cong s|k| \tag{83}$$

where $s \equiv$ speed of sound.

Problem 8: Follow the steps indicated in the text and explicitly diagonalize $\mathscr{H}_{ph}$. Obtain ω_k, and give an expression for the speed of sound, s.

The trace over each mode k can be performed separately when there is no interaction, as is the case in Eq. (82). Each mode contributes a factor,

$$Z_k = Tr\{e^{-\beta\hbar\omega_k(n_k+\frac{1}{2})}\} = \sum_{n_k=0}^{\infty} e^{-\beta\hbar\omega_k(n_k+\frac{1}{2})}$$

$$= e^{-\beta\hbar\omega_k\frac{1}{2}} + e^{-\beta\hbar\omega_k\frac{3}{2}} + e^{-\beta\hbar\omega_k\frac{5}{2}} + \cdots \tag{84}$$

and a free energy,

$$F_k = -\frac{1}{\beta} \ln Z_k = \frac{1}{\beta} \ln (2 \sinh \tfrac{1}{2}\beta\hbar\omega_k) \tag{85}$$

The partition sum is ΠZ_k, and the total phonon free energy is

$$F_{ph} = \frac{1}{\beta} \sum_k \ln (2 \sinh \tfrac{1}{2}\beta\hbar\omega_k) \tag{86}$$

To conclude, we note that the canonical transformation which displaced the lattice coordinates is not without physical implications. For if the atoms have moved, this should be immediately detectable as a change in length of the chain. Let us calculate the thermal average (TA) length, L,

$$L = Na + \left\langle x_{N+1} + \frac{J(a)\eta}{M\omega_0^2 a} \sum_{j<N+1} \sigma_j^z \sigma_{j+1}^z \right\rangle_{TA} - \langle x_1 \rangle_{TA}$$

$$= Na - \frac{\eta}{M\omega_0^2 a} U_I \tag{87}$$

with U_I = internal energy of Ising spins at zero magnetic field and constant separation. If we define the magnetic specific heat at constant separation and zero magnetic field as,

$$c_I = \frac{1}{N}\frac{dU_I}{dT}, \qquad h = 0 \qquad a = \text{const} \tag{88}$$

we can relate the coefficient of thermal expansion $\alpha \equiv dL/dT$, a mechanical property of the chain, to c_I, a magnetic thermodynamic function. Differentiating both sides of Eq. (87) with respect to the temperature, one obtains

$$\alpha \equiv \frac{dL}{dT} = -\frac{\eta Na}{M\omega_0^2 a^2} c_I \tag{89}$$

This is a fairly general result, and in the weak-coupling limit it can be shown to hold also for the Heisenberg model, and also for both Ising and Heisenberg models in three dimensions.[7] It is an interesting example of how a mechanical system can be used as a probe on the magnetic system and vice versa. Applications are discussed in Problems 9 and 10.

   Problem 9: An experiment assigns to α a maximum value α_m, at temperature T_m; assuming spins $s = \frac{1}{2}$, calculate $J(a)$.

   Problem 10: Use the formula for F_{ph}, Eq. (86), to obtain c_{ph} = phonon contribution to the specific heat. The following may be useful: $\sum_k = \frac{Na}{2\pi} \int_{-\pi}^{\pi} dk$, and $\omega_k \doteq s|k|$. Compare the asymptotic behaviors of c_{ph} and c_I in the neighborhoods of $T = 0$ and $T = \infty$.

ELEMENTARY SPIN-WAVE THEORY

In a first approximation, spin waves are Bosons carrying one unit of angular momentum $\hbar$ and described by a Hamiltonian

$$\mathcal{H} = \sum \hbar\omega_k a_k^* a_k \tag{90}$$

where at long wavelengths

$$\hbar\omega_k = Ds(ka)^2 \qquad \text{ferromagnetism}$$

$$= Cs(ka) \qquad \text{antiferromagnetism} \tag{91}$$

---

[7] D. C. Mattis and T. D. Schultz, "Theory of Magnetothermomechanics," *Phys. Rev.*, **129**: 175 (1963). Thus α should be discontinuous at T_c. A review of experimental magnetostriction is in W. J. Carr, *Magnetic Properties of Metals and Alloys*, chap.10, American Soc. for Metals, Cleveland, 1959.

The constants C, D are approximately equal to the exchange parameter J in a nearest-neighbor interaction model, and a = lattice parameter.

Using the simple linear spin-wave theory, we can reach some fairly interesting and noteworthy conclusions concerning the effects of temperature and dimensionality on long-range order. These will be carried to a more accurate evaluation in the following section.

The thermal average of the occupation number $\mathfrak{n}_k = a_k^* a_k$ is the famous Bose-Einstein function, and can be obtained from the partition sum for Bosons, Eq. (84) by the following technique:

$$\langle \mathfrak{n}_k \rangle_{TA} = -\frac{1}{\beta Z_k} \frac{\partial Z_k}{\partial \hbar \omega_k} - \frac{1}{2} = \frac{\partial F_k}{\partial \hbar \omega_k} - \frac{1}{2}$$

$$= \frac{1}{e^{\beta \hbar \omega_k} - 1} \qquad (92)$$

If a total of Ns magnons are excited, the spontaneous magnetization of the ferromagnet has vanished. In the case of the antiferromagnet, it can be assumed that with Ns magnons excited, the sublattice magnetization, or antiferromagnetic long-range order, has also vanished. Therefore let us investigate the implicit equation for T_c (or T_N)

$$Ns = \sum_k \langle \mathfrak{n}_k \rangle_{TA}$$

$$= \left(\frac{L}{2\pi}\right)^d \int_{B.z.} d\mathbf{k}(e^{\beta \hbar \omega_k} - 1)^{-1} \qquad (93)$$

with $d = 1$, 2, 3 indicating the number of dimensions, and B.z. the d-dimensional Brillouin zone.

It is correct to anticipate that the lack of long-range order will be manifested by a divergence at small k, long wavelengths, in which case the only solution to the equation above must be $T_c = 0$. In one dimension, the integrals

$$\int dx(e^{\beta Dsx^2} - 1)^{-1}$$

and

$$\int dx(e^{\beta Csx} - 1)^{-1}$$

are both divergent at $x = ka \to 0$, which confirms the absence of long-range order in one dimension at any finite temperature. This argument is not, however, ironclad. If there were an energy gap the integrals might not diverge; nevertheless, the absence of long-range order in one dimension can be proved in general by the following simple argument:

To break a long chain of N spins into two uncorrelated chains of lengths N_1 and $N - N_1$ respectively costs an energy rJ, where r = number of broken bonds is a number of order 1. This breakup of long-range order can be achieved N distinct ways, one for each position of the break. Thus a break alters the free energy in the amount

$$\delta F = rJ - kT \ln N \qquad (94)$$

For any finite temperature, the entropy term $\ln N$ dominates, (with the exception of pathologic interactions corresponding to $r > \ln N$). Also, in Problem 6 it was shown that the correlation between two spins decays exponentially with increasing distance, in the absence of applied magnetic (i.e., ordering) fields. In two dimensions, the energy required to separate a plane of $\sqrt{N} \times \sqrt{N}$ spins into two uncorrelated planes is $O(\sqrt{N})$, and so it is no longer necessarily advantageous to destroy long-range order at arbitrary finite temperature.

But in two dimensions, the integral

$$\int dx x (e^{\beta D s x^2} - 1)^{-1}$$

is still divergent at $x = 0$, and therefore the two-dimensional Heisenberg model, or two-dimensional collection of spin-waves, is thermodynamically unstable. It is interesting to note that quantum-mechanically speaking, the linear spin-wave theory we have been applying so far is itself invalid for the Heisenberg model in one or two dimensions. In a previous chapter, it was proved that two or more magnons in one- or two-dimensional ferromagnets form bound states which do not have the properties of ordinary magnons. Thus the quantum-mechanical instability has been reflected in the thermodynamics as well.

Such is not the case of the two-dimensional antiferromagnet, or of both species *in three dimensions*. Thus, in the case of the three-dimensional ferromagnet, we find for the relative magnetization $m(T) = \mathscr{M}(T)/\mathscr{M}(0)$,

$$m(T) = 1 - \left(\frac{T}{T_0}\right)^{\frac{3}{2}} \tag{95}$$

where

$$kT_0 = Ds^{\frac{2}{3}}\left[\frac{2\pi^2}{\displaystyle\int_0^\infty dx x^2 (e^{x^2} - 1)^{-1}}\right]^{\frac{2}{3}} = 6.7Ds^{\frac{2}{3}} \tag{96}$$

the celebrated *Bloch* $T^{\frac{3}{2}}$ *law* (cf. Fig. 8.5). The upper limits in the integration were taken to infinity, which is suggested by the rapid convergence at low temperatures (cf. Problem 11 for evaluation of the integral). However, this procedure is unsatisfactory at all but the lowest temperatures, and it must not be supposed, for example, that T_0 is the Curie temperature. An explanation follows.

BRILLOUIN ZONE EFFECTS

Debye's theory of the lattice specific heat yielded the correct high-temperature limiting form, the law of Dulong-Petit

$$c_v(T) = k \quad \text{per normal mode}$$

only when the finite extent of the Brillouin zone was taken into account. Similarly, the behavior of a ferromagnet at temperatures of the order of T_c requires that the finite range of the integrals be respected.

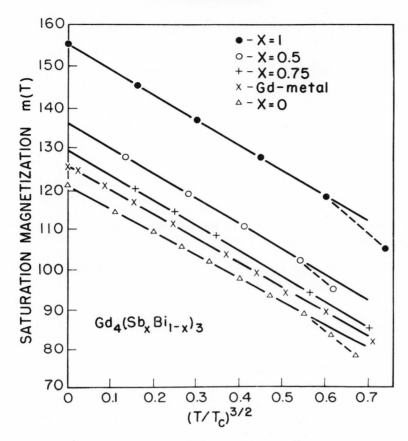

FIG. 8.5. Experimental verification of Bloch's $T^{3/2}$ law for several gadolinium alloy ferromagnets [after F. Holtzberg, T. McGuire, S. Methfessel, and J. Suits, *J. Appl. Phys.*, **35**: part 2, 1033 (1964)].

Consider a simple cubic ferromagnet with nearest-neighbor interactions and large spins $s \gg 1$. In a previous chapter, the spin-wave theory was justified by an expansion in powers of s^{-1}, and therefore this model has a degree of verisimilitude. Assuming

$$\hbar\omega_{\mathbf{k}} = 2sJ(3 - \cos k_x a - \cos k_y a - \cos k_z a) \tag{97}$$

which reduces to the long wavelength approximation if we choose $D = J$, $ka \ll 1$, the relative magnetization is

$$m(T) = 1 - \left(\frac{a}{2\pi}\right)^3 s^{-1} \int_{-\pi/a}^{\pi/a} dk_x \, dk_y \, dk_z (e^{\beta\hbar\omega_{\mathbf{k}}} - 1)^{-1}$$

$$= 1 - \left(\frac{a}{2\pi}\right)^3 s^{-1} \sum_{n=1}^{\infty} \int_{-\pi/a}^{\pi/a} dk_x \, dk_y \, dk_z \, e^{-n\beta\hbar\omega_{\mathbf{k}}} \tag{98}$$

Using the definition of the Bessel function of imaginary argument I_p,

$$I_p(z) = J_p(iz) = \frac{1}{2\pi} \int_{-\pi}^{\pi} d\theta \, e^{z \cos \theta} \cos p\theta = \left(\frac{z}{2}\right)^p \sum_{m=0}^{\infty} \frac{(z/2)^{2m}}{m!(|p| + m)!} \qquad (99)$$

we obtain[8]

$$m(T) = 1 - \frac{1}{S} \sum_{n=1}^{\infty} [e^{-ng} I_0(ng)]^3 \qquad (100)$$

with

$$g = \frac{2sJ}{kT} \qquad (101)$$

The Bessel function possesses an asymptotic expansion valid for large argument (i.e., low temperature in the present example)

$$I_0(z) \sim \frac{e^z}{(2\pi z)^{\frac{1}{2}}} \left[1 + \sum_{r=1}^{\infty} \frac{1^2 \times 3^2 \cdots (2r-1)^2}{r! 2^{3r} z^r}\right] = \frac{e^z}{(2\pi z)^{\frac{1}{2}}} \sum_{r=0}^{\infty} \frac{[\Gamma(r + \frac{1}{2})]^2}{\pi r! (2z)^r} \qquad (102)$$

which inserted into Eq. (100) generates the following series:

$$m(T) \cong 1 - B_{\frac{3}{2}}\left(\frac{T}{T_0}\right)^{\frac{3}{2}} - B_{\frac{5}{2}}\left(\frac{T}{T_0}\right)^{\frac{5}{2}} - B_{\frac{7}{2}}\left(\frac{T}{T_0}\right)^{\frac{7}{2}} \cdots \qquad (103)$$

Similar low-temperatures expansions can be obtained for other crystal structures, and for interactions longer-ranged than just nearest neighbor; only the numerical value of the B coefficients is affected. The asymptotic expansion of the Bessel function ceases to be accurate for

$$kT \gtrsim sJ$$

In the correspondence limit of classical spins, the Hamiltonian can be written

$$\mathscr{H} = -Js^2 \sum_{\substack{\text{nearest} \\ \text{neighb}}} \hat{\mathbf{u}}_i \cdot \hat{\mathbf{u}}_j$$

with $\hat{\mathbf{u}}_i = \mathbf{S}_i/s$ = unit vector, and therefore $kT_c \propto Js^2$ by simple dimensional arguments alone. [Hence $T_0 \propto S^{\frac{5}{3}}$, Eq. (96), is *not* a measure of the Curie temperature, as pointed out at the end of the preceding section.] For large but finite spins $s \gg 1$, the asymptotic expansion Eq. (102) therefore ceases to be of any use once

$$T \gtrsim \frac{1}{s} T_c \qquad (104)$$

As an alternative to numerical evaluation of the sum in Eq. (100), at temperatures $kT \gtrsim 6sJ$ it is permissible to expand the Bose-Einstein function in powers of $kT/\hbar\omega_{\mathbf{k}}$.

---

[8] Following T. Tanaka and S. J. Glass, to be published, S. H. Charap and E. L. Boyd, *Phys. Rev.*, **133**: A811 (1964).

(For $s \gtrsim 3$ this will be valid over a reasonable range of temperatures, up to and including T_c.) Thus

$$(e^{\hbar\omega_k/kT} - 1)^{-1} \doteq \frac{kT}{\hbar\omega_k} - \frac{1}{2} \tag{105}$$

retaining only leading terms. Over the range of temperatures $T \gtrsim T_c s^{-1}$ we then calculate

$$m(T) \cong 1 + \frac{1}{2s} - \frac{kT}{2Js^2}\left(\frac{a}{2\pi}\right)^3 \int_{-\pi/a}^{\pi/a} \frac{dk_x\, dk_y\, dk_z}{3 - \cos k_x a - \cos k_y a - \cos k_z a}$$

$$\cong 1 + \frac{1}{2s} - \frac{kT}{6Js^2}\, W \tag{106}$$

where W = Watson's integral = $1.516\ldots$, as given on p. 146. Calculating the Curie temperature T_c by setting $m(T_c) = 0$, we obtain

$$kT_c = 3.96Js^2\left(1 + \frac{1}{2s}\right) \qquad s \gg 1 \tag{107}$$

For comparison, the same lattice may be treated in the molecular field approximation, where each spin interacts with a molecular field,

$$\mathscr{H} = \mathbf{S}_i \cdot \mathbf{H}_m \tag{108}$$

made up of the average force exerted by its neighbors,

$$\mathbf{H}_m = 2J\langle\sum_{\delta}\mathbf{S}_\delta\rangle_{TA} \tag{109}$$

One may calculate $\langle\mathbf{S}_i\rangle_{TA}$ in the standard way, and then solve the molecular field equation,

$$\langle\mathbf{S}_i\rangle_{TA} = \langle\mathbf{S}_j\rangle_{TA} \qquad \text{for all } i, j \tag{110}$$

The temperature at which this constitutive equation ceases to have only a nontrivial solution is the Curie-Weiss temperature $T_c = \theta$, the temperature at which $\chi = C/(T - \theta) \to \infty$ (cf. Problem 17).

$$k\theta = 4Js^2\left(1 + \frac{1}{s}\right) \tag{111}$$

The agreement of this high-temperature theory with the low-temperature result is truly astounding. But very accurate high-temperature series extrapolation methods (cf. Eq. (138)) have shown *both* estimates to be some 30 percent too high.

Thus it is reasonable to believe that the linear spin-wave theory is adequate in the range

$$0 \leqslant T \leqslant \tfrac{2}{3}T_c \tag{112}$$

provided $s \gg 1$. Note that the validity of the power series expansion (103) is far more restricted, $0 \leqslant T \leqslant \dfrac{1}{s} T_c$.

Problem 11:   Find the coefficients $B_{n/2}$ in the series for $m(T)$, Eq. (103). The following *may* be useful:
The Riemann zeta function:

$$\zeta(s) = \frac{1}{\Gamma(s)} \int_0^\infty dx\, x^{s-1}(e^x - 1)^{-1} = \sum_{n=1}^\infty \frac{1}{n^s}$$

$$\zeta(\tfrac{3}{2}) = 2.612,\ \zeta(2) = \pi^2/6,\ \zeta(\tfrac{5}{2}) = 1.341,\ \zeta(\tfrac{7}{2}) = 1.127,\ \zeta(\infty) = 1$$

The gamma function:

$$\Gamma(s) = (s-1)\Gamma(s-1) \qquad \text{except} \qquad \Gamma(1) = 1 \qquad \text{and} \qquad \Gamma(\tfrac{1}{2}) = \sqrt{\pi}$$

Problem 12:   Calculate the specific heat for the simple cubic ferromagnet, at low temperatures and near T_c. How does the Dulong-Petit law at the upper temperatures compare with the molecular field theory? Plot the specific heat curves according to each theory, with particular reference to where they cross, and to the value at T_c.

Problem 13:   Repeat the analysis of the text for a nearest-neighbor *antiferromagnet*, using Eqs. (172) to (177) of Chapter 6 on spin-wave theory for the relevant formulas and numerical value of an important integral. How does kT_N compare with the molecular field value? What powers appear in the low-temperature series expansion?

Note: The Green function decomposition method employed in the book by Bonch-Bruevich and Tyablikov [9] gives results in substantial agreement with our Eq. (107) and so does not seem to offer any substantial advantage over conventional linear spin-wave theory below the Curie temperature. At least, it can be said that it does not suffer from some of the disadvantages of nonlinear spin-wave theory, which we shall detail in the succeeding section. The more recent work of Tahir-Kheli, Callen, and others on extending the Green function method offers great hope for the future understanding of the Heisenberg model; however, the best approximation is *not yet good enough* for an adequate understanding of the nature of the phase transition at T_c.

NONLINEAR SPIN-WAVE THEORY

The study of nonlinear spin-wave theory in a previous chapter (p. 156) established that *if* an expansion in powers of s^{-1} was valid, the leading "renormalization" in the magnon energy would be accomplished by replacement of $\hbar\omega_k$ by ε_k, with

$$\varepsilon_k = \hbar\omega_k - \frac{1}{Ns} \sum_{k'} \{\hbar\omega_k + \hbar\omega_{k'} - \hbar\omega_{k-k'} - \hbar\omega_0\} \mathfrak{n}_{k'} \tag{113}$$

In the thermodynamic theory, it will only be necessary to calculate the thermal average of the right-hand side. To tie in with previous notation, let the thermal average magnon energy be denoted $\hbar\omega_k(T) = \langle \varepsilon_k \rangle_{TA}$,

---

[9] Bonch-Bruevich and Tyablikov, *The Green Function Method in Statistical Mechanics*, North Holland Publishing Company, Amsterdam, 1962, chap. VII.

$$\hbar\omega_{\mathbf{k}}(T) = \hbar\omega_{\mathbf{k}}(0) - \frac{1}{Ns} \sum_{\mathbf{k}'} \{\hbar\omega_{\mathbf{k}}(0) + \hbar\omega_{\mathbf{k}'}(0) - \hbar\omega_{\mathbf{k}-\mathbf{k}'}(0) - \hbar\omega_0(0)\}\langle \mathfrak{n}_{\mathbf{k}'}\rangle_{TA} \quad (114)$$

with $\hbar\omega_{\mathbf{k}}(0) = \hbar\omega_{\mathbf{k}}$ = linear magnon energy. The Bose-Einstein function

$$\langle \mathfrak{n}_{\mathbf{k}'}\rangle_{TA} = \frac{1}{e^{\beta\hbar\omega_k(T)} - 1} \quad (115)$$

and the preceding equation *together form a set of implicit, coupled equations* for the determination of the magnon spectrum as function of the temperature.

Once again we use the simple cubic nearest-neighbor ferromagnet as the example in which to solve these equations. In this, we follow the work of Micheline Bloch.[10] Using Eq. (97) for the linear spin-wave energies, and making the self-consistent assumption

$$\langle \mathfrak{n}_{\mathbf{k}'}\rangle_{TA} = +\langle \mathfrak{n}_{-\mathbf{k}'}\rangle_{TA} \quad (116)$$

imposed by isotropy (the odd solution would require $\langle \mathfrak{n}_{\mathbf{k}'}\rangle_{TA}$ to be negative in some directions, which is impossible for an operator with the spectrum $0, +1, +2, \dots$), we find

$$1 + \cos k_x a \cos k_x' a - \cos k_x a - \cos k_x' a = (1 - \cos k_x a)(1 - \cos k_x' a)$$

as the x contribution to the sum over $\mathbf{k}'$, and similarly for the y and z contributions. Finally, taking full advantage of cubic symmetry, we transform the constitutive equation, Eq. (114), into the following form:

$$\hbar\omega_{\mathbf{k}}(T) = (\hbar\omega_{\mathbf{k}})\left(1 - \frac{1}{2NJs^2} \sum_{\mathbf{k}'} \hbar\omega_{\mathbf{k}'}\langle \mathfrak{n}_{\mathbf{k}'}\rangle_{TA}\right) \quad (117)$$

There is therefore a single temperature-dependent parameter

$$b(T) \equiv \frac{1}{2NJs^2} \sum_{\mathbf{k}'} \hbar\omega_{\mathbf{k}'}\langle \mathfrak{n}_{\mathbf{k}'}\rangle_{TA} \quad (118)$$

which enters into the formula for all magnons; we shall determine its value by use of Eq. (115) in Eq. (118):

$$
\begin{aligned}
b &= \frac{1}{2NJs^2} \sum_{\mathbf{k}'} \frac{\hbar\omega_{\mathbf{k}'}}{e^{\beta\hbar\omega_{\mathbf{k}'}} - 1} \\
&= \frac{a^3 2Js}{2Js^2(2\pi)^3} \int_{-\pi/a}^{\pi/a} \frac{dk_x\, dk_y\, dk_z(3 - \cos k_x a - \cos k_y a - \cos k_z a)}{e^{\beta\hbar\omega_{\mathbf{k}}} - 1} \\
&= \frac{3}{s} \sum_{n=1}^{\infty} e^{-3n\tilde{g}} I_0^2(n\tilde{g})[I_0(n\tilde{g}) - I_1(n\tilde{g})]
\end{aligned}
\quad (119)
$$

where $\qquad \tilde{\beta} = \beta(1 - b) \qquad \tilde{g} = g(1 - b) = \frac{2sJ}{kT}(1 - b) \qquad b = b(T)$

[10] M. Bloch, *Phys. Rev. Letters*, 9: 286 (1962). See also the generalization to nonnearest-neighbor interactions, L. Horwitz and D. Mattis, *Phys. Rev. Letters*, 10: 511 (1963).

The identity

$$I_1(z) = -\frac{d}{dz} I_0(z) \tag{120}$$

permits the asymptotic expansion of I_1 to be extracted from the formula previously given for I_0. As a consequence, we find a low-temperature power series for $b(T)$:

$$b(T) = C_{\frac{5}{2}}\left(\frac{T}{T_0}\right)^{\frac{5}{2}} + O(T^{\frac{7}{2}}) \tag{121}$$

Problem 14:   Calculate $C_{\frac{5}{2}}$ in Eq. (121).

We use this result in order to obtain the leading correction to the low-temperature series, Eq. (103) for the magnetization,[11] and denote it by D:

$$m(T) = 1 - \frac{1}{Ns} \sum_{\mathbf{k}} (e^{\beta\hbar\omega_{\mathbf{k}}} - 1)^{-1}$$

$$\cong 1 - B_{\frac{3}{2}}\left(\frac{T}{T_0}\right)^{\frac{3}{2}} - B_{\frac{5}{2}}\left(\frac{T}{T_0}\right)^{\frac{5}{2}} - B_{\frac{7}{2}}\left(\frac{T}{T_0}\right)^{\frac{7}{2}} - D_{\frac{9}{2}}\left(\frac{T}{T_0}\right)^4 \tag{122}$$

The first correction term that appears is seen to be of *higher order* than the leading terms retained in the original series expansion of $m(T)$, Eq. (103), and being T^4, is the first integral power of T to enter in the expansion. The evaluation of the coefficient of this correction term, $D_{\frac{9}{2}}$, is left as Problem 15.

Problem 15:   Calculate $D_{\frac{9}{2}}$, noting that $B_{\frac{3}{2}} = 1$, and using the result of Problem 14.

This state of affairs is quite reasonable; the nonlinearities do not make their effects felt at low temperatures where few magnons are excited, and so the corrections to the linear theory must be small. To gauge the importance of the nonlinearities, it is necessary to examine the region near the Curie temperature.

For the sake of definiteness, let us once more deal with large spins $s \gg 1$, so that the Curie temperature is of order $kT_c \sim Js^2$. For all temperatures obeying the inequality $kT \gg Js$, up to and including T_c, it is permissible to replace the Bose-Einstein function by the first two terms in an expansion in powers of T^{-1}, and so to obtain the equation

$$b = \frac{1}{2NJs^2} \sum_{\mathbf{k}} \hbar\omega_{\mathbf{k}}\left(\frac{kT}{(1-b)\hbar\omega_{\mathbf{k}}} - \frac{1}{2}\right) \tag{123}$$

which has the solution

$$1 - b = \frac{1}{2}\left(1 + \frac{3}{2s}\right) + \sqrt{\frac{1}{4}\left(1 + \frac{3}{2s}\right)^2 - \frac{kT}{2Js^2}} \tag{124}$$

---

[11] Due to F. J. Dyson, *Phys. Rev.*, **102**: 1230 (1956).

In the same range of temperature, the magnetization is given by

$$m(T) = 1 - \frac{1}{Ns} \sum_{\mathbf{k}} (e^{\beta\hbar\omega_{\mathbf{k}}} - 1)^{-1}$$

$$\cong 1 + \frac{1}{2s} - \frac{kT}{(1-b)6Js^2} W \tag{125}$$

A very strange phenomenon occurs. At a temperature $T_B \sim \frac{1}{8} T_c$ given by

$$kT_B = 2Js^2 \left[\frac{1}{2} \left(1 + \frac{3}{2s} \right) \right]^2 = 2Js^2 [1 - b(T_B)]^2 \tag{126}$$

the discriminant in the formula for $b(T)$, Eq. (124), vanishes. If T is raised above this value, $b(T)$ becomes complex and the formulas lose their meaning. We calculate $m(T_B)$ with the following result:

$$m(T_B) = 1 + \frac{1}{2s} - \frac{W}{6} \left(1 + \frac{3}{2s} \right)$$

$$= 0.75 + O(s^{-1}) \tag{127}$$

which is till very close to the saturation magnetization. At this temperature the *linear* spin-wave theory is still perfectly regular. But the *nonlinear* theory has broken down without an inordinate number of magnons excited, and merely because the self-consistency equations could no longer be satisfied. It indicates two possible remedies: (1) More terms in the perturbation theory (p. 157) must be kept, unless the expansion is nonconvergent. But (2) if unphysical states are doing the damage, they should be more effectively projected out, as in the exact Hamiltonian (p. 152).

Micheline Bloch[12] calculated $b(T)$ numerically for the case of $s = \frac{1}{2}$ and $s = 1$ with better results. She found a similar discontinuous behavior, but amazingly, the temperature T_B at which the equations ceased to be soluble agreed within a few per cent with the best high-temperature estimates of the Curie temperature, Eq. (138). The theory applied for small spins was more satisfactory than the correspondence limit treated in the present text in yet another respect: the magnetization for spins one-half was $m(T_B) \sim \frac{1}{3}$, appreciably closer to the exact value ($m(T_c) = 0$ by *definition*!) than found here. For further details, the reader is referred to the paper cited.

The nonlinear theory is in several respects less satisfactory than the linear spin-wave theory. This is comprehensible, if we accept that the perturbation theoretic expansion is an asymptotic series at $T \sim T_c$, and it is in the nature of such expansions that retaining more terms does not always increase the accuracy. The "phase transition" which occurs at T_B is due to the mathematical inadequacy of the model, and is not of physical significance. Yet there is no harm in calculating the specific heat, as is done in Problem 16; and near T_B one finds $c(T) \propto (T_B - T)^{-\frac{1}{2}}$. (As this is an integrable singularity, it is not prima-facie evidence of a first-order transition.) Finally, one should not take the present example too literally; for *longer-ranged* interactions such as the Ruderman-Kittel interaction in metals, the nonlinear terms in Eq. (113) can be much smaller (or sometimes much larger! this depends on k_F and is very structure sensitive)

---

[12] *Op. cit.*

than in the present model.[13] When they are small, a solution for $b(T)$ can exist over the entire range of temperature up until the Curie temperature, $m(T_c) = 0$. It is in such cases that the nonlinear spin-wave theory provides a physically meaningful model and useful approximation to the Heisenberg Hamiltonian.

Problem 16: Obtain a general formula for the specific heat in nonlinear spin-wave theory. Show that the first low-temperature correction to the linear theory is also T^4, as for $m(T)$. Show that near T_B, for arbitrary s, $c(T) \propto (T_B - T)^{-\frac{1}{2}}$ in the simple cubic, nearest-neighbor ferromagnet. Hint: the last part can be done without expanding the Bose-Einstein function, by a graphic qualitative analysis of the equations.

HIGH-TEMPERATURE EXPANSIONS [14]

Spin-wave theory breaks down above T_c, and perhaps well below that temperature (cf. nonlinear spin-wave theory). Molecular field theory in the simple version presented earlier cannot be correct above T_c, in general, for it predicts the absence of short-range order; and even refinements of this theory suffer from one shortcoming or another.

Because there is no known closed theory which can reliably predict the critical temperature of an arbitrary three-dimensional ferromagnet and its thermodynamic behavior at temperatures above T_c, it is interesting to expand the partition sum and all other thermodynamic functions obtained from it, in inverse powers of the temperature, and calculate the coefficients term by term. Not only does this provide a reliable direct means of comparing the models (e.g., Ising, or Heisenberg) with experiment, but by the use of powerful extrapolation techniques such as Padé approximants[15] it has been possible even to estimate the *nature* of the phase transition at T_c using data correlated from the high- and low-temperature series.

Given a density matrix

$$\rho = e^{-\mathcal{H}/kT} \tag{128}$$

and the definition of thermal average (TA) of an operator $\mathbf{R}$,

$$
\langle \mathbf{R} \rangle_{TA} = \frac{Tr\{\mathbf{R}\rho\}}{Tr\{\rho\}} = \frac{\langle \mathbf{R}\rho \rangle}{\langle \rho \rangle}
$$

$$
= \frac{\langle \mathbf{R} \rangle - \dfrac{1}{kT}\langle \mathbf{R}\mathcal{H} \rangle + \dfrac{1}{2!}\left(\dfrac{1}{kT}\right)^2 \langle \mathbf{R}\mathcal{H}^2 \rangle - \cdots}{1 - \dfrac{1}{kT}\langle \mathcal{H} \rangle + \dfrac{1}{2!}\left(\dfrac{1}{kT}\right)^2 \langle \mathcal{H}^2 \rangle - \cdots} \tag{129}
$$

where $\langle \mathbf{R} \rangle = Tr\{\mathbf{R}\}/Tr\{1\}$ = average of $\mathbf{R}$, is the same as the thermal average at $T = \infty$. The expansion in powers of T^{-1} which occurs in the denominator can be rationalized,

---

[13] D. Mattis and L. Horwitz, unpublished work.

[14] This material is based on E. Ambler, J. Eisenstein, and J. Schooley, "Traces of Products of Angular Momentum Matrices," *J. Math. Phys.*, **3**: 118 (1962).

[15] G. A. Baker, *Phys. Rev.*, **124**: 768 (1961) and *ibid.*, **129**: 99 (1963).

$$\langle \mathbf{R} \rangle_{TA} = \left(\langle \mathbf{R} \rangle - \frac{1}{kT} \langle \mathbf{R}\mathscr{H} \rangle + \frac{1}{2!} \left(\frac{1}{kT} \right)^2 \langle \mathbf{R}\mathscr{H}^2 \rangle - \cdots \right)$$

$$\times \left(1 + \frac{1}{kT} \langle \mathscr{H} \rangle + \left(\frac{1}{kT} \right)^2 \left(\langle \mathscr{H} \rangle^2 - \frac{1}{2!} \langle \mathscr{H}^2 \rangle \right) + \cdots \right) \tag{130}$$

This formula is sufficient for the calculation of almost all the important thermodynamic functions, with the exception of the magnetic susceptibility. For the latter it is convenient to split the Hamiltonian into two parts, with h = magnetic field, i.e., $\frac{1}{2} g \mu_B = 1$,

$$\mathscr{H} = \mathscr{H}_1 + h \mathscr{H}_2 \tag{131}$$

to which suitable constants have been added or subtracted (if necessary) to make the averages vanish,

$$\langle \mathscr{H}_1 \rangle = \langle \mathscr{H}_2 \rangle = 0 \tag{132}$$

The susceptibility is then

$$\chi = \lim_{h \to 0} \frac{M}{h} \tag{133}$$

and by Eq. (18), p. 226,

$$\chi = \frac{1}{kT} \langle \mathscr{H}_2^2 \rangle + \left(\frac{1}{kT} \right)^2 \left(-\frac{1}{2} \langle \mathscr{H}_2^2 \mathscr{H}_1 \rangle - \frac{1}{2} \langle \mathscr{H}_2 \mathscr{H}_1 \mathscr{H}_2 \rangle \right)$$

$$+ \left(\frac{1}{kT} \right)^3 \left(-\frac{1}{2} \langle \mathscr{H}_2^2 \rangle \langle \mathscr{H}_1^2 \rangle + \frac{1}{6} \langle \mathscr{H}_2^2 \mathscr{H}_1^2 \rangle + \frac{1}{6} \langle \mathscr{H}_2 \mathscr{H}_1 \mathscr{H}_2 \mathscr{H}_1 \rangle + \frac{1}{6} \langle \mathscr{H}_2 \mathscr{H}_1^2 \mathscr{H}_2 \rangle \right) + \cdots \tag{134}$$

The quantities in brackets are all traces over sums of spin operators if $\mathscr{H}$ refers to the Ising or Heisenberg models. In the Ising model, all operators commute so there remains only a counting problem; if an odd power $(S_i^z)^{2p+1}$ occurs, the trace vanishes. If an even power occurs, its trace can be easily found, and in particular for spins one-half, $(S_i^z)^2 = \frac{1}{4}$ = constant, the trace is trivial.

In the Heisenberg model mixed products of operators occur and different Cartesian components do not commute. An extract from extensive tables by Ambler, Eisenstein, and Schooley is appended to the present section, including all possible combinations of operators up to factors of six terms. Operators which can be obtained by cyclic permutations from those listed are, however, omitted.

There has lately been a strong development in the theory of *linked cluster expansions* of which the above represents a special case. For references, see Bibliography. In the use of this theory there is a heavy reliance on *Wick's theorem*, which permits the factorization of large products of operators which occur in the traces into products of traces involving two operators at a time. This theorem and the entire procedure and folklore of thermodynamic perturbation theory can be entirely adapted to the study of spin systems by the following technique: (1) For spins one-half use any of the Fermion representations on p. 78. (2) For arbitrary spins use Schwinger's coupled Boson

TABLE 8.1
Traces of Products of Angular Momentum Matrices

Operator	$j = 1/2$	1	3/2	2	5/2	3	7/2
J_x^2	1/2	2	5	10	35/2	28	42
$J_x J_y J_z$	$i/4$	i	$i5/2$	$i5$	$i35/4$	$i14$	$i21$
J_x^4	1/8	2	41/4	34	707/8	196	777/2
$J_x^2 J_y^2$	1/8	1	17/4	13	259/8	70	273/2
$J_x J_y J_x J_y$	$-1/8$	0	7/4	8	189/8	56	231/2
$J_x^3 J_y J_z$	$i/16$	i	$i41/8$	$i17$	$i707/16$	$i98$	$i777/4$
$J_x^2 J_y J_x J_z$	$-i/16$	0	$i7/8$	$i4$	$i189/16$	$i28$	$i231/4$
J_x^6	1/32	2	365/16	130	16355/32	1588	33501/8
$J_x^4 J_y^2$	1/32	1	125/16	37	4195/32	382	7725/8
$J_x^3 J_y J_x J_y$	$-1/32$	0	43/16	20	2781/32	284	6171/8
$J_x^2 J_y^2 J_z^2$	1/32	0	5/16	4	675/32	76	1749/8
$J_x^2 J_y J_x^2 J_y$	1/32	0	29/16	16	2403/32	256	5709/8
$J_x^2 J_y J_z^2 J_y$	1/32	1	101/16	25	2467/32	202	3765/8
$J_x^2 J_y J_z J_y J_z$	$-1/32$	0	19/16	8	1053/32	104	2211/8
$J_x J_y J_z J_x J_y J_z$	$-1/32$	-1	$-77/16$	-13	$-739/32$	-22	195/8
$J_x J_y J_x J_z J_y J_z$	1/32	0	5/16	4	675/32	76	1749/8

NOTE: $Tr\{J_x^2\} = Tr\{J_y^2\}$, etc.; $Tr\{J_x\} = 0$, etc.

SOURCE: E. Ambler, J. Eisenstein, and J. Schooley, *J. Math. Phys.*, **3**: 118 (1962).

representation, as Davis was the first to do.[16] The reason for resorting to these substitutions is that spins do not have the simple commutation properties of Fermions or Bosons, because the commutator (or anticommutator) of two spin operators is in general another operator, and not a c number. Thus Wick's theorem as used in the standard treatments does not apply directly.

One almost trivial application of the high-temperature expansion is the calculation of the Curie-Weiss constant C and the paramagnetic Curie temperature θ in the molecular field approximation, starting from a microscopic theory. Expansion of the susceptibility

$$\chi = \frac{C}{T - \theta} = \frac{C}{T} + \frac{C}{T}\frac{\theta}{T} + \cdots \tag{135}$$

and comparison with the present series yields

$$C = \frac{\langle \mathcal{H}_2^2 \rangle}{k} \tag{136}$$

and

$$k\theta = -\frac{1}{2} \frac{\langle \mathcal{H}_2^2 \mathcal{H}_1 \rangle + \langle \mathcal{H}_2 \mathcal{H}_1 \mathcal{H}_2 \rangle}{\langle \mathcal{H}_2^2 \rangle} \tag{137}$$

---

[16] H. L. Davis, "New Method for Treating the Antiferromagnetic Ground State," *Phys. Rev.*, **120**: 789 (1960).

Problem 17: Use the formula, Eq. (137), to derive Eq. (111) for the Curie temperature in the simple cubic ferromagnet of Eq. (97).

Rushbrooke and Wood[17] have carried the expansion out to many more terms and find the following formula fits the Curie temperature of the Heisenberg nearest-neighbor three-dimensional ferromagnets

$$k\theta = \frac{5J}{96}(z-1)[11s(s+1)-1] \tag{138}$$

to within 1 percent accuracy. The Curie temperature of three-dimensional Ising lattices is known to five decimal places by extrapolation from the high-temperature series expansions.[18,19]

---

[17] G. S. Rushbrooke and P. J. Wood, *Molec. Phys.*, **1**: 257 (1958).

[18] M. E. Fisher, *J. Math. Phys.*, **4**: 278 (1963): see the list on his p. 286.

[19] The interesting problem of the dilute, *random*, magnetic lattice has been given a solution (following a method due to R. Brout) by G. S. Rushbrooke, *J. Math. Phys.*, **5**: 1106 (1964).

CHAPTER 9

THE ISING MODEL

The two-dimensional Ising model of ferromagnetism or antiferromagnetism is one of the rare many-body problems that is exactly soluble *and* shows a phase transition. Although the exact solution in the absence of an external magnetic field was first given a generation ago by Lars Onsager,[1] who used the theory of Lie algebras, the flow of papers on both approximate and exact methods remains strong to the present day. One reason for this has been the interest in testing approximate methods on an exactly soluble problem. A second reason, no doubt, is the difficulty of the original Onsager method, and of the subsequent calculation by Yang of the spontaneous magnetization. The solution was first given by Onsager as a discussion remark following a paper presented to the New York Academy of Science in February, 1942 by Wannier; it was published two years later. The formula for the spontaneous magnetization

$$\boxed{\mathscr{M} = (1 - x^{-2})^{\frac{1}{8}}} \qquad \text{with } x = \sinh\frac{2J_1}{kT}\sinh\frac{2J_2}{kT} \qquad (0)$$

came subsequently:

> ... and required four years for its deciphered. It was first exposed to the public on 23 August 1948 on a blackboard at Cornell University on the occasion of a conference on phase transitions. Lazlo Tisza had just presented a paper on the General Theory of Phase Transitions. Gregory Wannier opened the discussion with a question concerning the compatibility of the theory with some properties of the Ising model. Onsager continued this discussion and then remarked that—incidentally the formula for the spontaneous magnetization of the two dimensional model is just that given by [0]. To tease a wider audience, the formula was again exhibited during the discussion which followed a paper by Rushbrooke at the first postwar IUPAP statistical mechanics meeting in Florence in 1948; it finally appeared in print as a discussion remark.[2] ... However, Onsager never published his derivation. The puzzle was finally solved by C. N. Yang and its solution published in 1952. Yang's analysis is very complicated.[3]

---

[1] L. Onsager, *Phys. Rev.*, **65**: 117 (1944). See also review articles: G. F. Newell and E. W. Montroll, *Rev. Mod. Phys.*, **25**: 353 (1953); C. Domb, (Adv. in Phys.) *Phil. Mag. Suppl.*, **9**: 151 (1960); T. Schultz, D. Mattis, and E. Lieb, *Rev. Mod. Phys.*, **36**: 856 (1964), on which the present chapter is based.
[2] L. Onsager, *Nuovo Cimento Suppl.*, **6**: 261 (1949).
[3] From Montroll, Potts, and Ward, "Correlations and Spontaneous Magnetization of the two-dimensional Ising Model," Onsager celebration issue, *J. Math. Phys.*, **4**: 308 (1963).

In the present chapter we shall rederive the principal properties found by these authors, using only elementary properties of spins one-half and their transformation to Fermions, thus requiring techniques no deeper than those used in the section on representation of spins one-half (see p. 78). *Ut lectum, ut solutum.*

Perhaps the Ising model will no longer find its place in textbooks of a generation hence, being considered too "trivial." But today a mastery of this model appears to be a sensible introduction to the unsolved problems of statistical mechanics, both within magnetism and without. It is therefore a fit subject with which to close this treatise, and we note that although the main results are for the two-dimensional net, all formulas up to (but not beyond) Eq. (30) can be trivially extended to three dimensions.

STATEMENT OF THE PROBLEM

Consider a set of spins one-half on a square lattice of M columns and N rows, interacting only with nearest neighbors and with a magnetic field h. Ultimately, we shall allow both M and N to tend to infinity keeping the ratio M/N fixed, and denote this by $\lim_{M, N \to \infty}$. Let the Hamiltonian be

$$\mathscr{H} = -J_1 \sum \sigma_{n, m}\sigma_{n+1, m} - J_2 \sum \sigma_{n, m}\sigma_{n, m+1} - h \sum \sigma_{n, m} \tag{1}$$

(nm) refers to the site in the nth row and mth column; J_1 and J_2 are the bond strengths within the rows and within the columns respectively. (For ferromagnetic coupling J_1 and $J_2 > 0$. If either is negative, it can be made effectively positive by transforming $\sigma \to -\sigma$ in every other column, row, or both. Then h term is modified, of course.) The Bohr magneton has been incorporated within h. Each $\sigma_{n, m}$ is $\sigma_{n, m}^z$, similar to a classical variable, but which takes on only the values ± 1. But as we know, the physical properties, such as the partition sum, do not depend on the particular representation, and later we shall wish to use instead of σ^z another Pauli spin matrix,

$$\sigma^x = \begin{vmatrix} 0 & 1 \\ 1 & 0 \end{vmatrix} \tag{2}$$

which has the same eigenvalues but is not trivially diagonal.

For boundary conditions, we may assume either that the lattice is wrapped on a torus, so that $N + 1 = 1$ and $M + 1 = 1$, or that the lattice has free ends. Each boundary condition has its separate advantages and disadvantages.[4] Hereafter, we make use of the fact that the free energy per spin, and other similar quantities, cannot depend on the boundary conditions chosen; so we shall make use of whatever simplest boundary conditions are available, often without specification.

The free energy per spin, **f**, is given by

$$e^{-\beta(NM)\mathbf{f}} = Z = \sum_{\sigma_{11} = \pm 1} \cdots \sum_{\sigma_{NM} = \pm 1} e^{-\beta\mathscr{H}} \tag{3A}$$

which is the usual formula

$$Z = Tr\{e^{-\beta\mathscr{H}}\} \tag{3B}$$

[4] Schultz, Mattis, and Lieb, *op. cit.*

written out explicitly. Besides the usual thermodynamic functions in zero magnetic field, which we shall examine particularly with respect to the phase transition, we shall also want to calculate the spontaneous magnetization, the high-temperature magnetic susceptibility, etc.

TRANSFER MATRIX

The transfer matrix formulation permits us to reduce the problem of a surface array of spins to one of a linear distribution of spins, that is, to reduce a matrix of dimensions 2^{NM} to one of dimensions 2^N. Even this reduction would not be sufficient in general, and it is a miracle that the eigenvalues of this particular matrix can be found—the reason that the two-dimensional Ising model occupies such a special place.

We have already encountered the transfer matrix, in solving the one-dimensional model in a magnetic field; the problem (of dimensionality 2^N in that case) was reduced to solving for the eigenvalues of a 2×2 transfer matrix. Let us entertain here a short discussion appropriate to two or more dimensions.

Consider each row (R) as a system with 2^M independent states. The way these states are labeled will be determined later quite naturally, so this need not preoccupy us at first. Let the jth state of the initial row R_0 be assigned a probability P_j, all the probabilities adding to unity, and let the set of these 2^M numbers be ordered as in a column vector,

$$\rho_0(R_0) = \begin{pmatrix} P_1 \\ P_2 \\ P_3 \\ \vdots \end{pmatrix} \qquad P_1 + P_2 + \cdots = 1 \qquad 0 \leqslant P_j \leqslant 1 \qquad (4)$$

We shall denote this, interchangeably, as the probability vector, or reduced density matrix of row R_0. If next we define $\mathcal{H}(R_1, R_0)$ as that part of the Hamiltonian containing the bonds internal to row R_1 and the connections between R_1 and R_0, then the probability vector for row R_1 is obtained by a sum over all states of R_0 weighted by their respective probabilities, i.e.,

$$z_1 \rho_1(R_1) = Tr_0 \{ e^{-\beta \mathcal{H}(R_1, R_0)} \rho_0(R_0) \} \qquad (5)$$

with the Boltzmann factor occupying its usual role of thermal probability, discussed in the previous chapter. On the left-hand side, a factor z_1 has been explicitly taken out of the density matrix for row R_1 in order that the probability vector $\rho_1(R_1)$ be normalized, in the sense that all its entries—which are probabilities—should add up to unity as in Eq. (4). It is now only a matter of a few steps to derive the all-important transfer matrix equations.

We merely assume as in Fig. 9.1 that the zeroth row is connected to a thermal reservoir appropriate to temperature T ($\beta = 1/kT$), which has the property that the reduced density matrix of row R_0 is the one appropriate to a row of spins at that temperature. As both factors on the right-hand side of the previous equation are characteristic of temperature T, it follows that $\rho_1(R_1)$ is also the reduced density matrix appropriate to that temperature for the spins of row R_1. This process may be

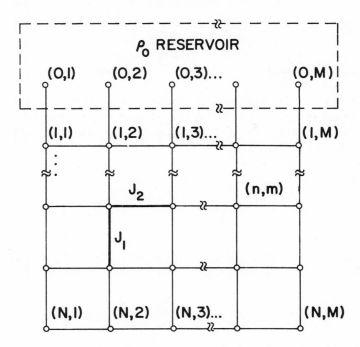

FIG. 9.1. Two-dimensional Ising lattice of $N + 1$ rows and M columns, in which zeroth row is connected to a special reservoir.

pursued to row R_2, etc., and we obtain

$$z\rho(R_{n+1}) = Tr_n\{e^{-\beta\mathcal{H}(R_{n+1}, R_n)}\rho(R_n)\} \tag{6}$$

as the universal equation for the common thermal density matrix $\rho(R)$ and eigenvalue z. The partition sum can then be expressed in the following revelatory manner:

$$Z = Tr_N Tr_{N-1}\{e^{-\beta\mathcal{H}(R_N, R_{N-1})}Tr_{N-2}\{\cdots Tr_0\{e^{-\beta\mathcal{H}(R_1, R_0)}\rho(R_0)\}\cdots\}\}$$

$$= Tr_N\rho(R_N)\cdot z^N$$

$$= z^N \tag{7}$$

To arrive at the second line, we took advantage of the eigenvalue equation above. The last line follows from the normalization condition, formally expressed as

$$Tr_n\rho(R_n) = 1 \tag{8}$$

The preceding derivation is the clearest one, based on the eigenvalue equation, Eq. (6), the partition function, Eq. (7), the normalization condition, Eq. (8), and a requirement that all the entries of $\rho(R)$ be positive since they are interpreted as probabilities. However, we could also have investigated the cyclic problem, in which the first row is tied to the Nth directly, the zeroth row and thermal bath having been eliminated. Equation (6) can also be used to diagonalize the full density matrix, but now all 2^M of its eigenvalues must be considered. The partition function is therefore

$$Z_{\text{cycl}} = \sum_{r=1}^{2^M} z_r^N \tag{9}$$

By a theorem of Frobenius, the largest eigenvalue of a matrix with all positive elements belongs to the eigenvector in which all entries are also positive; two such eigenvectors cannot in general be orthogonal, therefore this state is in general nondegenerate. It is readily identified as $\rho(R)$ derived above, with eigenvalue z. Let us label the other eigenvalues in order of decreasing magnitude: $z \equiv z_1$, then z_2, etc., so the partition sum becomes

$$Z_{\text{cycl}} = Z \cdot \sum_{r=1}^{2^M} \left(\frac{z_r}{z}\right)^N = Z \cdot \sum_{r=1}^{2^M} e^{-N \ln (z/z_r)} \tag{10}$$

The difference between $\ln Z_{\text{cycl}}$ and $\ln Z$ is properly seen to be in the nature of an end effect, whereas $\ln Z$ is itself extensive, that is, $O(MN)$. The magnitude of the end effect is actually calculable, but we shall not be interested in this.

.ELIMINATING THE TRACE

The next step is to perform the trace indicated in Eq. (6), and what results is a Schrödinger-like equation

$$z\rho(R) = \mathbf{V}(R)\rho(R) \tag{11}$$

where R stands symbolically for all 2^M configurations in an arbitrary row R, and $\mathbf{V}(R)$ is some sort of operator called the *transfer matrix*. The row density matrix $\rho(R)$ will play the role of a wavefunction, in fact it will be the "ground state" wavefunction belonging to the largest eigenvalue of $\mathbf{V}$.

   To derive this important equation (valid also in three or more dimensions) consider a typical bond joining the nth row to the $n + 1$st, $-J_1\sigma_{n, m}\sigma_{n+1, m}$, and the partial trace over the states only of $\sigma_{n, m}$. The result is a function ϕ only of $\sigma_{n+1, m}$, that is,

$$Tr_{(n, m)}\{e^{\beta J_1 \sigma_{n, m}\sigma_{n+1, m}}\rho(R_n)\} = \phi(\sigma_{n+1, m}) \tag{12}$$

neglecting for the moment all other spins in the problem. Because $\sigma_{n, m} = \pm 1$, $(\sigma_{n, m})^2 = (\sigma_{n, m})^4 = \cdots = 1$, and $(\sigma_{n, m})^3 = (\sigma_{n, m})^5 = \cdots = \sigma_{n, m}$, a Taylor series expansion of a function of this spin will contain but two terms. For example,

$$e^{\beta J_1 \sigma_{n, m}\sigma_{n+1, m}} = \cosh(\beta J_1) + \sigma_{n, m}\sigma_{n+1, m} \sinh(\beta J_1) \tag{13}$$

and similarly, we can always set

$$\rho(R_n) = A + \sigma_{n, m}B \tag{14}$$

where A and B are not functions of $\sigma_{n, m}$, but are functions of $\sigma_{n, m' \neq m}$. Multiply the two terms we have expanded and collect terms independent of $\sigma_{n,m}$ and those linear in $\sigma_{n,m}$:

$$e^{\beta J_1 \sigma_{n,m}\sigma_{n+1,m}}(A + \sigma_{n,m}B) = \cosh(\beta J_1)\{[A + \sigma_{n+1,m}B \tanh(\beta J_1)]$$
$$+ \sigma_{n,m}[B + \sigma_{n+1,m}A \tanh(\beta J_1)]\} \qquad (15)$$

The trace eliminates the latter, and supplies a factor 2 to the former. This gives us $\phi(\sigma_{n+1,m})$, and it is seen that in this process $\rho(\sigma_{n,m}) = A + \sigma_{n,m}B$ is replaced by

$$\rho\,(\sigma_{n+1,m} \tanh \beta J_1) = A + (\sigma_{n+1,m} \tanh \beta J_1)B \qquad (16A)$$

and a new factor of $2\cosh(\beta J_1)$ introduced as the result of taking the trace. Generalizing this observation, we define ρ by its expansion in products of σ's:

$$Tr_n\{e^{\beta J_1 \sigma_{n,m}\sigma_{n+1,m}}\rho(\sigma_{n,1}; \sigma_{n,2}; \sigma_{n,3}; \ldots; \sigma_{n,M})\}$$
$$= (2\cosh \beta J_1)^M \rho(t\sigma_{n+1,1}; t\sigma_{n+1,2}; t\sigma_{n+1,3}; \ldots; t\sigma_{n+1,M}) \qquad (16B)$$

where $t \equiv \tanh \beta J_1$. All the preceding is also valid if $\sigma^x_{n,m}$ replaces $\sigma_{n,m}$ everywhere, and at this juncture it is necessary to make this substitution. This is assumed in the following section.

THE REPRESENTATION

To make further progress, we must choose a definite representation and label the states of the reduced density matrix accordingly. In this manner the desired eigenvalue equation is obtained, although it remains to be solved.

Recall that $\rho(R)$ is a 2^M-dimensional column vector, with P_1 the weight of the first configuration, P_2 of the second, etc. Let us choose these configurations as follows:

$$\varphi_1 = |0\rangle = \text{the vacuum, that is, all spins down } (\sigma^z_m \varphi_1 = -\varphi_1)$$

$$\varphi_2 = \sigma^+_1|0\rangle = \sigma^x_1|0\rangle = \text{all spins down but the first}$$

$$\cdots \qquad\qquad \cdots$$

$$\varphi_{2^M} = \sigma^+_1\sigma^+_2\sigma^+_3 \cdots \sigma^+_M|0\rangle = \sigma^x_1\sigma^x_2\sigma^x_3 \cdots \sigma^x_M|0\rangle \qquad (17)$$

with "all spins reversed" as the last configuration. (For typographical reasons, the row index n is suppressed. This should not cause confusion as one stays within this row. The "first spin" means $m = 1$, etc.) We have indicated that $\sigma^x_m \equiv \sigma^+_m + \sigma^-_m$ can be used equally as well as the raising operator σ^+_m because of the definition of the vacuum,

$$\sigma^-_m|0\rangle = \text{zero} \qquad \text{for all } m \qquad (18)$$

In this language the reduced density matrix is

$$\rho(R) = \sum_{r=1}^{2^M} P_r \varphi_r \qquad (19)$$

The strange operator $\rho(t\sigma_1^x, t_2^x, \dots)$ defined by Eq. (16) is conveniently expressed in the new language, and it is an *exercise for the reader* to prove:

$$\rho(t\sigma_1^x; \cdots)|0\rangle = e^{(\ln t)\sum_{m=1}^{M}\sigma_m{}^+\sigma_m{}^-} \rho(\sigma_1^x; \cdots)|0\rangle \tag{20}$$

Hereafter we shall continue to let the Ising spins be aligned along the x direction, because of the convenient identity above. Of course

$$\sum_1^M \sigma_m^+\sigma_m^- \equiv \mathbf{N} \tag{21}$$

will be recognized as the total particle number *counting* operator, and to within an additive constant it equals S_{tot}^z in the new spin coordinate system.

THE EQUATION

The above has disposed of most of the preliminary and technical difficulties. What remains is a tangle of embarrassing notation. To make contact with the vast literature on the subject, we first introduce the following abbreviations:

$$\beta J_1 = K_1, \qquad \beta J_2 = K_2, \qquad \beta h = H, \qquad 2\tilde{K}_1 = -\ln(\tanh K_1) \tag{22}$$

and one of the many algebraic identities used by Onsager,

$$2K_1 = -\ln(\tanh \tilde{K}_1) \tag{23}$$

and use these to express $\mathbf{V}$, derived by the methods of the previous section, as the product of three factors:

$$\mathbf{V} = \mathbf{V}_1\mathbf{V}_2\mathbf{V}_3 \tag{24}$$

The first of these incorporates the counting operator,

$$\mathbf{V}_1 = (2\cosh K_1)^M e^{-2\tilde{K}_1\mathbf{N}}$$

$$= (2\sinh 2K_1)^{M/2} e^{-2\tilde{K}_1(\mathbf{N}-M/2)} \tag{25}$$

The factor in the exponent is now exactly $S_{\text{tot}}^z = \mathbf{N} - M/2$.

The next operator, $\mathbf{V}_2$, incorporates the bonds within row R, which have not come under examination as yet.

$$\mathbf{V}_2 = e^{K_2\sum\sigma_m{}^x\sigma_{m+1}{}^x} \tag{26}$$

Finally, the magnetic field enters through the third factor,

$$\mathbf{V}_3 = e^{H\sum\sigma_m{}^x} \cdot \tag{27}$$

The eigenvalue equation is thus

$$\boxed{z\rho = \mathbf{V}\rho} \qquad \mathbf{V} = \mathbf{V}_1\mathbf{V}_2\mathbf{V}_3 \tag{28}$$

Because $\mathbf{V}_1$ does not commute with either of the other two factors (note how maliciously a classical problem has been reexpressed in terms of noncommuting, genuinely quantum-mechanical operators!), $\mathbf{V}$ is not Hermitean. It is sometimes useful to symmetrize, or Hermitize, $\mathbf{V}$. The two obvious ways to do this:

$$\mathbf{V} \to (\mathbf{V}_2\mathbf{V}_3)^{\frac{1}{2}}\mathbf{V}_1(\mathbf{V}_3\mathbf{V}_2)^{\frac{1}{2}} \qquad \text{and} \qquad \mathbf{V} \to \mathbf{V}_1^{\frac{1}{2}}(\mathbf{V}_2\mathbf{V}_3)\mathbf{V}_1^{\frac{1}{2}} \tag{29}$$

have led various investigators to express their results in diverse forms. The richness of this problem probably has not yet been exhausted, and the author does not know of published versions based on such other symmetrized forms as, e.g.,

$$z\mathbf{V}_1^{-1}\rho = \mathbf{V}_2\mathbf{V}_3\rho \tag{30}$$

which is another pseudo-Schrödinger equation, familiar in the Heitler-London theory where there is an overlap matrix.

Solving the problem in the absence of an external field (next section), we shall soon discover the difficulties of introducing $H \neq 0$; and also understand the reason no method of solution has yet found an extension to three dimensions.

SOLUTION IN ZERO MAGNETIC FIELD

Consider the operators, first introduced on p. 78,

$$c_m = (-1)^{\sum\limits_{j \lessgtr m} n_j}\sigma_m^- \qquad c_m^* = (-1)^{\sum\limits_{j \lessgtr m} n_j}\sigma_m^+ \qquad \mathfrak{n}_m \equiv c_m^* c_m = \sigma_m^+\sigma_m^- \tag{31}$$

Inverting,

$$\sigma_m^- = (-1)^{\sum\limits_{j \lessgtr m} n_j}c_m \qquad \text{etc.} \tag{32}$$

It is a simple exercise to verify that the c's are Fermion operators, which anticommute

$$c_m c_{m'} + c_{m'} c_m \equiv \{c_m, c_{m'}\} = \{c_m^*, c_{m'}^*\} = 0$$

$$\{c_m, c_{m'}^*\} = \delta_{m,m'} \qquad c_m|0\rangle = 0 \tag{33}$$

Form the basic products of operators which occur in $\mathbf{V}_{1,2}$:

$$\mathbf{N} = \sum c_m^* c_m = \sum \mathfrak{n}_m$$

$$\sigma_m^+\sigma_{m+1}^- = c_m^* c_{m+1}$$

$$\sigma_m^+\sigma_{m+1}^+ = c_m^* c_{m+1}^* \tag{34}$$

$$\sigma_m^-\sigma_{m+1}^- = c_{m+1}c_m = -c_m c_{m+1}$$

Quadratic forms in spin operators remain quadratic forms in Fermions because of the unique choice of nearest-neighbor, linear ordering (cf. the similar XY model, p. 160). The difficulties which arise with next-nearest-neighbor interactions are typical of those we would encounter in extending the theory to three dimensions, where R is no longer a row but a plane of spins. It is then *impossible* for each spin to be numbered consecutively with its neighbors, and terms of the following sort arise:

$$\sigma_m^+ \sigma_{m+p}^- = c_m^*(-1)^{m<j\sum_{<m+p}^{n_j}} c_{m+p}$$

In such cases the transformation of Eqs. (31) and (32) is not of any practical use.

Returning to the problem at hand, viz., the operator

$$\mathbf{V} = (2\sinh 2K_1)^{M/2} e^{-2\bar{K}_1 \Sigma(n_m - \frac{1}{2})} e^{K_2 \Sigma(c_m^* - c_m)(c_{m+1}^* + c_{m+1})} \tag{35}$$

and the eigenvalue equation

$$\mathbf{V}\rho = z\rho \tag{36}$$

we may appreciate that it would be of the usual quadratic form were it not for the exponentiations. This need not deter us. First, make as usual a canonical transformation to running waves, c_q,

$$c_m = \frac{e^{-i\pi/4}}{\sqrt{M}} \sum_q e^{iqm} c_q \tag{37}$$

with c^* given by the Hermitean conjugate and the phase factor $e^{-i\pi/4}$ introduced for future convenience. Next we factor the matrices $\mathbf{V}_{1,2}$ into product matrices $\mathbf{V}_{1,2}(q)$:

$$\mathbf{V}_1 = \text{const } e^{-2\bar{K}_1 \Sigma(n_q - \frac{1}{2})}$$

$$= \text{const} \prod_{q>0} e^{-2\bar{K}_1(n_q + n_{-q} - 1)} \tag{38}$$

and
$$\mathbf{V}_2 = \prod_{q>0} e^{2K_2[\cos q(n_q + n_{-q}) + \sin q(c_q c_{-q} + \text{H.c.})]} \tag{39}$$

We have been intentionally cavalier about the mode $q = 0$, and indeed about the very values of the wavevectors $q \neq 0$. These are however discussed in Problems 1 and 2.

Problem 1: Show that $\mathbf{V}_1(0) = e^{-2\bar{K}_1(n_0 - \frac{1}{2})}$, $\mathbf{V}_2(0) = e^{(2K_2 \cdot n_0)}$. Also find $\mathbf{V}_{1,2}(\pi)$ by direct calculation.

Problem 2: Show that when $\mathbf{N}$ = even, $q = \pm\pi/M$, $\pm 3\pi/M \ldots$, $\pm(M-1)\pi/M$ (i.e., obey *anticyclic* boundary conditions); and when $\mathbf{N}$ = odd, $q = 0$, $\pm 2\pi/M$, $\pm 4\pi/M$, $\ldots$, $\pm(M-2)\pi/M$ (*cyclic* boundary conditions), assuming M is even. Hint: Investigate the bond $\sigma_M \sigma_1$ carefully. Cf. XY model, Chapter 6.

The factoring was a very important step, and could only be performed because the various $\mathbf{V}(q)$'s commute. It represents a real decomposition into normal modes, which allows the "wavefunction" itself to be factored

$$\rho = \prod \rho_q \tag{40}$$

as well as the eigenvalue

$$z = (2 \sinh 2K_1)^{M/2} \prod z_q \tag{41}$$

each of these being the solution of a 4×4 matrix equation,

$$\mathbf{V}_1(q)\mathbf{V}_2(q)\rho_q = z_q \rho_q \tag{42}$$

with
$$\mathbf{V}_1(q) = e^{-2\tilde{K}_1(\mathfrak{n}_q + \mathfrak{n}_{-q} - 1)}$$
$$\mathbf{V}_2(q) = e^{+2K_2[\cos q(\mathfrak{n}_q + \mathfrak{n}_{-q}) + \sin q(c_q c_{-q} + \text{H.c.})]} \qquad \text{for } q \neq 0, \pi \tag{43}$$

These reduce to 2×2 matrices for $q = 0$ and π (cf. Problem 1).

The 4×4 matrices have four eigenvalues, but we may still factor two of these, belonging to the eigenfunctions

$$\psi_1 = c_q^*|0\rangle \qquad \text{and} \qquad \psi_2 = c_{-q}^*|0\rangle \tag{44}$$

These must be eigenfunctions of $\mathbf{V}(q) \equiv \mathbf{V}_1(q)\mathbf{V}_2(q)$ since the latter is an operator which has nondiagonal matrix elements only between the unoccupied and doubly occupied states,

$$\psi_3 = |0\rangle \qquad \text{and} \qquad \psi_4 = c_{-q}^* c_{+q}^*|0\rangle \tag{45}$$

ψ_1 and ψ_2 are eigenfunctions of all the terms in the exponents of Eq. (43). Therefore, by inspection,

$$z_{1,q} = z_{2,q} = e^{2K_2 \cos q} \tag{46}$$

are the first two solutions of Eq. (42). In the subspace of the empty and doubly occupied states, the matrix $\mathbf{V}(q)$ can be rewritten in terms of pseudospin (Pauli) matrices,

$$\tau^z = \mathfrak{n}_q + \mathfrak{n}_{-q} - 1 \qquad \text{eigenvalues } \pm 1$$
$$\tau^x = c_q c_{-q} + c_{-q}^* c_q^* \qquad \text{eigenvalues } \pm 1 \tag{47}$$
and
$$\tau^y = i(c_q c_{-q} - c_{-q}^* c_q^*) \qquad \textit{idem}$$

and in terms of these:

$$\mathbf{V}_1(q)\mathbf{V}_2(q) = e^{-2\tilde{K}_1 \tau^z} e^{+2K_2[\cos q(\tau^z + 1) + \sin q(\tau^x)]}$$

$$= [\cosh 2\tilde{K}_1 - \tau^z \sinh 2\tilde{K}_1]$$

$$\cdot e^{2K_2}[\cosh 2K_2 + (\tau^z \cos q + \tau^x \sin q) \sinh 2K_2]$$

$$= e^{2K_2}[(\cosh 2\tilde{K}_1 \cosh 2K_2$$

$$- \cos q \sinh 2\tilde{K}_1 \sinh 2K_2) + \tau^x(\sin q \sinh 2K_2 \cosh 2\tilde{K}_1)$$

$$- i\tau^y(\sin q \sinh 2K_2 \sinh 2\tilde{K}_1) + \tau^z(\cos q \sinh 2K_2 \cosh 2\tilde{K}_1$$

$$- \sinh 2\tilde{K}_1 \cosh 2K_2)] \tag{48}$$

The final 2×2 matrix is immediately diagonalizable, yielding the last two eigenvalues. Or by an alternative procedure, we can substitute the electronic operators *back into* Eq. (48):

$$\mathbf{V}_1(q)\mathbf{V}_2(q) = e^{2K_2}[\cosh 2\tilde{K}_1 \cosh 2K_2 - \cos q \sinh 2\tilde{K}_1 \sinh 2K_2$$
$$+ (c_q c_{-q} + \text{H.c.})(\sin q \sinh 2K_2 \cosh 2\tilde{K}_1)$$
$$+ (c_q c_{-q} - c_{-q}^* c_q^*)(\sin q \sinh 2K_2 \sinh 2\tilde{K}_1)$$
$$+ (\mathfrak{n}_q + \mathfrak{n}_{-q} - 1)(\cos q \sinh 2K_2 \cosh 2\tilde{K}_1 - \sinh 2\tilde{K}_1 \cosh 2K_2)] \qquad (49)$$

which is valid for *all* four states $\psi_1, \ldots, \psi_4$. Then diagonalizing the complete matrix by means of the Valatin-Bogolubov transformation[5] (cf. p. 169) as it is known for Fermions:

$$c_q \to \cos \phi_q c_q + \sin \phi_q c_{-q}^* \qquad (50)$$

etc., and then reexponentiating, we find

$$\boxed{\mathbf{V}(q) = e^{2K_2 \cos q} e^{-\varepsilon_q(\mathfrak{n}_q + \mathfrak{n}_{-q} - 1)}} \qquad (51)$$

a diagonal matrix in the new operators, with ε_q the positive root of the transcendental equation,

$$\cosh \varepsilon_q = (\cosh 2K_2 \cosh 2\tilde{K}_1 - \cos q \sinh 2K_2 \sinh 2\tilde{K}_1) \qquad q \neq 0 \qquad (52)$$

The case of $q = 0$ was considered separately, in Problem 1. We had found that

$$\mathbf{V}(0) = e^{\tilde{K}_1} e^{2(K_2 - \tilde{K}_1)\mathfrak{n}_0} \qquad (53)$$

Combining all these results, we finally obtain for $\mathbf{V}$,

$$\mathbf{V} = (2 \sinh 2K_1)^{M/2} e^{-\Sigma \varepsilon_q(\mathfrak{n}_q - \frac{1}{2})} \qquad (54)$$

where the sum runs over all q, positive and negative. The largest eigenvalue of this operator is required, a simple task of setting some n_q's equal to unity, and others equal to zero.

At high temperature, all ε_q are positive, therefore all n_q must be zero if we are to attain the largest eigenvalue. Assuming cyclic boundary conditions are chosen (see Problem 2 for the meaning of these terms), one n_q must also be set equal to unity so that the number of particles N = odd. This obviously is less satisfactory, and leads to a smaller eigenvalue than the choice of *anticyclic* boundary conditions (N = even) in which the wavevector $q = 0$ does not appear at all, and the choice of *all* $n_q = 0$ is

---

[5] In its initial form, the eigenvalue equation, Eq. (42), is similar to the Bardeen, Cooper, and Schrieffer Hamiltonian in the theory of superconductivity. Our initial method of solution is also reminiscent of Anderson's pseudo-spin solution of the BCS Hamiltonian, *Phys. Rev.*, **112**: 1900 (1958).

allowed. Thus one possible eigenvalue, and in fact the maximum eigenvalue at high temperature ($\tilde{K}_1 > K_2$) is

$$z = (2 \sinh 2K_1)^{M/2} e^{M \int_{-\pi}^{\pi} dq \, \varepsilon_q/4\pi} \tag{55}$$

replacing sums by integrals as usual, in the limit $M \to \infty$. However, the situation changes abruptly when $\tilde{K}_1 = K_2$, and indeed this is how T_c will be defined. When $\tilde{K}_1 \leqslant K_2$, the choice of $n_0 = 1$ is better than $n_0 = 0$, and by choosing the cyclic boundary conditions compatible with $N = $ odd, we also obtain the same above z value to $O(e^{-M})$. Thus the "ground state" becomes twofold degenerate. (There is no violation of Frobenius' theorem, because these states are degenerate only in the limit $M \to \infty$.) This degeneracy expresses the twofold (spins up or down) degeneracy of the Ising ferromagnetic model, or (the AB sublattice interchange degeneracy) of the Ising antiferromagnetic model. It is also intimately associated with the existence of long-range order.

Although the expression for the partition sum does not appear symmetric in the two bond strengths $J_{1,2}$ (or $K_{1,2}$), it can be made so by use of Onsager's identity

$$\int_0^{2\pi} dt \ln(2 \cosh x - 2 \cos t) = 2\pi x \tag{56}$$

Thus $\mathbf{f} = -kT\left(\sqrt{\ln (2 \sinh 2K_1)} + \frac{1}{4\pi} \int_{-\pi}^{\pi} \varepsilon_q \, dq \right)$

$$= -kT\left[\ln 2 + \frac{2}{(2\pi)^2} \int_0^{\pi} d\omega \int_0^{\pi} d\omega \ln(\cosh 2K_1 \cosh 2K_2 \right.$$

$$\left. - \sinh 2K_1 \cos \omega - \sinh 2K_2 \cos \omega') \right] \tag{57}$$

The critical temperature determined by $K_2 = \tilde{K}_1$ is given by

$$\sinh \frac{2J_1}{kT_c} \sinh \frac{2J_2}{kT_c} = 1 \tag{58}$$

For $J_1 = J_2 = J$, the isotropic square lattice,

$$kT_c = \frac{2J}{\text{arc sinh}(1)} = \frac{2J}{\ln(1 + \sqrt{2})} = 2.27J \tag{59}$$

It is evident from the structure of the free energy formula exhibited in Eq. (57) that there is a branch cut at T_c, although it is also clear that the free energy is continuous—a postulate of thermodynamics which is here explicitly verified.

Early in the previous chapter we proved that the internal energy $u = \partial(\beta \mathbf{f})/\partial \beta$. Let us evaluate the internal energy for the isotropic square lattice; using the $\mathbf{f}$ given above, we find

$$u = -J(\coth 2K)\left[1 + \frac{2}{\pi}(2\tanh^2 2K - 1)K_1(k_1)\right] \tag{60}$$

with $k_1 = 2\sinh 2K/\cosh^2 2K$ and $K_1(k_1)$ defined as the complete elliptic integral of the first kind,

$$K_1(k_1) = \int_0^{\pi/2}(1 - k_1^2\sin^2\varphi)^{-\frac{1}{2}}\,d\varphi$$

When the internal energy is differentiated in turn to obtain the specific heat $c = du/dT$, a logarithmically singular behavior is found, shown in Fig. 9.2 and discussed in Problem 3. This logarithmic singularity is not limited to the isotropic case. In general, near $T = T_c$ some kind of a logarithmic singularity may be calculated from the formula for the free energy. If we fix $J_1 + J_2 = 2J$ (constant), then as $J_2 \to 0$, we recover the smooth one-dimensional specific heat (the singularity moves to $T = 0$ and the half-width of the logarithmic peak vanishes), and at $J_1 = J_2$ we obtain the broadest anomaly.

Problem 3: Taking a clue from the Landau theory of the previous chapter, expand f given in Eq. (57) about T_c and derive the results discussed in the text and displayed in Fig. 9.2.

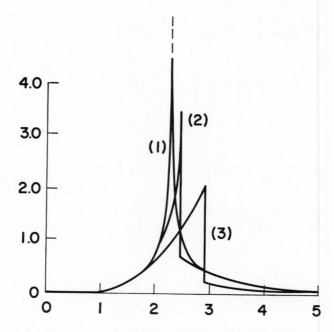

FIG. 9.2. *Exact* specific heat c/k versus kT/J for isotropic nearest-neighbor, square-lattice Ising model (curve 1) compared with various approximations: Kramers and Wannier approximation (curve 2) and Bethe method (similar to molecular field, curve 3). [After G. H. Wannier, *Revs. Mod. Phys.*, **17**: 50(1945).]

SPONTANEOUS MAGNETIZATION

One can make a plausible case for identifying the magnetization with the long-range order. For in the expression

$$\mathscr{M}^2(T) = \frac{\langle (\sum_i \sigma_{\mathbf{R}_i})^2 \rangle_{TA}}{MN}$$

$$= \lim_{R_{ij} \to \infty} \langle \sigma_{\mathbf{R}_i} \sigma_{\mathbf{R}_j} \rangle_{TA} \tag{61}$$

the division by MN eliminates all except the long-range correlations. Thus even though there are nonvanishing short-range correlations above T_c, $\mathscr{M}(T > T_c) = 0$, to $O(1/MN)$.

This formulation of $\mathscr{M}(T)$ obviates the necessity of inserting $\mathbf{V}_3$, p. 262, into the theory, and is the method chosen by Montroll, Potts, and Ward.[6] The first published method (by Yang) used $\mathbf{V}_3$. [Although the results obtained by either method are identical, Yang's approach is much more difficult. It can be summarized as follows: The magnetic field lifts the degeneracy between the two ground states which exist below T_c, and (much like the atomic Zeeman effect) the interaction energy is $-H\mathscr{M}(T)$, which is used to obtain $\mathscr{M}(T)$.]

It can be proved[7] that the long-range order in Eq. (61) is independent of the direction of $\mathbf{R}_{ij}$, even when the bonds are anisotropic, that is, $J_1 \neq J_2$. Therefore, the simplest thing to do is to pick two spins far apart on the same row and calculate their correlation as a function of T.

The relevant operator is $\sigma_i^x \sigma_j^x$, which we must translate into the Fermion operators using Eqs. (32) to (34). Here, it is slightly more convenient to use the identity (see the appropriate section on the representations of spins one-half in the chapter on angular momentum, p. 78).

$$(-1)^{n_m} \equiv (c_m^* + c_m)(c_m^* - c_m) \tag{62}$$

to obtain the compact formula

$$\sigma_i^x \sigma_j^x = (c_i^* - c_i)(c_{i+1}^* + c_{i+1})(c_{i+1}^* - c_{i+1}) \cdots (c_{j-1}^* + c_{j-1})(c_{j-1}^* - c_{j-1})(c_j^* + c_j) \tag{63}$$

The thermal average is nothing more than the "ground state" expectation value of this operator, in the "ground state" $|g\rangle$ appropriate to the largest eigenvalue. It may therefore be evaluated by Wick's theorem of field theory, which here states:

Associate the operators in all possible pairs, replace each pair by its ground-state expectation value and multiply the product by $(-1)^{\mathscr{P}}$ to take care of the number of anticommutators required to attain each permutation $\mathscr{P}$ of the operators. Finally, sum on all such permutations. (This defines, in effect, a *determinant*.)

The contractions which occur are of three types, two of which vanish,

$$(g|(c_m^* + c_m)(c_n^* + c_n)|g) = (g|(c_m^* - c_m)(c_n^* - c_n)|g) = 0 \tag{64}$$

---

[6] *Op. cit.*
[7] Schultz, Mattis, and Lieb, *op. cit.*

and the nonvanishing one,

$$(g|(c_m^* - c_m)(c_n^* + c_n)|g) \equiv a_{m,\,n-1} \tag{65}$$

Note that $n - 1$ is introduced in the definition of the matrix of importance in this problem. The evaluation is left as an exercise for the reader; it is a matter of performing the various transformations in the preceding section, taking due care of the signs and phase factors, to arrive at

$$a_{i,\,j} = a(i - j) = -\frac{1}{M} \sum_q e^{iq(i-j)} \cdot e^{-i(2\phi_q + q)} \tag{66}$$

A convenient formula for ϕ_q defined in Eq. (50) will be given subsequently.

The minus $(-)$ sign under odd permutations has the result that the long-range order is given by a determinant:

$$(g|\sigma_m^x \sigma_{m'}^x|g) = \begin{vmatrix} a_{m,\,m} & a_{m,\,m+1} & \cdots & a_{m,\,m'-1} \\ a_{m+1,\,m} & \cdot & & \cdot \\ \cdot & \cdot & & \cdot \\ a_{m'-1,\,m} & \cdot & \cdots & a_{m'-1,\,m'-1} \end{vmatrix} \tag{67}$$

which is a *Toeplitz* determinant, that is, the (i, j)th element depends only on the difference $(i - j)$. A Toeplitz determinant can differ from the corresponding *cyclic determinant* even when the size of the array becomes very large. For example, the former can vanish when the latter does not, as in the case of the 9×9,

$$\text{Toeplitz det} = \begin{vmatrix} 010000000 \\ 001000000 \\ \cdots \\ 000000001 \\ 000000000 \end{vmatrix} = \text{zero} \tag{68}$$

whereas by adding 1 in the lower left corner,

$$\text{Cyclic det} = \begin{vmatrix} 010000000 \\ 001000000 \\ \cdots \\ 000000001 \\ 100000000 \end{vmatrix} = 1 \tag{69}$$

Fortunately, there exists a theorem due to Szegö and Kac[8] which could be used by Montroll et al. to calculate the ratio of the Toeplitz to the cyclic determinant —asymptotically to $O(1/m' - m)$, which is to say, the leading correction term. The great value of this theorem is that the corresponding cyclic $a_{i,\,j}$ determinant is trivial to calculate. It is merely the product of the coefficients in a Fourier expansion of a typical row, which is precisely the product of the eigenvalues of the cyclic matrix (cf. p. 52).

---

[8] M. Kac, *Probability and Related Topics in Physical Sciences*, Interscience, New York, 1959.

Let the Fourier transform be

$$F(q) = \sum_m e^{iqm} a(m) \tag{70}$$

and in the limit $M \to \infty$ the cyclic determinant $C(F)$ is

$$C(F) = \prod_q f(q) = e^{M \int_{-\pi}^{\pi} \ln F(q)\, dq/2\pi} \tag{71}$$

The Kac-Szegö theorem yields the Toeplitz determinant $T(F)$ as,

$$T(F) = C(F) e^{\sum_{n=1}^{\infty} n k_n k_{-n}} \tag{72}$$

where
$$\ln F(q) \equiv \sum_{n=-\infty}^{\infty} k_n e^{inq} \tag{73}$$

In the case of actual interest, $\ln F(q) = +i(\phi_q + q)$ follows from Eq. (66), and as ϕ_q turns out to be odd, like q, we shall find that the integral in Eq. (71) vanishes and $C = 1$. The following, precise formula is a result of the calculations indicated previously:

$$e^{-2i\phi_q} = e^{iq} \left[\frac{(1 - x_1^{-1} e^{iq})(1 - x_2 e^{-iq})}{(1 - x_1^{-1} e^{-iq})(1 - x_2 e^{iq})} \right]^{\frac{1}{2}} \quad \text{for } T < T_c$$

$$= -\left[\frac{(1 - x_1^{-1} e^{iq})(1 - x_2^{-1} e^{iq})}{(1 - x_1^{-1} e^{-iq})(1 - x_2^{-1} e^{-iq})} \right]^{\frac{1}{2}} \quad \text{for } T > T_c \tag{74}$$

where
$$x_1 = (\cotanh \tilde{K}_1 \cotanh K_2) > 1$$

and
$$x_2 = \left(\frac{\cotanh K_2}{\cotanh \tilde{K}_1} \right) \gtrless 1 \quad \text{for } T \gtrless T_c \tag{75}$$

A series expansion of $+i(\phi_q + q)$ in powers of e^{iq} will yield the coefficients k_n by Eq. (73), and insertion of these into the formula for the Toeplitz form, Eq. (72), completes the process. The final formula is Eq. (0), as the reader might have guessed.

Above the Curie temperature the spontaneous magnetization vanishes. On the basis of exact series expansion methods Fisher[9] has estimated the following law for the magnetic susceptibility, $d\mathcal{M}/dH$,

$$\chi(T) = \frac{N\mu_B^2}{kT_c} \left(1 - \frac{T_c}{T} \right)^{-\frac{7}{4}} \quad T \gtrsim T_c \tag{76}$$

There is at present no known simple derivation of this result beside the series numerical approach, and it is evidently not valid when $T \gg T_c$, in the region of validity of the Curie-Weiss law. The exact susceptibility can be calculated (in principle) by expanding V_3 to second order in H, and solving for $z(H)$.

---

[9] M. E. Fisher, *J. Math. Phys.*, **4**: 278 (1963).

The very high accuracy series expansions of the three-dimensional Ising model have indicated results similar to many features of the exact two-dimensional solution. For example, there is a logarithmic singularity in the specific heat just as in two dimensions, phase-space arguments to the contrary notwithstanding. But it is an

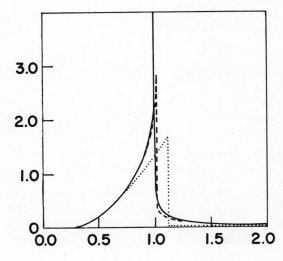

Fig. 9.3. Specific heat c/k versus kT/J for isotropic, nearest-neighbor, fcc Ising model, for which no analytical solution exists. Results of series methods exact everywhere except near T_c (solid curve) compared to Kikuchi approximation (dashed curve) and Bethe method (dotted curve). [After C. Domb (*Adv. in Phys.*), *Phil. Mag. Suppl.*, **9**: 151 (1960), where a review of these approximate methods will be found.]

asymmetric singularity, closer to the molecular field approximation than not. This is shown in Fig. 9.3. Near the Curie temperature, the three-dimensional susceptibility obeys the law

$$\chi(T) = \frac{N\mu_B^2}{kT_c}\left(1 - \frac{T_c}{T}\right)^{-\frac{5}{4}} \qquad T \gtrsim T_c \tag{77}$$

which is also closer to the molecular field Curie-Weiss law than the two-dimensional result. All these similarities are not unexpected as the number of neighbors to each spin has been increased, and therefore the likelihood of local fluctuations is less in three dimensions than in two, which is in closer accord with the premises of molecular field theory.

Future progress in this problem depends on the use of numerical or diagrammatical techniques and computer methods not within the scope of an introductory textbook on the theory of magnetism. This is therefore an appropriate place to end, and to refer the interested reader to the reviews[1] and other references in the Bibliography.

Problem 4: (a) For the general Ising model in arbitrary dimensions, $\mathscr{H} = -\sum_{(i,j)}J_{ij}\sigma_i\sigma_j - h\sum\sigma_i$, prove the following identity:

$$\mathscr{M}(T) = \langle\sigma_i\rangle_{TA} = \langle\tanh\{\sum_j J_{ij}\sigma_j + h\}/kT\rangle_{TA}$$

Hint: use Eq. (3) directly; do *not* use method of Doman and Ter Haar.[10] (b) Show how the (incorrect) substitution of $\tanh\langle\rangle_{TA}$ for the right-hand side $\langle\tanh\rangle_{TA}$ will yield the Curie-Weiss law.

---

[10] *Phys. Letters*, **2**: 15 (1962); cf. H. B. Callen, *Phys. Letters*, **4**: 161 (1963).

APPENDIX

TABLES FOR INDIRECT EXCHANGE THEORY

We give tabulated values of a quantity defined in Chapter 7,

$$WMF \equiv \sum_{i \neq 0} J(\mathbf{R}_i)$$

where the sum is over allowed lattice points

$$R_i = \sqrt{l^2 + m^2 + n^2} \qquad \text{except } R_i = 0$$

For the simple cubic lattice (sc) all integer values of l, m, and n are allowed. In the body-centered cubic lattice (bcc), only the integers l, m, n, *all* even or *all* odd, are allowed, and in the face-centered cubic structure (fcc),

$$l + m + n = \text{even integer}$$

is required.

The energy and the paramagnetic Curie temperature of the ferromagnetic state are proportional to $(-WMF)$ so that it is a necessary (but not sufficient) requirement for ferromagnetism to occur, that

$$WMF > 0$$

We have also calculated the energy of spiral configurations

$$S_i^z = 0 \qquad S_i^x = S \cos \mathbf{q} \cdot \mathbf{R}_i \qquad S_i^y = S \sin \mathbf{q} \cdot \mathbf{R}_i$$

for various values of the vector "pitch" $\mathbf{q}$, and referred that energy to the ferromagnetic energy (at $\mathbf{q} = 0$). The function, which contains this information, is denoted

$$\epsilon(\mathbf{q}) \equiv \sum_i J(\mathbf{R}_i)(1 - \cos \pi l q_x \cos \pi m q_y \cos \pi n q_z)$$

where the vector

$$\mathbf{q} = (q_x, q_y, q_z)$$

is allowed to vary along the (100) axis,

$$\mathbf{q} = (x, 0, 0) \qquad 0 \leq x \leq 1$$

and along the (110) axis,

$$\mathbf{q} = (x, x, 0) \qquad 0 \leq x \leq 1$$

and finally along the (111) axis

$$\mathbf{q} = (x, x, x) \qquad 0 \leq x \leq 1$$

for all three cubic structures. We recall that the value of $\mathbf{q}$, for which $\epsilon(\mathbf{q})$ has its minimum, gives the ground-state configuration. And that when this ground state is the ferromagnetic state, $\epsilon(\mathbf{q})$ is proportional to the frequency of a spin-wave vector $\mathbf{q}$. This function thus plays a dual role.

As we know, the number of conduction electrons per spin when the latter are in an sc array with magnetic lattice parameter $a = 1$, is

$$n_{\mathrm{sc}} = \frac{8\pi}{3}\left(\frac{k_F}{2\pi}\right)^3$$

For spins on a bcc lattice there are only one-quarter as many magnetic atoms, so that

$$n_{\mathrm{bcc}} = \frac{32\pi}{3}\left(\frac{k_F}{2\pi}\right)^3$$

and that for the fcc there are half as many as in the simple cubic, i.e.,

$$n_{\mathrm{fcc}} = \frac{16\pi}{3}\left(\frac{k_F}{2\pi}\right)^3$$

In the Tables, the value of WMF and of $\epsilon(\mathbf{q})$ along the three principal directions can be found directly for three cubic structures. *They must be used together with* Eq. (73), p. 202.

The calculations were performed with $\lambda \equiv 3.00$ in the dimensionless units.

The accuracy of the results extend to the third decimal place for all tabulated material corresponding to $k_F > 1$, and to no less than the second decimal place even for the smallest values of k_F. This was established by summing out to a radius $R_{\max}$ and observing convergence at $R_{\max} \approx 12$. We have chosen the even larger value of $R_{\max} = 20$ for all the tabulated data presented herewith, a cutoff which is sufficiently large for all practical purposes, and which involves summing over some 30,000 points in the sc lattice.

T A B L E I. Simple Cubic Magnetic Lattice

Magnetic lattice-constant $a = 1$. For each indicated value of $k_F = 2\pi\left(\dfrac{3n}{8\pi}\right)^{\frac{1}{3}}$, where $n =$ number of conduction electrons $\div$ number of magnetic atoms, we give the calculated value of

$$WMF = \sum_{\mathrm{all}\ i \neq 0} a^3 \frac{\sin \phi_i - \phi_i \cos \phi_i}{5\phi_i R_i^3} \cdot e^{-R_i/\lambda}$$

where

$$R_i = \sqrt{l_i^2 + m_i^2 + n_i^2} \qquad (l_i, m_i, n_i = \text{integers})$$

and $\phi_i = 2k_F R_i$, followed by the value of $\lambda = 3.00$, the magnetic lattice symmetry (here simple cubic) and a complete table of the spin waves along the principal axes,

$$\epsilon(q) = \sum_i \left(a^3 \frac{\sin \phi_i - \phi_i \cos \phi_i}{5\phi_i R^3} e^{-R_i/\lambda}\right)\left(1 - \cos l_i\pi q_x \cos m_i\pi q_y \cos n_i\pi q_z\right)$$

for

$$q = \begin{bmatrix} (1, 0, 0) \\ (1, 1, 0) \\ (1, 1, 1) \end{bmatrix} \cdot x$$

in the intervals $x = 0, \ldots (0.5) \ldots, 1.00$.

Table I (continued)

KF= 0.100   WMF= 2.429   LAMDA= 3.00   SC

x	100	110	111
0.	0.000	0.000	0.000
0.05	0.325	0.585	0.797
0.10	0.970	1.424	1.675
0.15	1.499	1.890	2.062
0.20	1.832	2.244	2.322
0.25	2.033	2.316	2.372
0.30	2.158	2.360	2.402
0.35	2.239	2.389	2.422
0.40	2.295	2.409	2.435
0.45	2.334	2.424	2.444
0.50	2.362	2.434	2.451
0.55	2.383	2.441	2.455
0.60	2.399	2.447	2.459
0.65	2.411	2.451	2.461
0.70	2.420	2.454	2.463
0.75	2.427	2.456	2.465
0.80	2.433	2.458	2.466
0.85	2.437	2.459	2.466
0.90	2.439	2.459	2.467
0.95	2.441	2.460	2.467
1.00	2.441	2.460	2.467

KF= 0.700   WMF= 13.909   LAMDA= 3.00   SC

x	100	110	111
0.	0.000	0.000	0.000
0.05	0.093	0.186	0.280
0.10	0.374	0.753	1.138
0.15	0.849	1.724	2.625
0.20	1.527	3.135	4.813
0.25	2.421	5.024	7.617
0.30	3.546	7.318	10.259
0.35	4.911	9.578	12.063
0.40	6.491	11.308	13.210
0.45	8.162	12.503	13.962
0.50	9.695	13.329	14.472
0.55	10.936	13.912	14.828
0.60	11.887	14.331	15.083
0.65	12.606	14.636	15.267
0.70	13.149	14.860	15.402
0.75	13.558	15.024	15.502
0.80	13.862	15.143	15.574
0.85	14.082	15.226	15.625
0.90	14.231	15.281	15.660
0.95	14.317	15.313	15.679
1.00	14.345	15.323	15.686

KF= 0.400   WMF= 11.750   LAMDA= 3.00   SC

x	100	110	111
0.	0.000	0.000	0.000
0.05	0.234	0.468	0.703
0.10	0.937	1.872	2.792
0.15	2.104	4.111	5.838
0.20	3.683	6.627	8.403
0.25	5.486	8.562	9.905
0.30	7.168	9.788	10.759
0.35	8.482	10.558	11.275
0.40	9.428	11.060	11.605
0.45	10.104	11.401	11.826
0.50	10.593	11.639	11.978
0.55	10.953	11.810	12.086
0.60	11.223	11.935	12.164
0.65	11.428	12.027	12.221
0.70	11.584	12.095	12.263
0.75	11.703	12.146	12.294
0.80	11.793	12.182	12.317
0.85	11.858	12.208	12.333
0.90	11.902	12.225	12.344
0.95	11.927	12.235	12.350
1.00	11.936	12.238	12.352

KF= 1.000   WMF= 12.816   LAMDA= 3.00   SC

x	100	110	111
0.	0.000	0.000	0.000
0.05	0.045	0.091	0.137
0.10	0.183	0.369	0.557
0.15	0.415	0.841	1.276
0.20	0.744	1.520	2.328
0.25	1.174	2.427	3.766
0.30	1.711	3.592	5.662
0.35	2.362	5.056	8.029
0.40	3.138	6.846	10.440
0.45	4.051	8.866	12.251
0.50	5.114	10.727	13.473
0.55	6.335	12.140	14.306
0.60	7.691	13.150	14.889
0.65	9.077	13.872	15.305
0.70	10.319	14.392	15.606
0.75	11.314	14.767	15.824
0.80	12.063	15.036	15.983
0.85	12.600	15.223	16.095
0.90	12.961	15.346	16.169
0.95	13.169	15.416	16.212
1.00	13.237	15.438	16.226

Table I (*continued*)

KF= 1.300 WMF= 9.967 LAMDA= 3.00

x	100	110	111	SC
0.	0.000	0.000	0.000	
0.05	0.024	0.048	0.072	
0.10	0.096	0.194	0.292	
0.15	0.217	0.440	0.668	
0.20	0.388	0.792	1.213	
0.25	0.609	1.258	1.949	
0.30	0.881	1.849	2.908	
0.35	1.207	2.581	4.137	
0.40	1.588	3.476	5.698	
0.45	2.028	4.564	7.640	
0.50	2.531	5.882	9.739	
0.55	3.101	7.446	11.439	
0.60	3.745	9.122	12.629	
0.65	4.470	10.575	13.455	
0.70	5.285	11.654	14.040	
0.75	6.188	12.421	14.458	
0.80	7.149	12.960	14.756	
0.85	8.065	13.330	14.965	
0.90	8.787	13.569	15.104	
0.95	9.230	13.704	15.183	
1.00	9.377	13.748	15.209	

KF= 1.900 WMF= 1.633 LAMDA= 3.00

x	100	110	111	SC
0.	0.000	-0.000	-0.000	
0.05	0.000	0.000	0.001	
0.10	0.001	0.002	0.005	
0.15	0.000	0.007	0.018	
0.20	-0.002	0.014	0.047	
0.25	-0.009	0.027	0.103	
0.30	-0.023	0.048	0.200	
0.35	-0.048	0.081	0.357	
0.40	-0.090	0.132	0.596	
0.45	-0.154	0.207	0.943	
0.50	-0.250	0.316	1.430	
0.55	-0.387	0.472	2.096	
0.60	-0.579	0.689	2.991	
0.65	-0.842	0.987	4.169	
0.70	-1.195	1.392	5.597	
0.75	-1.645	1.933	6.931	
0.80	-2.161	2.636	7.903	
0.85	-2.650	3.470	8.559	
0.90	-3.027	4.234	8.980	
0.95	-3.257	4.712	9.215	
1.00	-3.333	4.869	9.291	

KF= 2.500 WMF= -6.213 LAMDA= 3.00

x	100	110	111	SC
0.	-0.000	-0.000	-0.000	
0.05	-0.025	-0.051	-0.076	
0.10	-0.103	-0.204	-0.301	
0.15	-0.238	-0.460	-0.669	
0.20	-0.436	-0.824	-1.167	
0.25	-0.709	-1.296	-1.777	
0.30	-1.069	-1.878	-2.474	
0.35	-1.527	-2.568	-3.227	
0.40	-2.073	-3.352	-3.998	
0.45	-2.651	-4.199	-4.747	
0.50	-3.191	-5.062	-5.432	
0.55	-3.658	-5.889	-6.015	
0.60	-4.049	-6.655	-6.468	
0.65	-4.373	-7.360	-6.766	
0.70	-4.638	-8.021	-6.895	
0.75	-4.850	-8.670	-6.840	
0.80	-5.017	-9.344	-6.589	
0.85	-5.142	-10.070	-6.131	
0.90	-5.229	-10.777	-5.481	
0.95	-5.280	-11.270	-4.850	
1.00	-5.297	-11.439	-4.602	

KF= 1.600 WMF= 6.060 LAMDA= 3.00

x	100	110	111	SC
0.	0.000	0.000	0.000	
0.05	0.010	0.021	0.032	
0.10	0.043	0.087	0.132	
0.15	0.097	0.198	0.304	
0.20	0.171	0.357	0.556	
0.25	0.266	0.568	0.902	
0.30	0.380	0.835	1.358	
0.35	0.513	1.166	1.948	
0.40	0.662	1.570	2.703	
0.45	0.826	2.061	3.665	
0.50	1.003	2.655	4.890	
0.55	1.190	3.376	6.435	
0.60	1.383	4.254	8.200	
0.65	1.580	5.322	9.733	
0.70	1.773	6.578	10.834	
0.75	1.956	7.855	11.601	
0.80	2.120	8.881	12.136	
0.85	2.251	9.594	12.505	
0.90	2.336	10.050	12.746	
0.95	2.371	10.304	12.883	
1.00	2.375	10.385	12.927	

KF= 2.200 WMF= -2.723 LAMDA= 3.00

x	100	110	111	SC
0.	-0.000	-0.000	-0.000	
0.05	-0.011	-0.021	-0.032	
0.10	-0.043	-0.085	-0.125	
0.15	-0.100	-0.192	-0.275	
0.20	-0.184	-0.341	-0.472	
0.25	-0.300	-0.532	-0.703	
0.30	-0.455	-0.764	-0.952	
0.35	-0.657	-1.035	-1.196	
0.40	-0.919	-1.343	-1.414	
0.45	-1.255	-1.681	-1.577	
0.50	-1.681	-2.043	-1.656	
0.55	-2.209	-2.419	-1.621	
0.60	-2.819	-2.795	-1.440	
0.65	-3.443	-3.154	-1.079	
0.70	-4.003	-3.477	-0.500	
0.75	-4.467	-3.745	0.338	
0.80	-4.833	-3.938	1.429	
0.85	-5.109	-4.046	2.514	
0.90	-5.300	-4.067	3.280	
0.95	-5.413	-4.021	3.707	
1.00	-5.450	-3.980	3.844	

KF= 2.800 WMF= -7.576 LAMDA= 3.00

x	100	110	111	SC
0.	-0.000	-0.000	-0.000	
0.05	-0.051	-0.102	-0.152	
0.10	-0.207	-0.408	-0.604	
0.15	-0.469	-0.913	-1.332	
0.20	-0.830	-1.593	-2.287	
0.25	-1.242	-2.379	-3.380	
0.30	-1.637	-3.174	-4.507	
0.35	-1.977	-3.918	-5.596	
0.40	-2.256	-4.597	-6.620	
0.45	-2.479	-5.227	-7.584	
0.50	-2.656	-5.830	-8.505	
0.55	-2.793	-6.434	-9.399	
0.60	-2.899	-7.069	-10.282	
0.65	-2.979	-7.774	-11.168	
0.70	-3.038	-8.584	-12.065	
0.75	-3.081	-9.477	-12.979	
0.80	-3.111	-10.305	-13.904	
0.85	-3.132	-10.947	-14.816	
0.90	-3.145	-11.389	-15.658	
0.95	-3.152	-11.647	-16.337	
1.00	-3.154	-11.732	-16.638	

Table I (continued)

KF= 3.100   WMF= -4.673   LAMDA= 3.00   SC

x	100	110	111
0.	0.000	0.000	0.000
0.05	-0.077	-0.056	-0.066
0.10	-0.082	-0.181	-0.296
0.15	-0.125	-0.318	-0.575
0.20	-0.138	-0.449	-0.911
0.25	-0.118	-0.576	-1.319
0.30	-0.065	-0.711	-1.814
0.35	0.018	-0.872	-2.416
0.40	0.127	-1.077	-3.144
0.45	0.258	-1.354	-4.021
0.50	0.404	-1.732	-5.071
0.55	0.559	-2.248	-6.319
0.60	0.719	-2.907	-7.788
0.65	0.875	-3.605	-9.474
0.70	1.024	-4.207	-11.294
0.75	1.158	-4.683	-13.093
0.80	1.275	-5.047	-14.775
0.85	1.369	-5.315	-16.334
0.90	1.439	-5.499	-17.636
0.95	1.482	-5.607	-18.446
1.00	1.496	-5.642	-18.714

KF= 3.700   WMF= -0.858   LAMDA= 3.00   SC

x	100	110	111
0.	-0.000	0.000	-0.000
0.05	0.007	0.014	0.021
0.10	0.028	0.055	0.082
0.15	0.066	0.126	0.182
0.20	0.122	0.226	0.319
0.25	0.201	0.353	0.480
0.30	0.300	0.489	0.607
0.35	0.402	0.601	0.546
0.40	0.461	0.673	0.239
0.45	0.429	0.702	-0.190
0.50	0.288	0.687	-0.691
0.55	0.042	0.642	-1.288
0.60	-0.297	0.585	-2.029
0.65	-0.713	0.534	-2.913
0.70	-1.179	0.507	-3.756
0.75	-1.661	0.519	-4.424
0.80	-2.114	0.581	-4.927
0.85	-2.500	0.690	-5.292
0.90	-2.790	0.821	-5.541
0.95	-2.969	0.928	-5.686
1.00	-3.029	0.969	-5.734

KF= 4.300   WMF= 0.804   LAMDA= 3.00   SC

x	100	110	111
0.	-0.000	-0.000	-0.000
0.05	-0.082	-0.160	-0.234
0.10	-0.312	-0.555	-0.736
0.15	-0.636	-1.013	-1.151
0.20	-0.988	-1.429	-1.349
0.25	-1.309	-1.760	-1.341
0.30	-1.572	-1.994	-1.170
0.35	-1.766	-2.131	-0.880
0.40	-1.891	-2.181	-0.504
0.45	-1.949	-2.149	0.030
0.50	-1.941	-2.042	0.925
0.55	-1.869	-1.862	2.253
0.60	-1.733	-1.609	3.939
0.65	-1.535	-1.304	5.689
0.70	-1.280	-1.016	7.202
0.75	-0.996	-0.804	8.419
0.80	-0.728	-0.728	9.366
0.85	-0.513	-0.563	10.075
0.90	-0.362	-0.498	10.568
0.95	-0.273	-0.461	10.859
1.00	-0.243	-0.448	10.955

KF= 3.400   WMF= -0.661   LAMDA= 3.00   SC

x	100	110	111
0.	0.000	0.000	0.000
0.05	0.055	0.110	0.164
0.10	0.216	0.431	0.647
0.15	0.465	0.924	1.373
0.20	0.756	1.466	2.118
0.25	1.033	1.914	2.617
0.30	1.270	2.200	2.753
0.35	1.467	2.311	2.498
0.40	1.634	2.242	1.836
0.45	1.779	1.999	0.756
0.50	1.911	1.666	-0.697
0.55	2.036	1.390	-2.340
0.60	2.160	1.226	-3.951
0.65	2.288	1.155	-5.471
0.70	2.421	1.143	-6.950
0.75	2.559	1.160	-8.430
0.80	2.697	1.187	-9.764
0.85	2.827	1.214	-10.780
0.90	2.934	1.236	-11.472
0.95	3.006	1.250	-11.874
1.00	3.032	1.254	-12.006

KF= 4.000   WMF= -1.704   LAMDA= 3.00   SC

x	100	110	111
0.	-0.000	-0.000	-0.000
0.05	-0.037	-0.075	-0.112
0.10	-0.149	-0.302	-0.459
0.15	-0.336	-0.688	-1.057
0.20	-0.599	-1.212	-1.861
0.25	-0.938	-1.762	-2.613
0.30	-1.347	-2.215	-3.021
0.35	-1.811	-2.526	-3.002
0.40	-2.301	-2.675	-2.575
0.45	-2.765	-2.644	-1.830
0.50	-3.152	-2.461	-1.048
0.55	-3.444	-2.250	-0.511
0.60	-3.665	-2.128	-0.136
0.65	-3.850	-2.121	0.184
0.70	-4.013	-2.218	0.464
0.75	-4.155	-2.405	0.701
0.80	-4.274	-2.667	0.895
0.85	-4.367	-2.981	1.047
0.90	-4.435	-3.290	1.155
0.95	-4.475	-3.516	1.220
1.00	-4.489	-3.597	1.242

KF= 4.600   WMF= 7.512   LAMDA= 3.00   SC

x	100	110	111
0.	0.000	0.000	0.000
0.05	0.104	0.205	0.302
0.10	0.402	0.745	1.025
0.15	0.846	1.447	1.798
0.20	1.358	2.170	2.465
0.25	1.873	2.828	3.020
0.30	2.354	3.381	3.492
0.35	2.791	3.814	4.018
0.40	3.185	4.122	4.786
0.45	3.544	4.319	5.835
0.50	3.872	4.455	7.142
0.55	4.176	4.629	8.679
0.60	4.462	4.916	10.422
0.65	4.735	5.339	12.367
0.70	4.997	5.900	14.512
0.75	5.252	6.593	16.741
0.80	5.501	7.387	18.721
0.85	5.740	8.162	20.236
0.90	5.959	8.762	21.282
0.95	6.124	9.124	21.893
1.00	6.187	9.243	22.094

Table I (continued)

KF= 4.900   WMF= 7.987   LAMDA= 3.00   SC

x	100	110	111
0.	0.000	0.000	0.000
0.05	0.041	0.082	0.123
0.10	0.165	0.331	0.498
0.15	0.376	0.752	1.129
0.20	0.676	1.330	1.978
0.25	1.072	1.991	2.908
0.30	1.564	2.671	3.784
0.35	2.139	3.411	4.596
0.40	2.754	4.234	5.386
0.45	3.337	5.076	6.200
0.50	3.822	5.874	7.081
0.55	4.178	6.605	8.069
0.60	4.407	7.268	9.203
0.65	4.522	7.872	10.522
0.70	4.545	8.424	12.057
0.75	4.494	8.932	13.812
0.80	4.386	9.405	15.746
0.85	4.238	9.847	17.745
0.90	4.082	10.255	19.520
0.95	3.967	10.590	20.677
1.00	3.925	10.734	21.067

KF= 5.500   WMF= 2.608   LAMDA= 3.00   SC

x	100	110	111
0.	0.000	0.000	0.000
0.05	0.041	0.077	0.110
0.10	0.152	0.253	0.348
0.15	0.304	0.460	0.637
0.20	0.471	0.683	0.955
0.25	0.633	0.926	1.301
0.30	0.779	1.197	1.685
0.35	0.901	1.504	2.130
0.40	0.995	1.856	2.669
0.45	1.061	2.255	3.279
0.50	1.112	2.667	3.711
0.55	1.182	3.026	3.688
0.60	1.306	3.331	3.181
0.65	1.501	3.615	2.244
0.70	1.770	3.896	0.909
0.75	2.115	4.202	-0.806
0.80	2.526	4.569	-2.844
0.85	2.976	4.936	-5.015
0.90	3.394	5.225	-6.972
0.95	3.688	5.403	-8.271
1.00	3.794	5.462	-8.711

KF= 6.100   WMF= -7.269   LAMDA= 3.00   SC

x	100	110	111
0.	-0.000	-0.000	-0.000
0.05	-0.039	-0.079	-0.118
0.10	-0.151	-0.301	-0.450
0.15	-0.308	-0.616	-0.922
0.20	-0.478	-0.959	-1.444
0.25	-0.640	-1.295	-2.002
0.30	-0.793	-1.622	-2.730
0.35	-0.938	-1.982	-3.747
0.40	-1.082	-2.486	-5.077
0.45	-1.231	-3.206	-6.674
0.50	-1.391	-4.053	-8.324
0.55	-1.572	-4.921	-9.779
0.60	-1.786	-5.784	-11.004
0.65	-2.035	-6.643	-11.974
0.70	-2.298	-7.495	-12.477
0.75	-2.539	-8.349	-12.633
0.80	-2.733	-9.252	-12.724
0.85	-2.877	-10.206	-12.812
0.90	-2.975	-11.077	-12.887
0.95	-3.033	-11.669	-12.937
1.00	-3.052	-11.875	-12.955

KF= 5.200   WMF= 4.821   LAMDA= 3.00   SC

x	100	110	111
0.	0.000	0.000	0.000
0.05	-0.018	-0.036	-0.053
0.10	-0.071	-0.132	-0.166
0.15	-0.154	-0.226	-0.158
0.20	-0.256	-0.200	0.110
0.25	-0.359	-0.037	0.690
0.30	-0.437	0.513	1.602
0.35	-0.461	1.206	2.727
0.40	-0.408	2.027	3.740
0.45	-0.259	2.918	4.491
0.50	-0.009	3.877	5.013
0.55	0.343	4.890	5.358
0.60	0.775	5.875	5.568
0.65	1.236	6.698	5.675
0.70	1.662	7.266	5.706
0.75	2.018	7.556	5.686
0.80	2.301	7.588	5.636
0.85	2.518	7.403	5.582
0.90	2.670	7.097	5.545
0.95	2.760	6.839	5.541
1.00	2.790	6.745	5.552

KF= 5.800   WMF= -1.622   LAMDA= 3.00   SC

x	100	110	111
0.	0.000	-0.000	0.000
0.05	0.017	0.033	0.050
0.10	0.066	0.134	0.201
0.15	0.146	0.297	0.406
0.20	0.256	0.482	0.525
0.25	0.393	0.587	0.499
0.30	0.558	0.535	0.347
0.35	0.762	0.344	0.093
0.40	1.002	0.073	-0.253
0.45	1.251	-0.243	-0.695
0.50	1.474	-0.593	-1.239
0.55	1.648	-0.975	-1.908
0.60	1.759	-1.351	-2.831
0.65	1.800	-1.646	-4.217
0.70	1.764	-1.836	-5.980
0.75	1.647	-1.922	-7.924
0.80	1.448	-1.900	-9.755
0.85	1.178	-1.772	-11.183
0.90	0.886	-1.553	-12.166
0.95	0.656	-1.314	-12.737
1.00	0.570	-1.203	-12.925

KF= 6.400   WMF= -10.269   LAMDA= 3.00   SC

x	100	110	111
0.	-0.000	-0.000	-0.000
0.05	-0.013	-0.026	-0.039
0.10	-0.068	-0.140	-0.215
0.15	-0.200	-0.420	-0.658
0.20	-0.435	-0.926	-1.472
0.25	-0.784	-1.685	-2.704
0.30	-1.253	-2.675	-4.302
0.35	-1.848	-3.780	-6.022
0.40	-2.562	-4.880	-7.682
0.45	-3.359	-5.931	-9.325
0.50	-4.162	-6.925	-10.980
0.55	-4.892	-7.915	-12.462
0.60	-5.510	-8.985	-13.476
0.65	-6.008	-10.166	-13.941
0.70	-6.390	-11.404	-13.873
0.75	-6.662	-12.538	-13.319
0.80	-6.831	-13.416	-12.388
0.85	-6.906	-13.993	-11.332
0.90	-6.909	-14.311	-10.503
0.95	-6.879	-14.465	-10.019
1.00	-6.862	-14.513	-9.862

TABLE II. FCC Conduction-Band Model

Same instructions as for Table I, except

$$k_F = 2\pi\left(\frac{3n}{16\pi}\right)^{\frac{1}{3}}$$

The points (1, 0, 0), (1, 1, 0), and $(\frac{1}{2}, \frac{1}{2}, \frac{1}{2})$ are on the Brillouin zone boundary, the first two being equivalent. The values along the (1, 1, 1) axis for $x > \frac{1}{2}$ are redundant.

KF= 0.100 WMF= 1.195 LAMDA= 3.00

x	100	110	111 (FCC)
0.	0.000	0.000	0.000
0.05	0.162	0.293	0.398
0.10	0.485	0.712	0.837
0.15	0.749	0.945	1.030
0.20	0.916	1.060	1.116
0.25	1.016	1.121	1.159
0.30	1.078	1.156	1.183
0.35	1.119	1.178	1.197
0.40	1.146	1.192	1.205
0.45	1.165	1.201	1.209
0.50	1.179	1.207	1.211
0.55	1.190	1.211	1.209
0.60	1.197	1.214	1.205
0.65	1.203	1.216	1.197
0.70	1.207	1.217	1.183
0.75	1.211	1.217	1.159
0.80	1.213	1.217	1.116
0.85	1.215	1.217	1.030
0.90	1.216	1.217	0.837
0.95	1.216	1.217	0.398
1.00	1.217	1.217	0.000

KF= 0.700 WMF= 6.066 LAMDA= 3.00

x	100	110	111 (FCC)
0.	0.000	0.000	0.000
0.05	0.045	0.091	0.137
0.10	0.183	0.368	0.556
0.15	0.415	0.842	1.282
0.20	0.747	1.533	2.351
0.25	1.185	2.456	3.716
0.30	1.737	3.578	4.988
0.35	2.408	4.677	5.822
0.40	3.185	5.506	6.304
0.45	4.007	6.061	6.552
0.50	4.759	6.427	6.629
0.55	5.366	6.667	6.552
0.60	5.827	6.821	6.304
0.65	6.173	6.917	5.822
0.70	6.432	6.971	4.988
0.75	6.625	6.998	3.716
0.80	6.768	7.004	2.351
0.85	6.870	7.006	1.282
0.90	6.939	6.998	0.556
0.95	6.978	6.993	0.137
1.00	6.991	6.991	0.000

KF= 0.400 WMF= 5.574 LAMDA= 3.00

x	100	110	111 (FCC)
0.	0.000	0.000	0.000
0.05	0.117	0.234	0.350
0.10	0.467	0.933	1.392
0.15	1.049	2.049	2.909
0.20	1.836	3.302	4.184
0.25	2.735	4.264	4.924
0.30	3.573	4.869	5.335
0.35	4.226	5.244	5.572
0.40	4.695	5.483	5.709
0.45	5.028	5.641	5.780
0.50	5.268	5.745	5.780
0.55	5.444	5.815	5.780
0.60	5.575	5.860	5.709
0.65	5.673	5.888	5.572
0.70	5.747	5.905	5.335
0.75	5.803	5.913	4.924
0.80	5.845	5.915	4.184
0.85	5.875	5.915	2.909
0.90	5.895	5.913	1.392
0.95	5.907	5.912	0.350
1.00	5.911	5.911	0.000

KF= 1.000 WMF= 4.703 LAMDA= 3.00

x	100	110	111 (FCC)
0.	0.000	0.000	0.000
0.05	0.020	0.041	0.062
0.10	0.083	0.166	0.250
0.15	0.187	0.378	0.572
0.20	0.336	0.684	1.042
0.25	0.532	1.093	1.682
0.30	0.777	1.620	2.521
0.35	1.077	2.284	3.554
0.40	1.437	3.099	4.552
0.45	1.864	4.017	5.166
0.50	2.365	4.844	5.360
0.55	2.945	5.436	5.166
0.60	3.592	5.818	4.552
0.65	4.256	6.051	3.554
0.70	4.850	6.181	2.521
0.75	5.324	6.243	1.682
0.80	5.677	6.262	1.042
0.85	5.929	6.257	0.572
0.90	6.097	6.243	0.250
0.95	6.193	6.230	0.062
1.00	6.225	6.225	0.000

Table II (continued)

KF= 1.300 WMF= 2.363 LAMDA= 3.00 FCC

x	100	110	111
0.	0.000	0.000	0.000
0.05	0.008	0.015	0.023
0.10	0.031	0.062	0.094
0.15	0.071	0.142	0.212
0.20	0.128	0.255	0.380
0.25	0.202	0.405	0.599
0.30	0.297	0.597	0.870
0.35	0.412	0.835	1.192
0.40	0.551	1.132	1.559
0.45	0.716	1.501	1.935
0.50	0.911	1.961	2.135
0.55	1.138	2.521	1.935
0.60	1.404	3.120	1.559
0.65	1.712	3.595	1.192
0.70	2.069	3.878	0.870
0.75	2.476	4.011	0.599
0.80	2.917	4.049	0.380
0.85	3.344	4.034	0.212
0.90	3.682	4.000	0.094
0.95	3.890	3.970	0.023
1.00	3.958	3.958	0.000

KF= 1.600 WMF= -0.403 LAMDA= 3.00 FCC

x	100	110	111
0.	-0.000	0.000	-0.000
0.05	-0.002	-0.004	-0.006
0.10	-0.008	-0.016	-0.025
0.15	-0.017	-0.036	-0.059
0.20	-0.029	-0.066	-0.117
0.25	-0.043	-0.106	-0.212
0.30	-0.058	-0.156	-0.367
0.35	-0.074	-0.218	-0.623
0.40	-0.090	-0.288	-1.012
0.45	-0.103	-0.362	-1.413
0.50	-0.113	-0.433	-1.573
0.55	-0.120	-0.486	-1.413
0.60	-0.121	-0.500	-1.012
0.65	-0.117	-0.445	-0.623
0.70	-0.108	-0.302	-0.367
0.75	-0.096	-0.129	-0.212
0.80	-0.082	-0.033	-0.117
0.85	-0.072	-0.020	-0.059
0.90	-0.070	-0.045	-0.025
0.95	-0.077	-0.072	-0.006
1.00	-0.083	-0.083	-0.000

KF= 1.900 WMF= -3.013 LAMDA= 3.00 FCC

x	100	110	111
0.	-0.000	-0.000	-0.000
0.05	-0.012	-0.025	-0.038
0.10	-0.050	-0.100	-0.153
0.15	-0.111	-0.229	-0.357
0.20	-0.196	-0.415	-0.670
0.25	-0.305	-0.665	-1.128
0.30	-0.437	-0.984	-1.747
0.35	-0.591	-1.378	-2.382
0.40	-0.767	-1.851	-2.852
0.45	-0.965	-2.395	-3.126
0.50	-1.184	-2.979	-3.216
0.55	-1.426	-3.541	-3.126
0.60	-1.694	-4.017	-2.852
0.65	-1.991	-4.370	-2.382
0.70	-2.322	-4.582	-1.747
0.75	-2.686	-4.646	-1.128
0.80	-3.064	-4.555	-0.670
0.85	-3.406	-4.334	-0.357
0.90	-3.666	-4.089	-0.153
0.95	-3.825	-3.930	-0.038
1.00	-3.878	-3.878	-0.000

KF= 2.200 WMF= -4.645 LAMDA= 3.00 FCC

x	100	110	111
0.	-0.000	-0.000	-0.000
0.05	-0.028	-0.056	-0.084
0.10	-0.111	-0.226	-0.345
0.15	-0.250	-0.518	-0.802
0.20	-0.444	-0.940	-1.444
0.25	-0.693	-1.498	-2.105
0.30	-0.996	-2.167	-2.648
0.35	-1.354	-2.871	-3.060
0.40	-1.767	-3.533	-3.349
0.45	-2.234	-4.123	-3.521
0.50	-2.758	-4.639	-3.578
0.55	-3.335	-5.092	-3.521
0.60	-3.947	-5.488	-3.349
0.65	-4.551	-5.828	-3.060
0.70	-5.100	-6.113	-2.648
0.75	-5.570	-6.341	-2.105
0.80	-5.955	-6.507	-1.444
0.85	-6.254	-6.611	-0.802
0.90	-6.467	-6.655	-0.345
0.95	-6.595	-6.651	-0.084
1.00	-6.637	-6.637	-0.000

KF= 2.500 WMF= -3.912 LAMDA= 3.00 FCC

x	100	110	111
0.	-0.000	-0.000	-0.000
0.05	-0.055	-0.109	-0.162
0.10	-0.217	-0.420	-0.590
0.15	-0.482	-0.865	-1.099
0.20	-0.839	-1.340	-1.577
0.25	-1.273	-1.786	-2.008
0.30	-1.769	-2.199	-2.383
0.35	-2.312	-2.592	-2.696
0.40	-2.881	-2.975	-2.932
0.45	-3.441	-3.345	-3.080
0.50	-3.954	-3.692	-3.131
0.55	-4.402	-4.001	-3.080
0.60	-4.785	-4.270	-2.932
0.65	-5.107	-4.505	-2.696
0.70	-5.376	-4.723	-2.383
0.75	-5.595	-4.944	-2.008
0.80	-5.769	-5.191	-1.577
0.85	-5.901	-5.481	-1.099
0.90	-5.994	-5.780	-0.590
0.95	-6.049	-5.994	-0.162
1.00	-6.067	-6.067	-0.000

KF= 2.800 WMF= 0.743 LAMDA= 3.00 FCC

x	100	110	111
0.	0.000	0.000	0.000
0.05	0.029	0.053	0.074
0.10	0.102	0.149	0.188
0.15	0.183	0.205	0.245
0.20	0.241	0.208	0.223
0.25	0.273	0.197	0.139
0.30	0.300	0.224	0.033
0.35	0.336	0.318	-0.063
0.40	0.382	0.478	-0.132
0.45	0.436	0.681	-0.173
0.50	0.494	0.900	-0.186
0.55	0.553	1.103	-0.173
0.60	0.612	1.262	-0.132
0.65	0.667	1.346	-0.063
0.70	0.719	1.330	0.033
0.75	0.764	1.219	0.139
0.80	0.803	1.085	0.223
0.85	0.834	0.983	0.245
0.90	0.857	0.920	0.188
0.95	0.871	0.886	0.074
1.00	0.876	0.876	0.000

282

Table II (continued)

KF= 3.100   WMF= 4.684   LAMDA= 3.00   FCC

x	100	110	111
0.	0.000	0.000	0.000
0.05	0.031	0.061	0.091
0.10	0.138	0.269	0.391
0.15	0.342	0.653	0.903
0.20	0.654	1.199	1.514
0.25	1.079	1.816	2.151
0.30	1.612	2.406	2.803
0.35	2.236	2.944	3.412
0.40	2.915	3.434	3.891
0.45	3.599	3.885	4.187
0.50	4.247	4.299	4.286
0.55	4.837	4.673	4.187
0.60	5.361	5.010	3.891
0.65	5.820	5.357	3.412
0.70	6.213	5.752	2.803
0.75	6.543	6.166	2.151
0.80	6.811	6.548	1.514
0.85	7.018	6.863	0.903
0.90	7.166	7.095	0.391
0.95	7.237	7.237	0.091
1.00	7.284	7.284	0.000

KF= 3.700   WMF= 2.008   LAMDA= 3.00   FCC

x	100	110	111
0.	0.000	0.000	0.000
0.05	0.011	0.023	0.034
0.10	0.046	0.091	0.137
0.15	0.104	0.208	0.312
0.20	0.188	0.375	0.563
0.25	0.300	0.594	0.895
0.30	0.439	0.861	1.292
0.35	0.598	1.168	1.683
0.40	0.753	1.516	1.971
0.45	0.883	1.910	2.128
0.50	0.979	2.335	2.176
0.55	1.046	2.720	2.128
0.60	1.090	2.977	1.971
0.65	1.124	3.088	1.683
0.70	1.163	3.068	1.292
0.75	1.225	2.934	0.895
0.80	1.331	2.703	0.563
0.85	1.482	2.406	0.312
0.90	1.653	2.113	0.137
0.95	1.787	1.908	0.034
1.00	1.837	1.837	0.000

KF= 4.300   WMF= -4.674   LAMDA= 3.00   FCC

x	100	110	111
0.	-0.000	-0.000	-0.000
0.05	-0.057	-0.112	-0.165
0.10	-0.220	-0.406	-0.561
0.15	-0.464	-0.799	-1.016
0.20	-0.756	-1.241	-1.469
0.25	-1.069	-1.717	-1.939
0.30	-1.393	-2.227	-2.461
0.35	-1.725	-2.785	-3.073
0.40	-2.072	-3.404	-3.760
0.45	-2.438	-4.095	-4.336
0.50	-2.834	-4.826	-4.552
0.55	-3.266	-5.493	-4.336
0.60	-3.732	-5.989	-3.760
0.65	-4.214	-6.281	-3.073
0.70	-4.664	-6.400	-2.461
0.75	-5.038	-6.379	-1.939
0.80	-5.329	-6.242	-1.469
0.85	-5.548	-6.064	-1.016
0.90	-5.702	-5.927	-0.561
0.95	-5.793	-5.848	-0.165
1.00	-5.823	-5.823	-0.000

KF= 3.400   WMF= 5.342   LAMDA= 3.00   FCC

x	100	110	111
0.	0.000	0.000	0.000
0.05	0.049	0.099	0.148
0.10	0.196	0.392	0.590
0.15	0.431	0.865	1.300
0.20	0.734	1.462	2.180
0.25	1.077	2.124	3.096
0.30	1.451	2.824	3.904
0.35	1.859	3.543	4.516
0.40	2.314	4.198	4.945
0.45	2.814	4.702	5.211
0.50	3.377	5.072	5.306
0.55	4.004	5.399	5.211
0.60	4.688	5.729	4.945
0.65	5.398	6.068	4.516
0.70	6.082	6.415	3.904
0.75	6.693	6.764	3.096
0.80	7.207	7.117	2.180
0.85	7.613	7.470	1.300
0.90	7.907	7.800	0.590
0.95	8.086	8.050	0.148
1.00	8.146	8.146	0.000

KF= 4.000   WMF= -2.325   LAMDA= 3.00   FCC

x	100	110	111
0.	-0.000	-0.000	-0.000
0.05	-0.022	-0.045	-0.067
0.10	-0.089	-0.180	-0.273
0.15	-0.201	-0.410	-0.626
0.20	-0.359	-0.724	-1.104
0.25	-0.564	-1.066	-1.577
0.30	-0.813	-1.377	-1.900
0.35	-1.101	-1.635	-1.976
0.40	-1.413	-1.831	-1.900
0.45	-1.726	-1.958	-1.792
0.50	-2.017	-2.032	-2.030
0.55	-2.270	-2.116	-1.792
0.60	-2.529	-2.270	-1.900
0.65	-2.787	-2.513	-1.976
0.70	-3.067	-2.853	-1.900
0.75	-3.373	-3.262	-1.577
0.80	-3.704	-3.678	-1.104
0.85	-4.048	-4.063	-0.626
0.90	-4.362	-4.380	-0.273
0.95	-4.584	-4.591	-0.067
1.00	-4.664	-4.664	-0.000

KF= 4.600   WMF= -3.535   LAMDA= 3.00   FCC

x	100	110	111
0.	-0.000	-0.000	-0.000
0.05	0.019	0.035	0.050
0.10	0.067	0.103	0.106
0.15	0.117	0.108	0.106
0.20	0.129	-0.028	-0.454
0.25	0.063	-0.361	-1.167
0.30	-0.106	-0.909	-2.045
0.35	-0.386	-1.619	-2.855
0.40	-0.770	-2.370	-3.443
0.45	-1.224	-3.077	-3.790
0.50	-1.685	-3.701	-3.905
0.55	-2.105	-4.200	-3.790
0.60	-2.462	-4.546	-3.443
0.65	-2.754	-4.766	-2.855
0.70	-2.982	-4.645	-2.045
0.75	-3.151	-4.387	-1.167
0.80	-3.264	-4.050	-0.454
0.85	-3.326	-3.713	-0.030
0.90	-3.345	-3.443	0.106
0.95	-3.338	-3.338	0.050
1.00	-3.332	-3.332	-0.000

Table II (continued)

KF= 4.900   WMF= -2.546   LAMDA= 3.00   FCC

x	100	110	111
0.	-0.000	-0.000	-0.000
0.05	-0.045	-0.089	-0.133
0.10	-0.178	-0.353	-0.525
0.15	-0.395	-0.768	-1.097
0.20	-0.679	-1.247	-1.671
0.25	-0.982	-1.694	-2.173
0.30	-1.242	-2.079	-2.613
0.35	-1.428	-2.367	-2.975
0.40	-1.547	-2.549	-3.239
0.45	-1.636	-2.658	-3.399
0.50	-1.732	-2.730	-3.452
0.55	-1.854	-2.782	-3.399
0.60	-2.003	-2.850	-3.239
0.65	-2.175	-2.878	-2.975
0.70	-2.360	-2.910	-2.613
0.75	-2.550	-2.956	-2.173
0.80	-2.738	-3.026	-1.671
0.85	-2.915	-3.117	-1.097
0.90	-3.067	-3.187	-0.525
0.95	-3.169	-3.204	-0.133
1.00	-3.204	-3.204	-0.000

KF= 5.500   WMF= 6.964   LAMDA= 3.00   FCC

x	100	110	111
0.	0.000	0.000	0.000
0.05	0.094	0.185	0.275
0.10	0.369	0.710	1.044
0.15	0.805	1.506	2.166
0.20	1.366	2.452	3.411
0.25	1.991	3.425	4.603
0.30	2.621	4.368	5.653
0.35	3.231	5.245	6.543
0.40	3.814	6.030	7.281
0.45	4.370	6.711	7.839
0.50	4.904	7.264	8.067
0.55	5.425	7.652	7.839
0.60	5.942	7.876	7.281
0.65	6.452	7.992	6.543
0.70	6.952	8.091	5.653
0.75	7.435	8.233	4.603
0.80	7.896	8.434	3.411
0.85	8.319	8.650	2.166
0.90	8.670	8.830	1.044
0.95	8.903	8.944	0.275
1.00	8.983	8.983	0.000

KF= 6.100   WMF= -0.791   LAMDA= 3.00   FCC

x	100	110	111
0.	-0.000	-0.000	-0.000
0.05	-0.017	-0.034	-0.050
0.10	-0.063	-0.127	-0.191
0.15	-0.127	-0.257	-0.390
0.20	-0.189	-0.392	-0.607
0.25	-0.240	-0.515	-0.840
0.30	-0.276	-0.626	-1.126
0.35	-0.298	-0.721	-1.383
0.40	-0.305	-0.780	-1.564
0.45	-0.296	-0.789	-1.749
0.50	-0.272	-0.777	-1.847
0.55	-0.237	-0.788	-1.749
0.60	-0.207	-0.813	-1.564
0.65	-0.220	-0.811	-1.383
0.70	-0.305	-0.754	-1.126
0.75	-0.448	-0.661	-0.840
0.80	-0.613	-0.616	-0.607
0.85	-0.766	-0.683	-0.390
0.90	-0.886	-0.822	-0.191
0.95	-0.960	-0.942	-0.050
1.00	-0.986	-0.986	-0.000

KF= 5.200   WMF= 2.045   LAMDA= 3.00   FCC

x	100	110	111
0.	0.000	0.000	0.000
0.05	-0.011	-0.022	-0.032
0.10	-0.039	-0.069	-0.087
0.15	-0.072	-0.101	-0.064
0.20	-0.103	-0.058	0.097
0.25	-0.123	0.100	0.412
0.30	-0.122	0.383	0.878
0.35	-0.088	0.772	1.425
0.40	-0.012	1.220	1.878
0.45	0.114	1.688	2.148
0.50	0.291	2.168	2.237
0.55	0.517	2.644	2.148
0.60	0.781	3.064	1.878
0.65	1.056	3.347	1.425
0.70	1.309	3.430	0.878
0.75	1.522	3.299	0.412
0.80	1.693	3.004	0.097
0.85	1.824	2.647	-0.064
0.90	1.917	2.309	-0.087
0.95	1.973	2.073	-0.032
1.00	1.991	1.991	0.000

KF= 5.800   WMF= 4.840   LAMDA= 3.00   FCC

x	100	110	111
0.	0.000	0.000	0.000
0.05	0.040	0.079	0.119
0.10	0.158	0.319	0.480
0.15	0.358	0.724	1.074
0.20	0.641	1.284	1.848
0.25	1.011	1.957	2.750
0.30	1.473	2.685	3.646
0.35	2.033	3.378	4.400
0.40	2.675	3.952	4.920
0.45	3.343	4.390	5.161
0.50	3.968	4.717	5.223
0.55	4.514	4.981	5.161
0.60	4.975	5.205	4.920
0.65	5.354	5.397	4.400
0.70	5.655	5.552	3.646
0.75	5.881	5.673	2.750
0.80	6.035	5.773	1.848
0.85	6.120	5.870	1.074
0.90	6.148	5.982	0.480
0.95	6.149	6.094	0.119
1.00	6.146	6.146	0.000

KF= 6.400   WMF= -5.338   LAMDA= 3.00   FCC

x	100	110	111
0.	-0.000	-0.000	-0.000
0.05	-0.032	-0.065	-0.098
0.10	-0.138	-0.281	-0.428
0.15	-0.336	-0.692	-1.064
0.20	-0.639	-1.322	-1.999
0.25	-1.054	-2.127	-3.080
0.30	-1.583	-3.015	-4.156
0.35	-2.223	-3.876	-5.050
0.40	-2.956	-4.611	-5.647
0.45	-3.734	-5.170	-5.962
0.50	-4.481	-5.531	-6.048
0.55	-5.130	-5.712	-5.962
0.60	-5.641	-5.774	-5.647
0.65	-6.003	-5.824	-5.050
0.70	-6.214	-5.944	-4.156
0.75	-6.280	-6.048	-3.080
0.80	-6.218	-6.146	-1.999
0.85	-6.075	-6.102	-1.064
0.90	-5.918	-5.969	-0.428
0.95	-5.800	-5.821	-0.098
1.00	-5.756	-5.756	-0.000

TABLE III. Body-Centered Cubic Lattice

285

LAMDA = 3.00   BCC

KF= 0.100 WMF= 0.584 x	100	110	111	KF= 0.700 WMF= 2.416 x	100	110	111
0.	0.000	0.000	0.000	0.	0.000	0.000	0.000
0.05	0.081	0.146	0.199	0.05	0.021	0.043	0.064
0.10	0.242	0.356	0.418	0.10	0.086	0.173	0.261
0.15	0.374	0.472	0.514	0.15	0.195	0.395	0.602
0.20	0.457	0.529	0.557	0.20	0.351	0.720	1.105
0.25	0.507	0.559	0.578	0.25	0.558	1.154	1.747
0.30	0.538	0.576	0.589	0.30	0.819	1.677	2.333
0.35	0.558	0.586	0.595	0.35	1.137	2.179	2.696
0.40	0.571	0.592	0.598	0.40	1.505	2.529	2.881
0.45	0.581	0.595	0.599	0.45	1.894	2.719	2.961
0.50	0.587	0.596	0.599	0.50	2.247	2.778	2.980
0.55	0.592	0.595	0.599	0.55	2.526	2.719	2.970
0.60	0.595	0.592	0.599	0.60	2.732	2.529	2.953
0.65	0.598	0.586	0.599	0.65	2.881	2.179	2.947
0.70	0.599	0.576	0.599	0.70	2.987	1.677	2.961
0.75	0.601	0.559	0.599	0.75	3.062	1.154	2.994
0.80	0.602	0.529	0.600	0.80	3.114	0.720	3.042
0.85	0.602	0.472	0.601	0.85	3.149	0.395	3.096
0.90	0.603	0.356	0.602	0.90	3.172	0.173	3.144
0.95	0.603	0.146	0.603	0.95	3.184	0.043	3.176
1.00	0.603	0.000	0.603	1.00	3.188	0.000	3.188

Same instructions as for Table I, except

$$k_F = 2\pi \left(\frac{3n}{32\pi}\right)^{\frac{1}{3}}$$

The points (1, 0, 0) and (1, 1, 1) are equivalent points on the zone boundary, and (½, ½, 0) is also on the zone boundary. Values along (1, 1, 0) axis for $x > \frac{1}{2}$ are redundant.

LAMDA = 3.00   BCC

KF= 0.400 WMF= 2.572 x	100	110	111	KF= 1.000 WMF= 1.237 x	100	110	111
0.	0.000	0.000	0.000	0.	0.000	0.000	0.000
0.05	0.058	0.116	0.174	0.05	0.007	0.014	0.021
0.10	0.232	0.463	0.691	0.10	0.029	0.057	0.086
0.15	0.521	1.017	1.443	0.15	0.065	0.131	0.198
0.20	0.911	1.637	2.070	0.20	0.118	0.236	0.361
0.25	1.357	2.109	2.428	0.25	0.187	0.377	0.587
0.30	1.771	2.400	2.619	0.30	0.276	0.555	0.891
0.35	2.092	2.573	2.721	0.35	0.386	0.773	1.278
0.40	2.321	2.674	2.772	0.40	0.521	1.026	1.646
0.45	2.481	2.727	2.795	0.45	0.685	1.269	1.845
0.50	2.594	2.743	2.800	0.50	0.882	1.378	1.894
0.55	2.674	2.727	2.797	0.55	1.116	1.269	1.868
0.60	2.732	2.674	2.793	0.60	1.383	1.026	1.825
0.65	2.774	2.573	2.791	0.65	1.658	0.773	1.808
0.70	2.804	2.400	2.795	0.70	1.900	0.555	1.840
0.75	2.825	2.109	2.805	0.75	2.087	0.377	1.923
0.80	2.840	1.637	2.819	0.80	2.219	0.236	2.043
0.85	2.850	1.017	2.835	0.85	2.308	0.131	2.176
0.90	2.857	0.463	2.849	0.90	2.364	0.057	2.295
0.95	2.860	0.116	2.858	0.95	2.395	0.014	2.376
1.00	2.862	0.000	2.862	1.00	2.405	0.000	2.405

Table III (continued)

KF= 1.300 WMF= -0.343 LAMDA= 3.00 BCC

x	100	110	111
0.	0.000	-0.000	0.000
0.05	-0.003	-0.005	-0.007
0.10	-0.010	-0.020	-0.030
0.15	-0.021	-0.045	-0.071
0.20	-0.037	-0.084	-0.132
0.25	-0.056	-0.141	-0.218
0.30	-0.077	-0.224	-0.324
0.35	-0.100	-0.346	-0.439
0.40	-0.121	-0.513	-0.538
0.45	-0.140	-0.678	-0.579
0.50	-0.151	-0.746	-0.572
0.55	-0.152	-0.678	-0.598
0.60	-0.138	-0.513	-0.644
0.65	-0.101	-0.346	-0.654
0.70	-0.036	-0.224	-0.593
0.75	0.061	-0.141	-0.450
0.80	0.188	-0.084	-0.232
0.85	0.324	-0.045	0.029
0.90	0.435	-0.020	0.280
0.95	0.502	-0.005	0.459
1.00	0.524	-0.000	0.524

KF= 1.900 WMF= -2.019 LAMDA= 3.00 BCC

x	100	110	111
0.	-0.000	-0.000	-0.000
0.05	-0.031	-0.063	-0.095
0.10	-0.125	-0.251	-0.378
0.15	-0.281	-0.548	-0.818
0.20	-0.493	-0.889	-1.285
0.25	-0.755	-1.208	-1.656
0.30	-1.357	-1.480	-1.911
0.35	-1.655	-1.699	-2.073
0.40	-1.932	-1.857	-2.165
0.45	-2.183	-1.953	-2.210
0.50	-2.411	-1.985	-2.222
0.55	-2.622	-1.953	-2.214
0.60	-2.823	-1.857	-2.193
0.65	-3.021	-1.699	-2.169
0.70	-3.222	-1.480	-2.174
0.75	-3.420	-1.208	-2.321
0.80	-3.594	-0.889	-2.676
0.85	-3.725	-0.548	-3.131
0.90	-3.803	-0.251	-3.515
0.95	-3.829	-0.063	-3.751
1.00	-3.829	-0.000	-3.829

KF= 2.500 WMF= 2.367 LAMDA= 3.00 BCC

x	100	110	111
0.	0.000	0.000	0.000
0.05	0.041	0.082	0.123
0.10	0.164	0.324	0.480
0.15	0.364	0.697	0.979
0.20	0.633	1.136	1.454
0.25	0.941	1.577	1.850
0.30	1.248	1.961	2.195
0.35	1.516	2.252	2.514
0.40	1.736	2.446	2.813
0.45	1.918	2.553	3.052
0.50	2.086	2.587	3.148
0.55	2.253	2.553	3.061
0.60	2.426	2.446	2.908
0.65	2.603	2.252	2.809
0.70	2.783	1.961	2.814
0.75	2.960	1.577	2.781
0.80	3.123	1.136	2.901
0.85	3.262	0.697	3.040
0.90	3.368	0.324	3.220
0.95	3.434	0.082	3.390
1.00	3.456	0.000	3.456

KF= 1.600 WMF= -1.729 LAMDA= 3.00 BCC

x	100	110	111
0.	-0.000	-0.000	-0.000
0.05	-0.013	-0.027	-0.040
0.10	-0.053	-0.107	-0.163
0.15	-0.119	-0.247	-0.380
0.20	-0.211	-0.453	-0.704
0.25	-0.330	-0.732	-1.142
0.30	-0.474	-1.060	-1.667
0.35	-0.643	-1.361	-2.181
0.40	-0.834	-1.582	-2.579
0.45	-1.044	-1.714	-2.819
0.50	-1.268	-1.758	-2.898
0.55	-1.500	-1.714	-2.823
0.60	-1.732	-1.582	-2.635
0.65	-1.954	-1.361	-2.465
0.70	-2.159	-1.060	-2.377
0.75	-2.339	-0.732	-2.358
0.80	-2.489	-0.453	-2.393
0.85	-2.608	-0.247	-2.474
0.90	-2.697	-0.107	-2.592
0.95	-2.755	-0.027	-2.716
1.00	-2.776	-0.000	-2.776

KF= 2.200 WMF= 0.262 LAMDA= 3.00 BCC

x	100	110	111
0.	-0.000	-0.000	-0.000
0.05	-0.003	-0.005	-0.004
0.10	-0.008	-0.003	0.024
0.15	-0.008	0.017	0.120
0.20	0.001	0.053	0.283
0.25	0.021	0.099	0.495
0.30	0.047	0.149	0.729
0.35	0.077	0.196	0.956
0.40	0.104	0.234	1.148
0.45	0.121	0.259	1.280
0.50	0.120	0.268	1.329
0.55	0.096	0.259	1.272
0.60	0.048	0.234	1.082
0.65	-0.008	0.196	0.747
0.70	-0.057	0.149	0.338
0.75	-0.092	0.099	0.029
0.80	-0.114	0.053	-0.102
0.85	-0.128	0.017	-0.124
0.90	-0.136	-0.003	-0.131
0.95	-0.140	-0.005	-0.138
1.00	-0.141	-0.000	-0.141

KF= 2.800 WMF= 1.223 LAMDA= 3.00 BCC

x	100	110	111
0.	0.000	0.000	0.000
0.05	0.006	0.011	0.017
0.10	0.022	0.045	0.071
0.15	0.049	0.108	0.178
0.20	0.092	0.212	0.358
0.25	0.165	0.373	0.603
0.30	0.288	0.588	0.790
0.35	0.474	0.834	0.798
0.40	0.725	1.090	0.629
0.45	1.029	1.299	0.396
0.50	1.355	1.380	0.294
0.55	1.660	1.299	0.403
0.60	1.914	1.090	0.719
0.65	2.106	0.834	1.168
0.70	2.239	0.588	1.614
0.75	2.317	0.373	1.962
0.80	2.348	0.212	2.189
0.85	2.342	0.108	2.305
0.90	2.314	0.045	2.333
0.95	2.286	0.011	2.303
1.00	2.274	0.000	2.274

Table III (continued)

KF = 3.100   WMF = -0.442   LAMDA = 3.00   BCC

x	100	110	111
0.	0.000	0.000	0.000
0.05	-0.009	-0.018	-0.028
0.10	-0.029	-0.064	-0.103
0.15	-0.051	-0.123	-0.214
0.20	-0.070	-0.193	-0.367
0.25	-0.085	-0.279	-0.574
0.30	-0.095	-0.384	-0.807
0.35	-0.100	-0.514	-0.931
0.40	-0.102	-0.657	-0.901
0.45	-0.100	-0.778	-0.853
0.50	-0.091	-0.826	-0.839
0.55	-0.072	-0.778	-0.845
0.60	-0.048	-0.657	-0.846
0.65	-0.030	-0.514	-0.813
0.70	0.170	-0.384	-0.698
0.75	0.311	-0.279	-0.448
0.80	0.443	-0.193	-0.076
0.85	0.546	-0.123	0.277
0.90	0.619	-0.064	0.506
0.95	0.661	-0.018	0.633
1.00	0.675	0.000	0.675

KF = 3.700   WMF = -1.585   LAMDA = 3.00   BCC

x	100	110	111
0.	-0.000	-0.000	-0.000
0.05	-0.049	-0.095	-0.139
0.10	-0.186	-0.333	-0.449
0.15	-0.382	-0.603	-0.752
0.20	-0.602	-0.830	-0.981
0.25	-0.820	-0.998	-1.126
0.30	-1.025	-1.111	-1.209
0.35	-1.216	-1.184	-1.275
0.40	-1.404	-1.228	-1.348
0.45	-1.604	-1.251	-1.400
0.50	-1.822	-1.258	-1.417
0.55	-2.062	-1.251	-1.401
0.60	-2.323	-1.228	-1.436
0.65	-2.608	-1.184	-1.669
0.70	-2.915	-1.111	-1.998
0.75	-3.240	-0.998	-2.049
0.80	-3.573	-0.830	-2.540
0.85	-3.901	-0.603	-3.116
0.90	-4.180	-0.333	-3.733
0.95	-4.367	-0.095	-4.240
1.00	-4.432	-0.000	-4.432

KF = 4.300   WMF = 1.140   LAMDA = 3.00   BCC

x	100	110	111
0.	0.000	0.000	0.000
0.05	-0.001	-0.001	0.000
0.10	0.000	0.019	0.056
0.15	0.017	0.108	0.261
0.20	0.067	0.288	0.595
0.25	0.163	0.529	0.927
0.30	0.306	0.742	1.182
0.35	0.480	0.877	1.318
0.40	0.658	0.946	1.328
0.45	0.826	0.978	1.283
0.50	1.002	0.987	1.262
0.55	1.213	0.978	1.278
0.60	1.462	0.946	1.296
0.65	1.734	0.877	1.270
0.70	2.010	0.742	1.285
0.75	2.268	0.529	1.458
0.80	2.492	0.288	1.790
0.85	2.668	0.108	2.215
0.90	2.793	0.019	2.590
0.95	2.868	-0.001	2.818
1.00	2.893	0.000	2.893

KF = 3.400   WMF = -1.601   LAMDA = 3.00   BCC

x	100	110	111
0.	-0.000	-0.000	-0.000
0.05	-0.011	-0.022	-0.034
0.10	-0.045	-0.093	-0.143
0.15	-0.108	-0.228	-0.353
0.20	-0.212	-0.458	-0.660
0.25	-0.371	-0.781	-0.970
0.30	-0.588	-1.127	-1.230
0.35	-0.850	-1.426	-1.433
0.40	-1.128	-1.657	-1.572
0.45	-1.394	-1.813	-1.635
0.50	-1.626	-1.872	-1.638
0.55	-1.814	-1.813	-1.668
0.60	-1.956	-1.657	-1.757
0.65	-2.049	-1.426	-1.877
0.70	-2.093	-1.127	-2.011
0.75	-2.087	-0.781	-2.147
0.80	-2.032	-0.458	-2.226
0.85	-1.935	-0.228	-2.186
0.90	-1.815	-0.093	-2.019
0.95	-1.710	-0.022	-1.786
1.00	-1.668	-0.000	-1.668

KF = 4.000   WMF = 0.994   LAMDA = 3.00   BCC

x	100	110	111
0.	0.000	0.000	0.000
0.05	0.048	0.093	0.136
0.10	0.181	0.324	0.438
0.15	0.370	0.580	0.720
0.20	0.575	0.786	0.901
0.25	0.763	0.940	1.015
0.30	0.912	1.064	1.129
0.35	1.009	1.161	1.269
0.40	1.052	1.230	1.428
0.45	1.044	1.287	1.580
0.50	0.991	1.272	1.650
0.55	0.893	1.287	1.582
0.60	0.742	1.230	1.440
0.65	0.541	1.161	1.291
0.70	0.317	1.064	1.136
0.75	0.109	0.940	0.902
0.80	-0.063	0.786	0.523
0.85	-0.195	0.580	0.139
0.90	-0.287	0.324	-0.141
0.95	-0.341	0.093	-0.305
1.00	-0.359	0.000	-0.359

KF = 4.600   WMF = 0.580   LAMDA = 3.00   BCC

x	100	110	111
0.	0.000	0.000	0.000
0.05	0.009	0.017	0.024
0.10	0.031	0.049	0.052
0.15	0.054	0.055	0.001
0.20	0.061	0.024	-0.114
0.25	0.052	-0.009	-0.182
0.30	0.053	-0.008	-0.140
0.35	0.096	0.104	-0.047
0.40	0.199	0.253	0.059
0.45	0.369	0.372	0.164
0.50	0.606	0.414	0.210
0.55	0.899	0.372	0.195
0.60	1.227	0.253	0.253
0.65	1.560	0.104	0.453
0.70	1.884	-0.008	0.797
0.75	2.195	-0.009	1.256
0.80	2.491	0.024	1.747
0.85	2.768	0.055	2.221
0.90	3.005	0.049	2.673
0.95	3.171	0.017	3.061
1.00	3.231	0.000	3.231

Table III (continued)

KF= 4.900   WMF= -0.063   LAMDA= 3.00   BCC

x	100	110	111
0.	0.000	0.000	0.000
0.05	-0.019	-0.038	-0.056
0.10	-0.059	-0.111	-0.156
0.15	-0.088	-0.165	-0.223
0.20	-0.090	-0.182	-0.252
0.25	-0.059	-0.181	-0.284
0.30	0.005	-0.184	-0.372
0.35	0.099	-0.189	-0.533
0.40	0.211	-0.198	-0.742
0.45	0.321	-0.225	-0.908
0.50	0.412	-0.247	-0.969
0.55	0.474	-0.225	-0.902
0.60	0.508	-0.198	-0.697
0.65	0.516	-0.189	-0.392
0.70	0.502	-0.184	-0.085
0.75	0.469	-0.181	0.159
0.80	0.414	-0.182	0.323
0.85	0.334	-0.165	0.396
0.90	0.248	-0.111	0.355
0.95	0.183	-0.038	0.227
1.00	0.160	0.000	0.160

KF= 5.500   WMF= -1.488   LAMDA= 3.00   BCC

x	100	110	111
0.	-0.000	-0.000	-0.000
0.05	-0.019	-0.039	-0.060
0.10	-0.078	-0.171	-0.266
0.15	-0.185	-0.409	-0.608
0.20	-0.344	-0.713	-0.926
0.25	-0.554	-0.980	-1.050
0.30	-0.799	-1.141	-0.998
0.35	-1.058	-1.206	-0.860
0.40	-1.324	-1.214	-0.673
0.45	-1.603	-1.199	-0.478
0.50	-1.891	-1.188	-0.386
0.55	-2.174	-1.199	-0.481
0.60	-2.440	-1.214	-0.708
0.65	-2.681	-1.206	-1.008
0.70	-2.896	-1.141	-1.448
0.75	-3.083	-0.980	-1.990
0.80	-3.237	-0.713	-2.526
0.85	-3.344	-0.409	-2.985
0.90	-3.401	-0.171	-3.291
0.95	-3.424	-0.039	-3.409
1.00	-3.429	-0.000	-3.429

KF= 6.100   WMF= 1.638   LAMDA= 3.00   BCC

x	100	110	111
0.	0.000	0.000	0.000
0.05	0.050	0.099	0.146
0.10	0.197	0.374	0.528
0.15	0.432	0.744	0.939
0.20	0.728	1.086	1.207
0.25	1.039	1.336	1.288
0.30	1.322	1.490	1.218
0.35	1.552	1.583	1.071
0.40	1.730	1.637	0.884
0.45	1.876	1.652	0.685
0.50	2.012	1.651	0.582
0.55	2.148	1.652	0.692
0.60	2.291	1.637	0.934
0.65	2.448	1.583	1.229
0.70	2.624	1.490	1.609
0.75	2.819	1.336	2.029
0.80	3.010	1.086	2.413
0.85	3.170	0.744	2.775
0.90	3.286	0.374	3.101
0.95	3.356	0.099	3.309
1.00	3.379	0.000	3.379

KF= 5.200   WMF= -0.237   LAMDA= 3.00   BCC

x	100	110	111
0.	-0.000	-0.000	-0.000
0.05	0.017	0.035	0.052
0.10	0.067	0.132	0.198
0.15	0.136	0.259	0.381
0.20	0.194	0.362	0.481
0.25	0.213	0.393	0.421
0.30	0.183	0.328	0.256
0.35	0.104	0.191	0.131
0.40	-0.017	0.042	0.045
0.45	-0.179	-0.072	-0.022
0.50	-0.374	-0.115	-0.046
0.55	-0.590	-0.072	-0.052
0.60	-0.803	0.042	-0.137
0.65	-0.994	0.191	-0.323
0.70	-1.157	0.328	-0.581
0.75	-1.294	0.393	-0.844
0.80	-1.404	0.362	-1.076
0.85	-1.486	0.259	-1.294
0.90	-1.540	0.132	-1.459
0.95	-1.569	0.035	-1.551
1.00	-1.578	-0.000	-1.578

KF= 5.800   WMF= -0.720   LAMDA= 3.00   BCC

x	100	110	111
0.	-0.000	-0.000	-0.000
0.05	-0.045	-0.084	-0.119
0.10	-0.160	-0.257	-0.319
0.15	-0.302	-0.413	-0.454
0.20	-0.441	-0.521	-0.527
0.25	-0.561	-0.602	-0.554
0.30	-0.655	-0.677	-0.539
0.35	-0.721	-0.747	-0.486
0.40	-0.760	-0.801	-0.411
0.45	-0.781	-0.832	-0.356
0.50	-0.799	-0.844	-0.337
0.55	-0.831	-0.832	-0.359
0.60	-0.894	-0.801	-0.439
0.65	-0.994	-0.747	-0.562
0.70	-1.122	-0.677	-0.697
0.75	-1.271	-0.602	-0.841
0.80	-1.434	-0.521	-1.027
0.85	-1.602	-0.413	-1.251
0.90	-1.754	-0.257	-1.531
0.95	-1.862	-0.084	-1.789
1.00	-1.901	-0.000	-1.901

KF= 6.400   WMF= 0.615   LAMDA= 3.00   BCC

x	100	110	111
0.	0.000	0.000	0.000
0.05	-0.009	-0.017	-0.026
0.10	-0.037	-0.070	-0.098
0.15	-0.086	-0.137	-0.156
0.20	-0.137	-0.151	-0.092
0.25	-0.156	-0.072	-0.039
0.30	-0.109	0.065	0.099
0.35	-0.016	0.207	0.061
0.40	0.214	0.325	-0.021
0.45	0.462	0.399	-0.076
0.50	0.742	0.423	-0.095
0.55	1.044	0.399	-0.058
0.60	1.362	0.325	0.085
0.65	1.681	0.207	0.336
0.70	1.991	0.065	0.670
0.75	2.287	-0.072	1.091
0.80	2.565	-0.151	1.605
0.85	2.822	-0.137	2.165
0.90	3.047	-0.070	2.684
0.95	3.211	-0.017	3.096
1.00	3.273	-0.000	3.273

BIBLIOGRAPHY

Introduction

Of several books or reviews that fell into my hands at an early stage in the manuscript, the following were particularly rewarding: P. W. Anderson, *"Theory of Magnetism"*, lecture notes, University of Tokyo, 1953–1954. The Proc. 1952 Maryland Magnetism Conference, *Rev. Mod. Phys.*, January, 1953, entire issue. A. Herpin, "Magnétisme," in De Witt et al. (eds.), *Physique des Basses Températures* (*Low Temperature Physics*), Gordon & Breach, New York, 1962, pp. 309–409; and C. Kittel, "Magnons," in *ibid.*, pp. 443–478. It is a pleasure to acknowledge my debt to the authors of these works.

This Bibliography is intended mainly to carry on beyond where the text leaves off. Therefore many titles are quoted on aspects not previously covered; and conversely, subjects adequately discussed in the text will in general not be included in this listing and should be sought in the Index. It is desirable for the reader to scan the entire list, for some titles included under one chapter heading may be useful for another chapter as well.

Chapter 1. History of the Theory of Magnetism

J. B. Porta, *Natural Magick*, Naples, 1589, 1st English ed., 1658, with the second edition of 1669 being "even more scarce than the first, whose soiled and damaged examples testify to the fact that it was used and worn out by the practical man and in the laboratory." From reprint of 1st ed., Basic Books, Inc., New York, 1957, preface. A pleasureful treatise on "the causes of wonderful things" such as "counterfeiting gold," the "wonders of the loadstone," "beautifying women," "cookery," etc.

W. Gilbert, *On the Magnet*, in Latin (*De Magnete*), London, 1600, trans. (for tercentenary), Gilbert Club, London (of which Lord Kelvin was president). This 1900 edition was a private one limited to 250 copies, but a faithful, indeed luxurious, reproduction was made available by Basic Books, Inc., New York, 1958. The reader should shun an inferior translation by P. F. Mottelay, 1893, a bibliographer whose main contribution was the thorough but uncritical *Bibliographical History of Electricity and Magnetism*, London, 1922, covering the period up to and including Faraday.

E. Whittaker, *A History of the Theories of Aether and Electricity*, Harper & Row, New York, 1960, vols. I, II. A most complete scientific and bibliographical history of electricity and magnetism from earliest times up to and including the advent of quantum mechanics. Free use of equations is delightful for the scientific reader, but makes this work inaccessible to the layman, who will have to turn to sections of F. Cajori, *A History of Physics*, Dover, New York, 1962, or the very interesting and diversified *Histoire de la Science*, Maurice Daumas (ed.): *Encyclopédie de la Pléiade*, Paris, 1957 (in French), or to similar historical or philosophical accounts.

J. C. Maxwell, *A Treatise on Electricity and Magnetism*, 1874. Extremely famous and complete account of the theory before the discovery of the electron. Available as a reprint,

Dover, New York, 1954, as are Maxwell's collected works, any of which should be read by those who agree with his remark that it "is of great advantage to the student of any subject to read in the original ... for science is always most completely assimilated when it is found in its nascent state. Every student of science should, in fact, be an antiquary in his subject." Some polishing and pruning transformed the voluminous *Treatise* into J. H. Jeans, *The Mathematical Theory of Electricity and Magnetism*, Cambridge, 1907. One follows subsequent history with the 2nd ed., revised to include "motion of the electrons," 1911; 4th ed., revised to incorporate the theory of relativity, 1919; and 5th ed., 1925, incorporating the quantum theory of Bohr.

J. A. Ewing, *Magnetic Induction in Iron and other Metals*, Electrician Publishing Co., London, 1900. Covers more technical aspects of magnetism. It was Ewing, for example, who coined the word "hysteresis." The authoritative modern successor to this work is R. M. Bozorth, *Ferromagnetism*, Van Nostrand, Princeton, N.J., 1951, 1000 pp., collected facts and figures about magnetic materials, including a chronological bibliography covering many important papers and books on technical aspects of magnetism published from 1850 to 1950.

The development of the theory can be followed in the Proc. 6th Solvay Congress, Brussels, October, 1930, Magnétisme, Gauthier-Villars, Paris, 1932, particularly W. Pauli, "L'électron Magnétique," and reviews by Weiss and Heisenberg, among others (all in French). Thence to the forties in J. H. Van Vleck, "A Survey of the Theory of Ferromagnetism," *Rev. Mod. Phys.*, **17**: 27 (1945). Starting with the January, 1953, issue of *Rev. Mod. Phys.* (previously mentioned), the proceedings of yearly magnetics conferences in the United States have been "... written with a pen of iron, and with the point of a diamond ...", most recently in supplementary issues of the *J. Appl. Phys.* See also *Nuovo Cimento Suppl.*, **6** (1957). For example, from Proc. 10th Conference, *J. Appl. Phys.*, **35**, pt. 2, March, 1964, we find the following types of categories discussed: Band-Theoretic View of Ferromagnetic Nickel, Large Magnetic Film Memories, Applications and Instrumentation, Spin Waves and Thin Films, Nuclear and Antiferromagnetic Resonance, Soft Magnetic Materials, Ferromagnetic Resonance and Relaxation, Magnetization Processes, Magnetic Transitions and Ordering, Hard Magnetic Materials, Superconductors, Exchange Interactions, Ferrites and Garnets, Rare-Earth Metals and Alloys, and Band Theory of Magnetism and Spin Waves. Such proceedings, covering a wide spectrum of problems in the subject, are "of great advantage to the student," in the words of Maxwell.

Chapter 2. Exchange

J. C. Slater, *Quantum Theory of Molecules and Solids*, McGraw-Hill, New York, 1963, vol. I. Critical analysis and textbook of molecular theory. See also A. Freeman, et al., *Phys. Rev.*, **125**: 1978 (1962).

P. O. Löwdin, "Quantum Theory of Cohesive Properties of Solids," *Advances in Phys.* (*Phil. Mag.Suppl.*), **5**: 1 (1956). Extension of molecular theory to solids, including an early matrix analysis of nonorthogonality problem.

Chapter 3. Quantum Theory of Angular Momentum

Aside from texts exclusively on angular momentum such as those already cited in this chapter, the reader might consult any book similar to V. Heine, *Group Theory in Quantum Mechanics*, Pergamon, New York, 1960, where the theory of angular momentum and its applications are developed by the group theoretical methods of Wigner et al. Applications to the solid state are particularly extensive in a forthcoming book on group theory by Melvin Lax, but the following articles should also prove useful: P. Meijer, "Calculation of Wave Functions in a Symmetrical Crystalline Field," *Phys. Rev.*, **95**: 1443 (1954). G. Trammell, "Symmetry Functions of the Cube," *J. Math. Phys.*, **4**: 431 (1963). Dorothy Bell, "Group Theory and Crystal Lattices," *Revs. Mod. Phys.*, **26**: 311 (1954).

Y. Yafet, "*g*-factors and Spin-Lattice Relaxation of Conduction Electrons," in F. Seitz and D. Turnbull (eds.), *Solid State Physics*, Academic, New York, 1963, vol. 14, pp. 1–98.

Chapter 4. Many-Electron Wavefunctions

H. Weyl, *The Theory of Groups and Quantum Mechanics*, 2nd ed., (transl.) Dover, New York, 1930. Early, quaint treatment of "resonance between equivalent individuals," fully justified David Hilbert's pessimistic remark, "Physics is becoming too difficult for the physicist." Written before the famous paper of P. Jordan and E. Wigner, *Z. Phys.*, **47**: 631 (1928). The theory of permutations is now in the standard arsenal of the physicist, but the reader may wish to refresh his knowledge and study about Young's tableaux in B. R. Judd, *Operator Techniques in Atomic Spectroscopy*, McGraw-Hill, New York, 1963.

J. S. Griffith, *The Theory of Transition-Metal Ions*, Cambridge, 1961. Discusses effects of crystal fields on the ions, as well as many other important theoretical subjects which we have barely touched on. There are also available Hartree-Fock calculations of the iron transition series by R. E. Watson, *Tech. Rept. No.* 12, Solid State and Molecular Theory Group, M.I.T., 1959, unpublished. Compare with experimental data in Charlotte E. Moore, *Atomic Energy Levels*, vol. 2, U.S. National Bureau of Standards Circular 467, Aug. 15, 1952. Compare also with far less detailed compilation, *American Institute of Physics Handbook*, McGraw-Hill, New York, 1963.

E. Lieb and D. Mattis, "Theory of Ferromagnetism and the Ordering of Electronic Energy Levels," *Phys. Rev.*, **125**: 164 (1962), supplies the basis of the energy-level ordering theorems proved in Chapter 4.

Chapter 5. Semiclassical Theory of Magnetism

D. J. Craik and R. S. Trebble, "Magnetic Domains," *Repts. Progr. Phys.*, XXIV: 116 (1961). Survey on the various method of investigating domains—e.g., Bitter patterns, electron microscopy, and magneto-optic effects: well illustrated.

"The word ferrimagnetism was coined by Néel (1948) to describe the properties of those substances which below a certain temperature exhibit spontaneous magnetization arising from a *non-parallel* alignment of atomic magnetic moments." From a review of the physical properties of ferrimagnetism, W. P. Wolf, in *ibid.*, p. 212 (italics mine).

Chapter 6. Magnons-Quantum Theory of Spin Waves in Insulators

Following F. Bloch's fundamental "Zur Theorie des Ferromagnetismus," *Z. Physik.*, **61**: 206 (1930), in which the $T^{\frac{3}{2}}$ law was deduced from linear spin-wave theory, T. Holstein and H. Primakoff formalized this procedure including dipolar anisotropy in "Field Dependence of the Intrinsic Domain Magnetization of a Ferromagnet," *Phys. Rev.*, **58**: 1098 (1940), by the introduction of the use of Boson field operators. All attempts to take into account interactions among these Bosons in the three-dimensional problem were unfruitful, until F. J. Dyson wrote "General Theory of Spin-Wave Interactions," *Phys. Rev.*, **102**: 1217 (1956), which presented the first rigorous solution of the scattering problem at long wavelengths.

Antiferromagnetism in all its aspects, including linear magnon theory, is reviewed by T. Nagamiya, K. Yosida, and R. Kubo, *Advances in Phys.* (*Phil. Mag. Suppl.*),(13) **4**: 1 (1955). Nonlinear effects are in T. Oguchi, *Phys. Rev.*, **117**: 117 (1960).

F. Keffer's article on spin waves, to appear in the *Handbuch der Physik ca.* 1966, is an easy to read and general review of all aspects of the theory.

The use of neutrons was reported by B. N. Brockhouse, "Scattering of Neutrons by Spin Waves in Magnetite," *Phys. Rev.*, **106**: 859 (1957). L. Van Hove, "Time-Dependent Correlations between Spins, and Neutron Scattering in Ferromagnetic Crystals," *Phys. Rev.*,

95: 1374 (1954), gave the theory of neutron-magnon scattering; but more importantly, was perhaps the first application in the Western literature of solid-state physics, of the two-particle correlation function, or Green function.

Chapter 7. Magnetism and Magnons in Metals

J. C. Slater, H. Statz, and G. F. Koster, *A Two-Electron Example of Ferromagnetism*, *Phys. Rev.*, **91**: 1323 (1953) included correlation and Hund's rule energies, and solved the problem of two electrons in an empty band about as far as it was possible to go. Unfortunately, two electrons do not make a Fermi sea, and their technique (elimination of center of mass motion, etc.) does not seem capable of generalization.

In an investigation of the properties of MnO_2, A. Yoshimori, *J. Phys. Soc. Japan*, **14**: 807 (1959), discovered that over a certain range of next-nearest-neighbor exchange parameters, a spiral spin configuration would be stable. He denoted it a *screw-type structure* and found for the magnons a linear dependence on wavevector, as in antiferromagnets.

Y. A. Rocher, "L'Étude de la Structure Électronique des Métaux des Terres Rares," *Advances in Phys.* (*Phil. Mag. Suppl*), (43) **11**: 233 (1962), studies the electronic and magnetic properties of the lanthanides ($4f$ shell) and plutonium ($5f$).

The theory of magnetism in metals can be considered as the high density limit of the magnetic impurity problem, when a magnetic solute atom occupies every site in the solvent metal. Therefore the study of the impurity problem is a field of special importance, first considered by N. F. Mott, *Proc. Phys. Soc.* (*London*), **A62**: 416 (1949), and J. Friedel, *Nuovo Cimento Suppl.*, **7**: 287 (1958); later by P. W. Anderson, *Phys. Rev.*, **124**: 41 (1961), and P. A. Wolff, *Phys. Rev.*, **124**: 1030 (1961). An interesting approach by H. Suhl and D. R. Fredkin, *Phys. Rev.*, **131**: 1063 (1963), should be noted, as well as the extension of Anderson's treatment to two-impurity atom clusters by S. Alexander and P. W. Anderson, *Phys. Rev.*, **133**: A1594 (1964).

A theory of *s-d* or *s-f* coupling in the indirect exchange mechanism was developed by the following: T. Kasuya, *Progr. Theoret. Phys.* (*Kyoto*), **16**: 45 (1956). K. Yosida, *Phys. Rev.*, **106**: 893 (1957). P. de Gennes, *C.R. Acad. Sci. Paris*, **247**: 1836 (1958). S. H. Liu, *Phys. Rev.*, **121**: 451 (1961). A. Abrikosov and L. Gor'kov, *Zh. Exsperim. i Teor. Fiz.*, **43**: 2230 (1962). T. Kaplan and D. Lyons, *Phys. Rev.*, **129**: 2072 (1963). Calculations by R. Watson and A. Freeman, *Phys. Rev. Letters*, **6**: 277, and *erratum*, 388 (1961), revealed that rare-earth ions "carry a 'paired' electron spin density which is negative in their outer reaches ... antiparallel to the $4f$ spin direction." The first systematic calculation of the ground-state long-range order in the indirect exchange theory was in D. Mattis and W. Donath, *Phys. Rev.*, **128**: 1618 (1962).

A *strong-coupling* theory of indirect exchange was proposed by H. Fröhlich and F. Nabarro, *Proc. Roy. Soc.* (*London*), **A175**: 382 (1940), for the case of nuclear hyperfine indirect interactions. But it is now clear that the weak-coupling Ruderman-Kittel interaction, M. A. Ruderman and C. Kittel, *Phys. Rev.*, **96**: 99 (1954), is the correct one to use. This need not be the case in electronic magnetism, however, and the idea has been resuscitated by S. V. Vonsovskii, *JETP* (USSR), **16**: 981 (1946); C. Zener, *Phys. Rev.*, **81**: 440 (1951); and lately in a Green function formulation by R. A. Tahir-Kheli and D. Ter Haar, *Phys. Rev.*, **130**: 108 (1963).

The interaction between electrons and magnons and the resultant "drag" on the former is the subject of a paper by T. Wolfram and J. Callaway, *Phys. Rev.*, **127**: 1605 (1962).

Magnons in metals have been discussed by the following: C. Herring and C. Kittel, *Phys. Rev.*, **81**: 869 (1951). C. Herring, *Phys. Rev.*, **87**: 60 (1952). T. Izuyama, *Progr. Theoret. Phys.* (*Kyoto*), **23**: 969 (1960). T. Ruijgrok, *Physica*, **28**: 877 (1962). M. M. Antonoff, *Bull. Am. Phys. Soc.*, **8**: 227 (1963). E. D. Thompson, *Ann. Phys.* (*N.Y.*), **22**: 309 (1963). D. Mattis, *Phys. Rev.*, **132**: 2521 (1963), *J. Appl. Phys.*, **35**: 1085 (1964), and *Bull. Am. Phys. Soc.*, **9**: 559 (1964). T. Izuyama and R. Kubo, *J. Appl. Phys.*, **35**: 1074 (1964). T. Nakamura, *Phys. Rev. Letters*, **12**: 279 (1964). T. Izuyama, *Phys. Rev. Letters*, **12**: 585 (1964). The last three in this list have analyzed magnon-magnon interactions in metals, without achieving agreement regarding the result.

D. Pines, *The Many-Body Problem*, Benjamin, New York, 1962. A good introduction to the study of the many-electron system. Of the many books and reviews on the Green function technique in the many-body problem, none is clearer than D. Zubarev, "Double-Time Green Functions in Statistical Physics," *Soviet Phys.—Usp.*, **3**: 320 (1960), [from the Russian, *Usp. Fiz. Nauk*, **71**: 71 (1960)]; and A. Alekséev, "The Application of the Methods of Quantum Field Theory in Statistical Physics," *Soviet Phys. Usp.*, **4**: 23 (1961), [from the Russian, *Usp. Fiz. Nauk*, **73**: 41 (1961).] And none is more erudite than C. De Dominicis and P. Martin, "Stationary Entropy Principle, etc.," *J. Math. Phys.*, **5**: 14 and 31 (1964), "sufficiently general to encompass systems which have several components, with Bose or Fermi statistics. ..." These references overlap, and extend, the following chapter as well.

Chapter 8. Elementary Statistical Mechanics

The basic variational theorem for the free energy at finite temperature was given by R. E. Peierls, *Phys. Rev.*, **54**: 918 (1938). Compare the derivation by T. Schultz, *Nuovo Cimento*, **8**: 943 (1958).

A linked cluster expansion for the free energy of the Heisenberg ferromagnet was used to investigate the self-consistency of the molecular field theory and its various extensions (constant-coupling approximation, Oguchi, Bethe-Peierls-Weiss, and other methods) in B. Strieb, H. Callen, and G. Horwitz, "Cluster Expansion for the Heisenberg Ferromagnet," *Phys. Rev.*, **130**: 1798 (1963). See also R. Stinchcombe, G. Horwitz, F. Englert, and R. Brout, *Phys. Rev.*, **130**: 155 (1963). The Oguchi method extended to next-nearest neighbors is used to calculate magnetic short-range order and specific heat in ferromagnets and antiferromagnets by J. S. Smart, *J. Phys. Chem. Solids*, **20**: 41 (1961).

The bases for modern thermodynamic spin-wave theories were laid in F. J. Dyson, "Thermodynamic Behavior of an Ideal Ferromagnet," *Phys. Rev.*, **102**: 1230 (1956).

Watson's integrals for the simple, body- and face-centered cubic structures, enable all Brillouin zone effects to be correctly taken into account. G. Watson, *Quart. J. Math.*, **10**: 266 (1939).

Chapter 9. The Ising Model

"The 'Ising Model' of ferromagnetism was first proposed by Wilhelm Lenz (1888–1957) in 1920. Ernst Ising, a graduate student working with Lenz at Hamburg, worked out the statistical mechanical properties of the model in one dimension in 1925 ... " This quote is from S. G. Brush, *History of the Lenz-Ising Model* (Report UCLR–7940 dated June 19, 1964, available at Clearing House for Federal Scientific and Technical Information, Natl. Bureau of Stand., U.S. Dept. of Commerce, Springfield, Virginia; price $3.00). This report includes an extensive bibliography on its subject and related matters.

E. W. Montroll, "Lattice Statistics," in E. F. Beckenbach (ed.), *Applied Combinatorial Mathematics*, to be published. "Concerned with the counting of the number of ways certain events can occur on a lattice ... in the limit of large ... one and two dimensional lattices." The *random walk*, the *Pfaffian* and *dimer* problems are shown to be eventually all related to the Ising model.

The Ising model connects to the "statistical theory of equations of state and phase transitions" by way of two interesting papers by that title: T. D. Lee and C. N. Yang, *Phys. Rev.*, **87**: 404 and 410 (1952).

INDEX

Additional authors, subjects, and titles are listed in the Bibliography.

DATE DUE